COMPREHENSIVE BIOCHEMISTRY

SOLE DISTRIBUTORS FOR THE UNITED STATES AND CANADA:

AMERICAN ELSEVIER PUBLISHING COMPANY, INC.

52, Vanderbilt Avenue, New York 17, N.Y.

SOLE DISTRIBUTORS FOR GREAT BRITAIN:

ELSEVIER PUBLISHING COMPANY LIMITED

12B, Rippleside Commercial Estate, Ripple Road, Barking, Essex

Library of Congress Catalog Card Number 62–10359

With 24 illustrations and 3 tables

COMPREHENSIVE BIOCHEMISTRY

COMPREHENSIVE BIOCHEMISTRY

SECTION I (VOLUMES I–4)

PHYSICO-CHEMICAL AND ORGANIC ASPECTS
OF BIOCHEMISTRY

SECTION II (VOLUMES 5–11)

CHEMISTRY OF BIOLOGICAL COMPOUNDS

SECTION III

BIOCHEMICAL REACTION MECHANISMS

SECTION IV

METABOLISM

SECTION V

CHEMICAL BIOLOGY
GENERAL INDEX

COMPREHENSIVE BIOCHEMISTRY

EDITED BY

MARCEL FLORKIN

Professor of Biochemistry, University of Liège (Belgium)

AND

ELMER H. STOTZ

Professor of Biochemistry, University of Rochester, School of Medicine and Dentistry, N.Y. (U.S.A.)

VOLUME 11

WATER-SOLUBLE VITAMINS, HORMONES, ANTIBIOTICS

ELSEVIER PUBLISHING COMPANY

AMSTERDAM · LONDON · NEW YORK

1963

CONTRIBUTORS TO THIS VOLUME

E. P. ABRAHAM, M.A., D.Phil., F.R.S.

Reader in Chemical Pathology, Sir William Dunn School of Pathology,
University of Oxford and Fellow of Lincoln College, Oxford (Great Britain)

GUILLERMO ARROYAVE, Ph.D.

Chief, Division of Physiological Chemistry, Instituto de Nutrición de Centro América
y Panamá (INCAP), Guatemala (Central America)

RICARDO BRESSANI, M.S., Ph.D.

Chief, Division of Agricultural Chemistry and Food Analysis, Instituto de Nutrición
de Centro América y Panamá (INCAP), Guatemala (Central America)

KARL FOLKERS, Ph.D., D.Sc.

Executive Director, Fundamental Research, Merck Sharp & Dohme Research Laboratories, Merck & Co., Inc., Rahway, N.J. (U.S.A.)

P. KARLSON, Ph.D.

Professor of Physiological Chemistry, Physiologisch-chemisches Institut der Universität,
Goethestrasse 33, München (Deutschland)

J. P. LAMBOOY, Ph.D.

University of Rochester, Medical Center, Rochester, N.Y. (U.S.A.)

C. H. MONFOORT, Ph.D.

Laboratory of Physiological Chemistry, State University, Utrecht (The Netherlands)

Professor Dr. KURT MOTHES

Direktor des Universitätsinstituts für Allgemeine Botanik und des Akademieinstituts
für Biochemie der Pflanzen, Am Kirchtor 1, Halle/Saale (Deutschland)

WILLIAM SHIVE, Ph.D.

Professor of Chemistry, Department of Chemistry, The University of Texas,
Austin 12, Texas (U.S.A.)

ESMOND E. SNELL, B.A., M.A., Ph.D.

Professor of Biochemistry, Department of Biochemistry, University of California,
Berkeley 4, Calif. (U.S.A.)

L. H. STERNBACH, M.Pharm., Ph.D.

Chemical Research Department, Hoffmann-La Roche Inc., Nutley, N.J. (U.S.A.)

ELIZABETH P. STEYN-PARVÉ, Ph.D.

Professor of Physiological Chemistry, Laboratory of Physiological Chemistry, State University, Utrecht (The Netherlands)

BRUCE B. STOWE, M.A., Ph.D.

Assistant Professor of Botany, Department of Biology, Yale University, New Haven, Conn. (U.S.A.)

Dr. H. VELDSTRA

Professor of Biochemistry, Department of Biochemistry, University of Leiden, Wassenaarseweg 64, Leiden (The Netherlands)

ARTHUR F. WAGNER, Ph.D.

Research Associate, Fundamental Research, Merck Sharp & Dohme Research Laboratories, Merck & Co., Inc., Rahway, N.J. (U.S.A.)

CHARLES A. WEST. Ph.D.

Associate Professor, Department of Chemistry, University of California, Los Angeles 24, Calif. (U.S.A.)

ROGER J. WILLIAMS, Ph.D., D.Sc.

Director, Clayton Foundation Biochemical Institute, The University of Texas, Austin 12, Texas (U.S.A.)

GENERAL PREFACE

The Editors are keenly aware that the literature of Biochemistry is already very large, in fact so widespread that it is increasingly difficult to assemble the most pertinent material in a given area. Beyond the ordinary textbook the subject matter of the rapidly expanding knowledge of biochemistry is spread among innumerable journals, monographs, and series of reviews. The Editors believe that there is a real place for an advanced treatise in biochemistry which assembles the principal areas of the subject in a single set of books.

It would be ideal if an individual or small group of biochemists could produce such an advanced treatise, and within the time to keep reasonably abreast of rapid advances, but this is at least difficult if not impossible. Instead, the Editors with the advice of the Advisory Board, have assembled what they consider the best possible sequence of chapters written by competent authors; they must take the responsibility for inevitable gaps of subject matter and duplication which may result from this procedure.

Most evident to the modern biochemist, apart from the body of knowledge of the chemistry and metabolism of biological substances, is the extent to which he must draw from recent concepts of physical and organic chemistry, and in turn project into the vast field of biology. Thus in the organization of Comprehensive Biochemistry, the middle three sections, Chemistry of Biological Compounds, Biochemical Reaction Mechanisms, and Metabolism may be considered classical biochemistry, while the first and last sections provide selected material on the origins and projections of the subject.

It is hoped that sub-division of the sections into bound volumes will not only be convenient, but will find favour among students concerned with specialized areas, and will permit easier future revisions of the individual volumes. Toward the latter end particularly, the Editors will welcome all comments in their effort to produce a useful and efficient source of biochemical knowledge.

Liège/Rochester
July 1962

M. FLORKIN
E. H. STOTZ

PREFACE TO SECTION II

(VOLUMES 5–11)

Section II on the Chemistry of Biological Compounds deals with the organic and physical chemistry of the major organic constituents of living material. A general understanding of organic and physical chemistry is presumed, but the reader will find the special topics in Section I of value in the fuller understanding of several parts of Section II. The Editors have made special effort to include a sound treatment of the important biological high polymers, including sections on their shape and physical properties. A number of substances peculiar to plants, certain isoprenoids, flavonoids, tannins, lignins, and plant hormones, often omitted from textbooks of biochemistry, are included. Nevertheless, it is inevitable that some omissions, hopefully minor ones, have occurred. The only intentional omission is the chemistry of the coenzymes and certain components of biological oxidation, which will be covered in connection with their function in Section III.

The previous policy of dividing the section into smaller volumes has been continued, resulting in seven volumes for Section II. Two of the volumes each contain a complete area, namely Carbohydrates (Volume 5) and Sterols, Bile Acids and Steroids (Volume 10). Comments from readers will be appreciated by the Editors and be most helpful for possible future revisions.

Liège/Rochester   M. FLORKIN
December 1962   E. H. STOTZ

CONTENTS

Part A

WATER-SOLUBLE VITAMINS

Chapter I. Thiamine

by E. P. Steyn-Parvé and C. H. Monfoort

Chapter II. Riboflavin and Closely Related Flavins

by J. P. Lambooy

Chapter III. Niacin

by G. ARROYAVE AND R. BRESSANI

Chapter IV. Vitamin B$_6$

by E. E. SNELL

Chapter V. Pantothenic Acid

by R. J. WILLIAMS, p. 59

Chapter VI. Biotin

by L. H. Sternbach

Chapter VII. Folic Acid and Pteridines

by W. Shive

Chapter VIII. Vitamin B_{12}

by A. F. Wagner and K. Folkers

Part B

HORMONES

Chapter IX. Plant Hormones

Section a. Indole Auxins of Plants

by B. B. STOWE

Chapter IX. Plant Hormones

Section b. Synthetic Auxins

by H. VELDSTRA

Chapter IX. Plant Hormones

Section c. Gibberellins

by CH. A. WEST

Chapter IX. Plant Hormones

Section d. Purines and Other Compounds

by K. Mothes

Chapter X. Insect Hormones

by P. Karlson

Part C

ANTIBIOTICS

Chapter XI. The Antibiotics

by E. P. Abraham

COMPREHENSIVE BIOCHEMISTRY

SECTION I (VOLUMES 1–4)

Physico-Chemical and Organic Aspects of Biochemistry

Volume 11

Part A

WATER-SOLUBLE VITAMINS

Chapter I

Thiamine

ELIZABETH P. STEYN-PARVÉ AND C. H. MONFOORT

*Laboratory of Physiological Chemistry, State University, Utrecht
(The Netherlands)*

1. Discovery and isolation

In 1890 the Dutch physician Eijkman, working in Java, observed that fowls, mainly fed upon polished rice, developed a disease characterized by a weakness of the legs, a loss of balance, paralyses and a drastic drop of body temperature just before death. Microscopic examination revealed a degeneration of the peripheral nervous system. Sometimes the spinal marrow was also affected. He gave this disease the name of *polyneuritis gallinarum*. It did not develop on a diet of unpolished rice. Once developed, it could be cured by administering rice polishings or by feeding unpolished rice[1].

As the disease also occurred upon feeding rice starch or other kinds of starch, but not upon feeding meat, Eijkman suggested that a toxic principle, formed from starch in the intestine, would cause the observed degeneration of the nervous system. Rice polishings would contain an antidote.

In 1901 Grijns, also working in Java, arrived at the conclusion that *polyneuritis gallinarum* should be regarded as a partial starvation and that "there occur in various natural foods substances, which cannot be absent without serious injury to the nervous system"[2]. He was therefore the first to advance an explanation which later proved to be correct.

Another ten years were to elapse before Funk gave the name of "vitamine" to the substance whose absence from foodstuffs was responsible for the development of polyneuritis[3]. Later the term vitamin(e) was applied to the whole group of organic compounds, small amounts of which are essential to the health of man and beast. The various vitamins were distinguished by prefixes or subscripts, and later still by giving them names from which the word "vitamin" had disappeared completely. As years went by, the substance connected with polyneuritis has been called: vitamine, vitamine B, vitamin B_1, oryzanin, toruline, antineuritic vitamin, anti-beriberi vitamin and aneurin. These names have now been almost universally superseded by *thiamine*.

Ever since his first observations on *polyneuritis gallinarum* in 1890, Eijkman was aware of the resemblance between this disease of fowls and human beriberi. Vorderman obtained more certainty for a common basis of these two diseases in 1896, when he established that in prisons in Java where polished rice was the staple diet beriberi was far more frequent than in prisons where unpolished rice was provided.

Grijns and many others after him have attempted to extract and isolate the antineuritic substance from rice polishings. Of the early attempts those of Funk attracted most notice. He made use of extraction with dilute acid or acidified alcohol. His conclusion of 1912, that the substance would be a pyrimidine base, prompted his naming it "vitamine" ("an organic base essential for life")[3]. But the active product he isolated still only contained very little of this principle.

The isolation of thiamine as an essentially pure, crystalline compound was only achieved in 1926 by Jansen and Donath, working in the same laboratory in Java where Eijkman and Grijns had once carried out their investigations[4]. The following points were fundamental for their success:

(*1*) A fairly rapid and very reliable method, employing rice birds, for testing the activity of successive steps in the purification;

(*2*) The inclusion in their procedure of an adsorption step: adsorption onto fuller's earth ("acid clay"), still quite unusual in those days;

(*3*) The use of a then uncommonly large amount of starting material (rice polishings).

For the rest they employed precipitating agents that were already in use in the days of Funk.

2. Occurrence

Thiamine is present in all living organisms; this is easy to understand, for it is essential for life. Man and beast are dependent upon the synthetic ability of plants and micro-organisms for their supply of thiamine. Good sources of the vitamin are cereals (flour of high extraction percentage), legumes, yeast, potatoes, liver, kidney, pork and, generally speaking, all foodstuffs that are not too far refined. Wheat flour for white bread, corn starch, cane sugar, etc., are too far refined.

3. Structure

Thiamine chloride hydrochloride, the form in which the vitamin is usually isolated or prepared, has the empirical formula $C_{12}H_{18}N_4OSCl_2$ and structure (I).

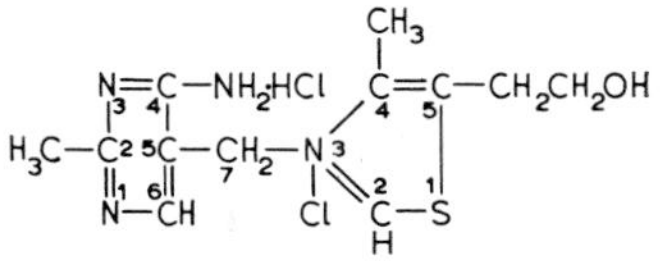

$$
\begin{array}{c}
\text{(I)}
\end{array}
$$

(I)

It consists of a pyrimidine derivative, 2-methyl-4-aminopyrimidine* and a thiazole derivative, 4-methyl-5-(β-hydroxy)ethylthiazole, linked by a methylene bridge.

In the elucidation of the structure of thiamine[5] (1934–1936) Williams and collaborators have had a major share, but important contributions also came from the laboratories of Todd and Bergel in Great Britain and Windaus and I. G. Farben in Germany. Williams *et al.* made the important observation that thiamine is quantitatively split by neutral sulfite solution at room temperature as follows:

$$C_{12}H_{18}N_4OSCl_2 + Na_2SO_3 \longrightarrow \underset{(A)}{C_6H_9N_3SO_3} + \underset{(B)}{C_6H_9NOS} + 2\,NaCl$$

Product A proved to contain a sulfonic group: it yielded sulfuric acid on treatment with water at 200° and sulfurous acid with alkali. Its absorption in the ultraviolet was suggestive of a pyrimidine nucleus. This suggestion was confirmed and the exact structure of the pyrimidine part of the vitamin established by the synthesis of 2,5-dimethyl-4-aminopyrimidine (II), which proved to be identical with the product obtained from compound A by treatment with metallic sodium in liquid ammonia.

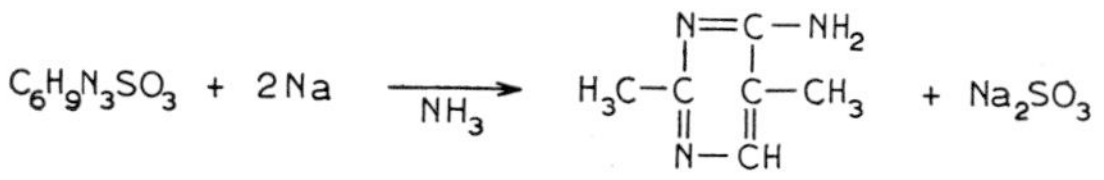

$$\underset{(A)}{C_6H_9N_3SO_3} + 2\,Na \xrightarrow{NH_3} \underset{(II)}{} + Na_2SO_3$$

(A)   (II)

To ascertain the position of the sulfonic group in primary cleavage product A, Williams *et al.* prepared 2-methyl-4-hydroxypyrimidine-5-methyl sulfonic acid (III) by treating previously synthesized 2-methyl-4-hydroxy-5-ethoxy-methylpyrimidine (XI, see p. 7) with sodium sulfite. This proved identical with the product obtained from (A) by acid hydrolysis.

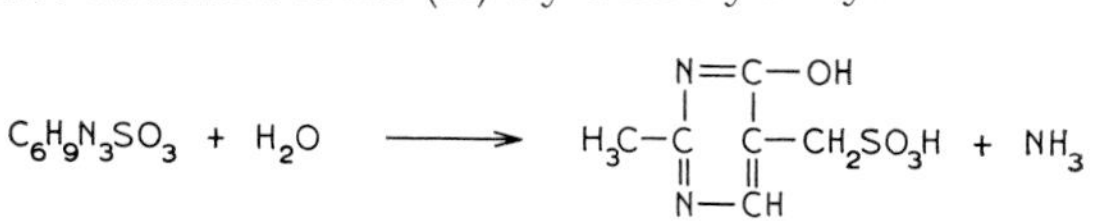

$$\underset{(A)}{C_6H_9N_3SO_3} + H_2O \longrightarrow \underset{(III)}{} + NH_3$$

(A)   (III)

* Positions 4 and 6 in the pyrimidine ring are equivalent, so this compound is often also indicated as 2-methyl-6-aminopyrimidine.

So structure IV could be assigned to A:

$$\begin{matrix} & N=C-NH_2 \\ & | \quad | \\ H_3C-C & C-CH_2SO_3H \\ & || \quad || \\ & N-CH \end{matrix}$$

(IV)

Confirmation of the structure of the pyrimidine part of the vitamin soon followed when Grewe synthesized 2-methyl-4-amino-5-aminomethylpyrimidine (V, see p. 8), a product obtained by Windaus et al. upon oxidizing thiamine with barium permanganate. From (V) Grewe was able to prepare a sulfonic acid derivative (IV), which proved to be identical with Williams's primary cleavage product A.

The identification of fragment B of the vitamin molecule gave less trouble. It was recognized as a thiazole derivative by Clarke and Gurin[6]. On oxidation with nitric acid it yielded 4-methylthiazole-5-carboxylic acid (VI), a compound that had already been synthesized in 1890. It appeared to contain an aliphatic hydroxyl group which could be replaced by chlorine without much change in the U.V. absorption spectrum, so it could be reconstructed as having structure VII.

(VI)   (VII)   (VIII)

4-methyl-5(β-hydroxy)
ethylthiazole

The OH group was deduced to be in the β-position, because the vitamin is optically inactive and B did not give an iodoform reaction. Confirmation of structure VII soon followed when Buchman[7], and later Andersag and Westphal[8], synthesized this compound, and it proved to be identical with B.

That the pyrimidine nucleus is linked to the thiazole nucleus through the nitrogen atom of the latter soon became apparent. A comparison of the behaviour of thiamine and its thiazole moiety towards certain chemical reagents indicated the presence of a quaternary nitrogen in the former. Moreover, upon potentiometric titration of thiamine with alkali it behaved exactly as an addition product (VIII) of VII and methyl iodide.

The point of attachment on the pyrimidine fragment was of course already marked by the position of the sulfonic group introduced during the sulfite cleavage of the vitamin. Thus, in 1936, the structure I could be assigned to thiamine, ten years after the crystalline vitamin was first obtained.

4. Synthesis

(a) Chemical synthesis[9]

As the proof for the structure of thiamine had depended so largely upon the synthesis of certain breakdown products, the complete synthesis of the vitamin was accomplished very soon afterwards. The first publication came from Williams and Cline[10] in the U.S.; hard on their heels followed Todd and Bergel[11] in England and Andersag and Westphal[8] in Germany.

One can conceive of three possibilities for the synthesis of thiamine:

(*1*) Building up the pyrimidine and thiazole moieties separately, then connecting both parts.

(*2*) Building up the pyrimidine part with an aminomethyl group in position 5, elongating this side chain, and ring closure to form the thiazole part.

(*3*) Building up the thiazole part, attaching a suitable side chain to the nitrogen, and achieving ring closure of the pyrimidine part.

The first method was followed by Williams *et al.*, while Todd and Bergel chose the second route. Andersag and Westphal tried both methods, with slight modifications. Both are now used in the industrial preparation of thiamine. The third method has also been described, but does not seem to have found much application.

(*i*) To synthesize the pyrimidine part, Williams *et al.* condensed acetamidine (IX) with ethyl sodioformyl-β-ethoxypropionate (X) to form 2-methyl-4-hydroxy-5-ethoxymethylpyrimidine (XI).

An amino group was substituted for the hydroxyl group in position 4 by successive treatment with $POCl_3$ and alcoholic ammonia. For the ensuing synthesis of thiamine, the ethoxy group in position 7 was then replaced by bromine, so that 2-methyl-4-amino-5-bromomethylpyrimidine hydrobromide was obtained (XII).

The amino group in position 4 could also be introduced directly by condensing either acetamidine with ethoxymethylene malononitrile (XIII), or acetimino ether (XIV) with aminomethylene malononitrile (XV). The resulting 2-methyl-4-amino-5-cyanopyrimidine (XVI) was then catalytically hydrogenated to form 2-methyl-4-amino-5-aminomethylpyrimidine (V, Grewe[12]).

(*ii*) Numerous ways have been developed for synthesizing the thiazole part of thiamine (VII). Williams's collaborator Buchman[7] employed a reaction between thioformamide (XVII) and γ-chloro-γ-acetopropanol (XVIII). Instead of XVIII, γ-halogeno-γ-acetopropylacetate is also used. The ring closure takes place readily.

(*iii*) The two ring systems are easily linked together when the bromopyrimidine compound XII is heated with the thiazole compound VII.

Thiamine bromide hydrobromide

Williams *et al.* replaced the bromine ions by chlorine ions by shaking a solution of the bromide with an aqueous suspension of silver chloride.

(*iv*) Todd and Bergel followed the alternative procedure (2) of elongating the side chain in position 5 of the pyrimidine part. They were able to thioformylate 2-methyl-4-amino-5-aminomethylpyrimidine (V) by treatment with potassium dithioformate and obtained 2-methyl-4-amino-5-thioformylaminomethylpyrimidine (XIX).

$$
\underset{(V)}{\overset{\displaystyle N=C-NH_2}{\underset{\displaystyle N-CH}{H_3C-C\;\;\;C-CH_2NH_2}}} + HCSSK \longrightarrow \underset{(XIX)}{\overset{\displaystyle N=C-NH_2}{\underset{\displaystyle N-CH}{H_3C-C\;\;\;C-CH_2N-C=S}}} + KSH
$$

XIX was then heated with γ-chloro-γ-acetopropylacetate and thiazolium ring closure achieved; the acetyl group was saponified during the process and thiamine chloride was obtained directly.

$$
\underset{(XIX)}{\overset{\displaystyle N=C-NH_2}{\underset{\displaystyle N-CH}{H_3C-C\;\;\;C-CH_2-N}}} +
\overset{\displaystyle H_3C\;\;\;CH_2CH_2OCOCH_3}{\underset{\displaystyle Cl}{O=C-CH}}
\longrightarrow
\underset{\text{Thiamine chloride}}{\overset{\displaystyle N=C-NH_2}{\underset{\displaystyle N-CH}{H_3C-C\;\;\;C-CH_2-N}}}
+ CH_3COOH
$$

(b) Biological synthesis

Most higher plants are able to synthesize thiamine. This takes place in the leaves. Very little is known about the details of the process. It seems very likely that the pyrimidine and thiazole moieties are built up separately and then linked together, for some plant materials are able to effect this combination of the two fragments[13]. We know nothing about the biogenesis of the separate fragments. Isolated pea roots can synthesize the thiazole fragment from thioformamide and γ-chloro-γ-acetopropanol (see p. 8), but it is not known whether this is a general reaction by which thiazole is formed in plants.

In the microbial world there are many organisms that are autotrophic as regards thiamine. Others are able to synthesize the vitamin if one, or both, moieties are provided; some require the complete molecule[14].

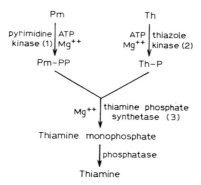

Fig. 1. Synthesis of thiamine by cell-free extracts of baker's yeast.

Animals cannot synthesize thiamine, although there are enzymes in rabbit liver and kidney capable of uniting the pyrimidine and thiazole fragments.

Recently, the mechanism has been established by which this union of the two fragments is achieved by cell-free extracts of baker's yeast (*Saccharomyces cerevisiae*)[15,16]. It proceeds[16] according to the diagram shown in Fig. 1. 2-Methyl-4-amino-5-hydroxymethylpyrimidine (Pm) is enzymically phosphorylated in position 7 by ATP in the presence of Mg^{2+} ions, to form the pyrophosphate derivative. The thiazole part (Th) is similarly phosphorylated (in the aliphatic side chain), but in this case the monophosphate derivative is formed. Both intermediates are linked together by a third enzyme, and pyrophosphate (or possibly two successive orthophosphate molecules) is split off. The primarily formed thiamine monophosphate is dephosphorylated by a phosphatase. Enzyme (1) has been separated from enzymes (2) and (3).

5. The fate of thiamine in living organisms

All living organisms are able to phosphorylate thiamine, with the aid of ATP, to form thiamine pyrophosphate (TPP). This form of the vitamin is ubiquitous in nature, and predominates in animals and many yeasts. In many plants, however, free thiamine is the prevailing form. Very small amounts of thiamine monophosphate and triphosphate have been reported to occur in animal tissues, but confirmation is required. Only in milk appreciable amounts of thiamine monophosphate have been found. Under certain conditions the pyrophosphate ester of thiamine disulfide has been encountered in yeast. Its presence has also been claimed in animal tissues, but this again requires confirmation.

The enzyme thiaminokinase, catalysing the reaction between thiamine and ATP, has been partially purified from liver and yeast by various investigators[17,18]. It has been established that the reaction proceeds as follows[19]:

$$\text{Thiamine} + \text{ATP} \xrightarrow[\text{thiaminokinase}]{Mg^{++}} \text{Thiamine pyrophosphate} + \text{AMP}$$

TPP cannot pass through the cell membrane and penetrate into the cell (at least not in animal tissues and yeast), but thiamine can. So if TPP is required inside the cell, it will have to be formed there *in situ* from thiamine.

Phosphatases capable of catalysing the dephosphorylation of TPP to thiamine have been encountered in animal tissues and in yeasts, and will probably be found in all living organisms. A kidney phosphatase and the acid yeast phosphatase (pH optimum ± 4) have been shown to remove the phosphate groups one by one. The phosphatases cannot attack TPP when it is bound to protein. In rat liver a large proportion of the TPP was shown to be present in the cytoplasm in free condition. Hence in the liver cell *in vivo* a barrier must exist, separating TPP from the phosphatase able to hydrolyse it.

The acid yeast phosphatase mentioned above is markedly inhibited by thiamine, and to a lesser degree by the pyrimidine part of the vitamin, not only when TPP is the substrate, but also when other phosphate esters, such as α- or β-glycerophosphate, are used. Animal phosphatases do not appear to be inhibited by thiamine[20].

Human beings and laboratory animals receiving a diet adequate in thiamine excrete the vitamin in the urine*. When extra thiamine is administered the excretion also increases. But always only part of the ingested thiamine reappears in the urine as such. The remainder must be broken down in the body, but how this happens is completely obscure.

Thiamine labelled with ^{35}S or ^{14}C in the thiazole nucleus has been injected into rats[21,22]. The bulk of the radioactivity excreted in the urine was recovered as unchanged thiamine, but many other radioactive products were also discerned. Three of these were tentatively identified as thiochrome, thiamine disulfide and thiazole. In the experiments with ^{35}S, a considerable amount of radioactivity was recovered as sulfate. This indicates that a breakdown and oxidation of thiamine does take place, and there our knowledge ends for the moment.

Enzymes destroying thiamine have been encountered in some species: in a number of fresh-water fish, in very few salt-water fish, in some shellfish and crustacea, in bracken ferns and in three species of intestinal bacteria. They have all received the name of "thiaminase", but it is very probable that we have to do with several, different, enzymes[20,23]. They all bring about a fission of the thiamine molecule, liberating the thiazole part, but only in one case, that of thiaminase of *Bacillus aneurinolyticus* Kimura *et* Aoyana, reasonable proof has been obtained of a hydrolytic fission, yielding both moieties of the vitamin molecule: 2-methyl-4-amino-5-hydroxymethylpyrimidine and 4-methyl-5(β-hydroxy)-ethylthiazole.

In all other cases the breakdown appeared to be stimulated by a number of amines and heterocyclic bases. Partly purified thiaminase preparations were even completely inactive unless such a compound was present. Isolation and identification of the reaction products confirmed the suspicion that a transfer reaction was taking place:

$$Pym \cdot CH_2 \cdot Th^+ + HX \longrightarrow Pym \cdot CH_2 \cdot X + Th + H^+$$
or:
$$Pym \cdot CH_2 \cdot Th^+ + Y \longrightarrow Pym \cdot CH_2 \cdot Y^+ + Th$$

---

* This is a simple test to see if the thiamine intake is satisfactory.

References p. 21

Pym stands for 2-methyl-4-aminopyrimidine, Th is the thiazole portion of the vitamin. HX can be an amine, such as aniline or hypotaurine, Y a strong base, such as pyridine. These reactions can be regarded as transmethylations involving a substituted methyl group (Pym·CH$_2$—).

The elucidation of this reaction gave an explanation for earlier observations that extracts of bracken or clam could be separated by dialysis into a heat-labile component (enzyme) and a heat-stable component (coenzyme), both required for enzymic activity. The "coenzyme" is evidently an acceptor base or possibly a mixture of several such bases. For instance, Hennessy *et al.* showed that crude extracts of clam form icthiamine from added thiamine. This ability is lost upon dialysis, but can be restored by adding hypotaurine, so this base will be at least one of the acceptors for the reaction in crude extracts[24].

$$\text{Pym·CH}_2\text{·Th}^+ \;+\; \text{H}-\overset{\displaystyle O}{\underset{\displaystyle O}{\overset{\|}{\underset{\|}{S}}}}-\text{CH}_2\text{CH}_2\text{NH}_2 \;\longrightarrow\; \text{Pym·CH}_2-\overset{\displaystyle O}{\underset{\displaystyle O}{\overset{\|}{\underset{\|}{S}}}}-\text{CH}_2\text{CH}_2\text{NH}_2 \;+\; \text{Th} \;+\; \text{H}^+$$

Hypotaurine   Icthiamine

The literature concerning thiaminases is still confused in some respects. Thus, according to some reports, bracken and other plants would contain heat-stable substances capable of destroying thiamine; evidently not enzymes, but often mentioned together with these. Some have later been identified as flavonoids, phenols and tannins. In one report thiaminase has been claimed to occur in tissues of rabbits and chickens[25], but this has never been confirmed.

The seemingly erratic distribution of thiaminases in nature makes the function of such an enzyme rather enigmatic. However, many more tissues, hitherto negative, might appear to contain a thiaminase if re-examined with a suitable acceptor for the reaction.

It has been repeatedly suggested that the main role of thiaminase *in vivo* would be not the decomposition, but the synthesis of thiamine. Indeed, thiamine has been formed by the enzyme, starting from a Pym·CH$_2$·Y$^+$ conjugate and the thiazole moiety, but the equilibrium was far to the side of decomposition of the vitamin.

6. Chemical and physical properties

Thiamine chloride hydrochloride (mol.wt. 337.28) forms colourless monoclinic crystals, m.p. 248–250° (under decomposition). Under certain conditions it also crystallizes with m.p. 232–234° (dimorphism). It has a characteristic odour and a slightly bitter taste. The chloride hydrochloride crystallizes from alcohol–water solutions as the hemihydrate, but on exposure to air the water content can vary from nearly 1 mole to almost zero, depending on the atmospheric humidity. Thiamine is not sensitive to atmospheric oxygen. It is readily soluble in water, sparingly soluble in ethanol (more soluble in methanol), and practically insoluble in ether, benzene, chloroform, hexane.

The aqueous solution is strongly acid (1% w/v: pH 3.13). At a pH below 5, solutions can be sterilized at 110° without loss of the vitamin, but it is rapidly destroyed when a solution is heated to this temperature at a pH above 5. Thiamine is very sensitive to alkali; in solution at a pH above 7 it is already destroyed at room temperature (thiazole ring opens). The solution exhibits two absorption bands in the ultraviolet, at 233 and 267 mμ.

Sulfite at room temperature cleaves the molecule into its pyrimidine and thiazole parts. Ferricyanide in alkaline solution oxidizes thiamine to thiochrome, a compound with intense blue fluorescence.

Thiamine gives a number of colour reactions. With diazotized sulfanilic acid and formaldehyde a pink colour is produced; with diazotized p-aminoacetophenone a red-purple colour. Potassium bismuth iodide gives an orangered precipitate. Coloured precipitates are also obtained with picrolonic acid, gold chloride, mercuric chloride and iodine. Thiamine is further precipitated by picric acid and a variety of alkaloidal reagents.

7. Methods of assay

Since thiamine was first discovered, countless methods have been developed for its determination: biological methods, using either test animals or microorganisms, and chemical methods. Many of them have gradually been abandoned and therefore will not be discussed in detail here. For particulars, the reader may be referred to reviews on this subject[26,27].

For the determination of thiamine pyrophosphate (the most abundant form of thiamine in animal tissues) a sensitive manometric procedure exists, based upon its function as a coenzyme of yeast carboxylase.

(a) Animal methods

Biological assay methods using animals were the first to be developed. They were the only practicable methods in the days before pure thiamine became available. They are specific, but also expensive, in terms of time, animals, and material under assay. Therefore they have been abandoned for routine use and are only occasionally employed for a specific purpose, for instance to test the physiological availability of the vitamin in certain foodstuffs and diets.

The animal methods can be classified as follows:

(*i*) *Protective methods*

Protective methods, based on the prevention of polyneuritis. They were generally carried out with birds (fowls, pigeons, rice birds), because these animals develop characteristic symptoms of polyneuritis in several weeks on a simple diet of washed polished rice and water, before other disturbances appear on this multiple-deficient diet. By adding the material under assay to the basal diet at different levels, the minimum protective amount is determined.

(*ii*) *Growth methods*

Growth methods, based on the rate of growth of young animals, have mostly made use of young rats, fed a basal diet composed of purified carbohydrate, fat, protein, salts, autoclaved yeast and cod liver oil. In long-term growth tests, varying quantities of the material under assay are added to the basal diet and the amount of thiamine is computed from the growth response over a number of weeks. In short-term growth tests, young rats receive the basal diet until their growth curves definitely begin to decline. A single oral dose of the material is then administered, causing a temporary gain in weight. The time this effect lasts is proportional to the amount of thiamine administered. This test is economical in terms of time, material, and animals, which can be used repeatedly.

An ingenious and sensitive method elaborated by Van 't Hoog[28] makes use of the requirement for thiamine of *Drosophila* for normal development and metamorphoses. The material to be tested is added in different levels to the nutrient medium on which washed *Drosophila* eggs are allowed to develop.

Generally speaking, growth methods are not as specific as protective or curative methods. Therefore precautions must be taken to ensure that the growth response measured derives solely from thiamine.

(*iii*) *Curative methods*

Curative methods mostly make use of rats that have developed symptoms of polyneuritis after several weeks on a thiamine-deficient diet. After a single dose of the material under assay either the "length of cure", or the "percentage cure" during 4 days, is taken as a measure of the amount of thiamine. Such tests are also economical as regards time and material.

(*iv*) *The bradycardia test*

The bradycardia test makes use of the fall in heart rate of rats during the development of polyneuritis. A single dose of thiamine elicits a temporary rise in heart rate. The duration of the effect is proportional to the amount of the vitamin administered. The test is not easy to reproduce and perhaps not very specific. It also requires an electrocardiograph.

(b) Microbiological methods

Most methods for the determination of thiamine employing micro-organisms measure the growth of the latter, in terms of turbidity of the culture, on thiamine-free nutrient media supplemented with small amounts of the vitamin. They are still used fairly frequently, because they are very sensitive, fairly rapid, and inexpensive.

Many of the micro-organisms proposed, even some that have been extensively used, show a certain lack of specificity: their requirement for thiamine as a growth factor can also be met by the pyrimidine and thiazole moieties of the molecule, either singly or in combination. Such is the case for the yeast *Saccharomyces cerevisiae* and the mould *Phycomyces blakesleeanus*.

Strictly specific for thiamine are the yeast *Kloeckera brevis*[29] and the bacteria *Lactobacillus fermentum*[30] [36] and *Lactobacillus viridescens*[31]. The first will measure 0.2–2.0 mμg of thiamine, the two latter 5–40 mμg. They all also respond to thiamine pyrophosphate, but to a different degree; therefore the material under assay should be hydrolysed by a phosphatase preparation prior to assay.

Certain mutant strains of *Escherichia coli* have also been profitably used for the determination of thiamine[27].

In this section a method developed by Schultz, Atkin and Frey may also be mentioned, based on the stimulation by thiamine of the fermentation of glucose by baker's yeast (*S. cerevisiae*) in the presence of ammonium sulfate. Carried out in a Warburg apparatus, it can measure 0.01–0.02 μg of thiamine[32]. This method has been widely used. The effect of thiamine on fermentation has been shown to depend quantitatively upon the formation of carboxylase: the coenzyme being derived from thiamine, and ammonium sulfate in the medium providing material for the synthesis of enzyme protein[33]. Under the circumstances of the test carboxylase is evidently a limiting enzyme for fermentation.

(c) Chemical methods

For routine determinations of thiamine chemical methods are the most widely used. There are two methods whose specificity has been well established, and that are rapid and reasonably accurate and sensitive.

Before either one can be applied, the material under assay has to undergo a preliminary treatment:

(i) The vitamin must be extracted from the material. This is usually achieved by heating to 100° in dilute acid, at pH 2 to 3.

(ii) The phosphate esters of thiamine must be hydrolysed. Most workers use the commercially available "Takadiastase" preparation for this purpose, but an also easily procurable preparation of alkaline-washed, acetone-dried baker's yeast is greatly to be preferred[34], because it acts much more rapidly.

(*iii*) In many cases the vitamin has to be separated from interfering substances, or concentrated, by an adsorption and elution step. The adsorbing materials most frequently used are the acid clay Frankonite and the artificial zeolite Decalso. Bentonite is also a good adsorbent for thiamine.

The colorimetric azo method of Melnick and Field makes use of the red compound formed when diazotized *p*-aminoacetophenone reacts with thiamine in alkaline solution[35,36]. The reaction is performed on the thiamine extract after preliminary treatment as above. The red pigment is extracted with xylene. This extraction makes the method specific for thiamine. The compound formed from its phosphate esters is insoluble in xylene. The preferred range of thiamine for this determination is 20 to 100 μg. Many minor modifications and simplifications have been proposed.

The thiochrome method is based on the observation by Barger *et al.* that oxidation with alkaline ferricyanide converts thiamine into a compound with intense blue fluorescence: thiochrome[37].

Thiochrome

Jansen adapted this reaction for the quantitative determination of thiamine[38]. The oxidation with ferricyanide in alkaline medium is carried out on an extract of the vitamin treated as mentioned above. The thiochrome formed is extracted into isobutanol and the fluorescence of the extract measured. The fluorescent products formed from the thiamine phosphates are only slightly soluble in isobutanol.

The preferred range of thiamine for this determination is 0.5 to 2.5 μg. A micromethod developed by Burch *et al.*[39] permits determination of 2 to 5 mμg.

Many modifications and simplifications have also been proposed for this procedure[27]. It demands a critical approach, for there are many possible sources of error, but by its rapidity and sensitivity it has become the procedure of choice for the chemical determination of thiamine.

Both chemical methods allow determination of esterified as well as free thiamine by running two determinations, one with and one without the phosphatase treatment.

(d) Other methods

In recent years methods have been worked out for the separation of thiamine and its phosphate esters with the aid of chromatography and electrophoresis.

Small amounts of thiamine and its derivatives can be satisfactorily separated by chromatography on paper[40]. Location of the spots by applying the thiochrome procedure to the paper permits detection of 5 mμg of thiamine. Naiman's potassium bismuth iodide reagent is less sensitive (limit 0.1 μg). It imparts an orange-pink colour to the spots[41].

Extremely small amounts (down to $5 \cdot 10^{-4}$ μg) can be detected with the very sensitive "bioautographic" technique[42,43]. The developed chromatogram is brought into brief contact with the surface of a nutrient agar, lacking thiamine and seeded with an organism requiring this vitamin for growth. Upon incubation of the agar plate growth zones appear, corresponding to the zones of migration of the compounds on the original chromatogram.

Separation by paper electrophoresis is also feasible but requires about 10 μg of each compound[40]. Electrophoresis in agar gel is more sensitive[43].

For preparative purposes, successful separation has been carried out by column chromatography on ion exchange resins (Amberlite IRC 50 and XE 64) and by electrophoresis in cellulose columns[40].

(e) Test for physiological availability

A method for estimating the availability to man of thiamine in foodstuffs is based on the observation that the urinary excretion of thiamine parallels the intake, if the test subject is normal and subsisting on an adequate diet. Thiamine in urine is determined chemically[44].

8. Function and mechanism of action

Thiamine has a physiological function in the form of thiamine pyrophosphate. This compound is the coenzyme of a number of enzymes involved in carbohydrate metabolism: carboxylase, pyruvic dehydrogenase, α-ketoglutaric dehydrogenase, transketolase, phosphoketolase. Thiamine monophosphate and thiamine triphosphate cannot replace the pyrophosphate ester in this function; a supposed activity of the triphosphate was later shown to be due to its partial hydrolysis to the pyrophosphate[45].

It has been suggested that thiamine would also have a second function, in particular in brain, not requiring preliminary phosphorylation to thiamine pyrophosphate[46]; but the supporting evidence for this theory subsequently proved to be inadequate[47,48].

The connection between the known physiological activity of thiamine and the clinical symptoms manifest in thiamine deficiency is still completely obscure, although the activity of many of the enzymes mentioned above is then depressed.

It has long been a puzzle how one and the same coenzyme could be active in such widely different reactions as those catalysed by the enzymes mentioned above, until the realization dawned that they could all be grouped together under the common denominator: transfer of aldehyde. This suggested the possible occurrence of an intermediate aldehyde–coenzyme or aldehyde–enzyme complex, a surmise which recent studies have proved to be correct.

According to Breslow, the "active aldehyde" intermediate in the decarboxylation of pyruvate could be an α-hydroxyethyl derivative of thiamine pyrophosphate, the substituent being attached in position 2 to the thiazole ring[49]. His starting point was the observation that thiazolium salts easily lose a proton at C-2. Thus a stable and reactive zwitterion results that could be capable of forming an acyl carbanion derivative. The near-by aminopyrimidine ring would have an inductive effect upon electron withdrawal at C-2. Breslow pictures the formation of acetoin from pyruvate and acetaldehyde* as follows:

* A reaction catalysed by pyruvic dehydrogenase and by carboxylase.

Indeed both α-lactylthiamine pyrophosphate (XX) and α-hydroxyethyl-thiamine pyrophosphate (XXI) have been isolated and identified as products after incubation of pyruvate with a purified carboxylase preparation[50,51]. When [2-14C]pyruvate is used, the radioactivity is found in the thiazole part of the molecule after sulfite cleavage of XXI. Acetaldehyde is formed from pyruvic acid by yeast carboxylase by enzymic cleavage of intermediate XXI, liberating thiamine pyrophosphate[52]. XXI has also been identified as inter-mediate in the formation of acetyl-coenzyme A from pyruvic acid by pyruvic oxidase[53]. The transketolase reaction has been shown to proceed via a gly-colaldehyde–enzyme intermediate[54]; here one may expect to find dihydroxy-ethylthiamine pyrophosphate as "active glycol-aldehyde". Such exper-iments strongly support Breslow's concept of the reaction mechanism.

9. Essential groups in the molecule; antithiamines

Once the structure of thiamine was definitely established, the question arose which groups of the molecule are essential for its vitamin activity. This was shown to be the case[55] for:

(*1*) The methylene bridge. The analogous 3-pyrimidylthiazolium salt is inactive.

(*2*) The amino group in position 4 on the pyrimidine ring. Replacement by a hydroxyl group gives a compound with antithiamine activity: oxythi-amine (see below).

(*3*) Hydrogen at position C-2 of the thiazolium ring. Methylation gives an inactive compound, entirely in agreement with Breslow's mechanism of thiamine action.

(*4*) A β-hydroxyethyl group in position 5 of the thiazolium ring. Activity is lost upon replacing this group by hydrogen. The need for a free hydroxyl group is obvious, for here phosphorylation takes place when thiamine is converted into thiamine pyrophosphate.

(*5*) The thiazole ring. Pyrithiamine, the analogous compound in which the thiazole ring has been replaced by a pyridine ring, is a potent antivitamin (see below).

It is possible to introduce some changes in the vitamin molecule and still retain vitamin activity. For instance, when the methyl group in position 2 on the pyrimidine ring is replaced by ethyl, the product still exhibits activity, albeit much reduced. The corresponding propyl derivative is inactive; the butyl derivative has antithiamine properties, and so have 2-alkylthio deriv-atives.

Thiamine disulfide (the product of condensation of two thiamine molecules after opening of the thiazole ring and oxidation) still has the complete biological activity of thiamine[56]. So have allithiamine (XXII), a product of

the action of an extract of garlic upon thiamine, and its homologue dithio-
propylthiamine (XXIII). In fact, these two compounds are better absorbed
from the intestine than thiamine. They cause a higher and longer-lasting
rise of thiamine pyrophosphate activity in the liver, of total thiamine in
blood, and of thiamine excretion in urine[57].

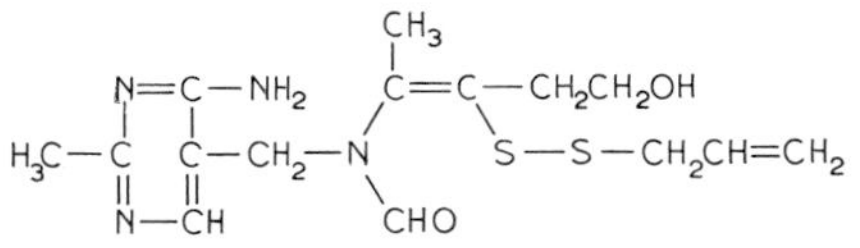

(XXII) 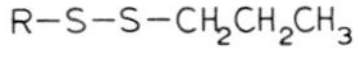   (XXIII)

The antithiamines studied best are pyrithiamine (XXIV) and oxythiamine[58]
(XXV). Pyrithiamine is the most potent antagonist of the two.

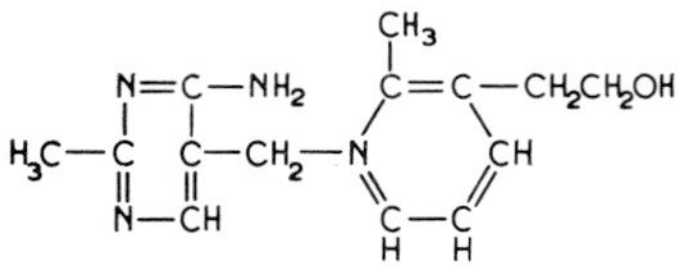

(XXIV) 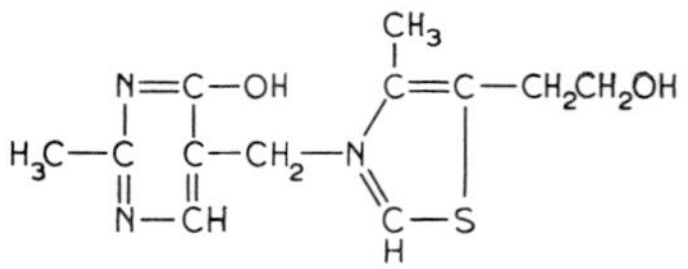   (XXV)

When it is given to animals, together with otherwise adequate amounts of
thiamine, thiamine pyrophosphate soon disappears from the tissues and
symptoms of polyneuritis become manifest[47,48]. When oxythiamine is given
the decrease in thiamine pyrophosphate is much slower, and polyneuritis is
seldom observed before death.

The antagonistic action of these compounds would seem to be due to their
fairly close structural relationship with thiamine. As soon as the structure
of an analogue deviates too far from that of the vitamin it loses its anti-
metabolite properties: oxypyrithiamine, combining the modifications of
XXIV and XXV, is inert[58].

Experiments with enzyme systems *in vitro* make it seem likely that
pyrithiamine acts mainly by inhibition of thiamine pyrophosphate synthesis
(it is a strong inhibitor of animal thiaminokinase, in contrast to oxythiamine),
while oxythiamine presumably is only active after phosphorylation (oxythiamine pyrophosphate is a powerful competitor of thiamine pyrophosphate
for a number of enzymes requiring the latter, far more so than pyrithiamine
pyrophosphate)[59].

REFERENCES

1 C. EIJKMAN, *Arch. pathol. Anat. Physiol.*, *Virchow's*, 148 (1897) 523.
2 G. GRIJNS, *Researches on Vitamins 1900–1911*, J. Noorduyn, Gorinchem, 1935, p. 37, 38.
3 C. FUNK, *J. State Med.*, 20 (1912) 341.
4 B. C. P. JANSEN AND W. F. DONATH, *Koninkl. Ned. Akad. Wetenschap.*, *Proc.*, 29 (1926) 1390.
5 R. R. WILLIAMS AND R. D. SPIES, *Vitamin B_1 (Thiamin) and its Use in Medicine*, MacMillan, New York, 1939, p. 144.
6 H. T. CLARKE AND S. GURIN, *J. Am. Chem. Soc.*, 57 (1935) 1876.
7 E. R. BUCHMAN, *J. Am. Chem. Soc.*, 58 (1936) 1803.
8 H. ANDERSAG AND K. WESTPHAL, *Ber.*, 70 (1937) 2035.
9 H. M. WUEST in W. H. SEBRELL AND R. S. HARRIS (Eds.), *The Vitamins*, Vol. III, Academic Press, New York, 1954, p. 409.
10 R. R. WILLIAMS AND J. K. CLINE, *J. Am. Chem. Soc.*, 58 (1936) 1504.
11 A. R. TODD AND F. BERGEL, *J. Chem. Soc.*, (1937) 364.
12 R. GREWE, *Z. Physiol. Chem.*, *Hoppe-Seyler's*, 242 (1936) 89.
13 J. BONNER AND H. BONNER, *Vitamins and Hormones*, 6 (1948) 225.
14 J. M. VAN LANEN AND F. W. TANNER, *Vitamins and Hormones*, 6 (1948) 163.
15 I. G. LEDER, *Biochem. Biophys. Research Communs.*, 1 (1959) 63.
16 G. W. CAMIENER AND G. M. BROWN, *J. Biol. Chem.*, 235 (1960) 2404, 2411.
17 F. LEUTHARDT AND H. NIELSEN, *Helv. Chim. Acta*, 35 (1952) 1196.
18 E. P. STEYN-PARVÉ, *Biochim. Biophys. Acta*, 8 (1952) 310.
19 O. FORSANDER, *Societas Scientiarum Fennica, Commentationes Physico-Mathematicae*, Vol. 19, 1946, no. 22.
20 H. G. K. WESTENBRINK, *Proc. Fourth Int. Congress Biochem.*, Vol. IX, 1958, 73.
21 P. T. McCARTHY, L. R. CERECEDO AND E. V. BROWN, *J. Biol. Chem.*, 209 (1954) 611.
22 J. M. IACONO AND B. C. JOHNSON, *J. Am. Chem. Soc.*, 79 (1957) 6321.
23 A. FUJITA, *Advances in Enzymol.*, 15 (1954) 389.
24 E. E. KUPSTAS AND D. J. HENNESSY, *J. Am. Chem. Soc.*, 79 (1957) 5217, 5220, 5222.
25 J. C. SOMOGYI, *Die Antianeurin-Faktoren, Intern. Z. Vitaminforsch.*, (1952) Beiheft no.6.
26 Ref. 5, p. 197.
27 O. MICKELSEN AND R. S. YAMAMOTO in D. GLICK (Ed.), *Methods of Biochemical Analysis*, 6 (1958) 191.
28 E. G. VAN 'T HOOG, *Z. Vitaminforsch.*, 4 (1935) 300.
29 E. HOFF-JØRGENSEN AND B. HANSEN, *Acta Chem. Scand.*, 9 (1955) 562.
30 H. P. SARETT AND V. H. CHELDELIN, *J. Biol. Chem.*, 155 (1944) 153.
31 R. H. DEIBEL, J. B. EVANS AND C. F. NIVEN JR., *J. Bacteriol.*, 74 (1957) 818.
32 L. ATKIN, A. S. SCHULTZ AND C. N. FREY, *J. Biol. Chem.*, 129 (1939) 471.
33 T. J. M. MAESEN, *Biochim. Biophys. Acta*, 12 (1953) 445.
34 H. G. K. WESTENBRINK AND A. F. WILLEBRANDS, *Z. Vitaminforsch.*, 14 (1944) 291.
35 D. MELNICK AND H. FIELD JR., *J. Biol. Chem.*, 127 (1939) 515, 531.
36 P. GYÖRGY AND S. H. RUBIN in P. GYÖRGY (Ed.), *Vitamin Methods*, Vol. I, Academic Press, New York, 1950, p. 217.
37 G. BARGER, F. BERGEL AND A. R. TODD, *Nature*, 136 (1935) 259.
38 B. C. P. JANSEN, *Rec. trav. chim.*, 55 (1936) 1046.
39 H. B. BURCH, O. A. BESSEY, R. H. LOVE AND O. H. LOWRY, *J. Biol. Chem.*, 198 (1952) 447.
40 D. SILIPRANDI AND N. SILIPRANDI, *Biochim. Biophys. Acta*, 14 (1952) 52.
41 W. BARTLEY, *Biochem. J.*, 56 (1954) 379.
42 W. A. WINSTEN AND E. EIGEN, *Proc. Soc. Exptl. Biol. Med.*, 67 (1948) 513.
43 G. MARTEN, *Nature*, 176 (1955) 1064.
44 D. MELNICK AND B. L. OSER, *Vitamins and Hormones*, 5 (1947) 39; D. MELNICK, M. HOCHBERG AND B. L. OSER, *J. Nutrition*, 30 (1945) 67.
45 K. H. KIESSLING, *Biochim. Biophys. Acta*, 20 (1956) 293.
46 D. W. WOOLLEY AND R. B. MERRIFIELD, *Federation Proc.*, 11 (1952) 458; *Bull. soc. chim. biol.*, 36 (1954) 1207.

[47] L. DE CARO, G. RINDI, V. PERRI AND G. FERRARI, *Experientia*, 12 (1956) 300.
[48] J. C. KOEDAM, *Biochim. Biophys. Acta*, 29 (1958) 333; J. C. KOEDAM AND E. P. STEYN-PARVÉ, *Koninkl. Ned. Akad. Wetenschap. Proc.*, C62 (1959) 400.
[49] R. BRESLOW, *J. Am. Chem. Soc.*, 80 (1958) 3719; R. BRESLOW AND E. MCNELIS, *J. Am. Chem. Soc.*, 81 (1959) 3080.
[50] G. CARSON AND G. M. BROWN, *J. Biol. Chem.*, 235 (1960) PC 3.
[51] H. HOLZER AND K. BEAUCAMP, *Biochim. Biophys. Acta*, 46 (1961) 226.
[52] P. SCRIBA, S. SCHNEIDER AND H. HOLZER, *Biochim. Biophys. Acta*, 54 (1961) 115.
[53] H. W. GOEDDE, H. INOUYE AND H. HOLZER, *Biochim. Biophys. Acta*, 50 (1961) 41.
[54] A. G. DATTA AND E. RACKER, *J. Biol. Chem.*, 236 (1961) 624.
[55] F. BERGEL AND A. R. TODD, *J. Chem. Soc.*, (1937) 1504.
[56] G. BONVICINO AND D. J. HENNESSY, *Intern. Z. Vitaminforsch.*, 30 (1959) 97.
[57] D. HIOCO, R. TIXIER AND A. UZAN, *Bull. soc. chim. biol.,* 41 (1959) 1075.
[58] L. R. CERECEDO, *Am. J. Clin. Nutrition*, 3 (1955) 273.
[59] J. C. KOEDAM AND E. P. STEYN-PARVÉ, *Koninkl. Ned. Akad. Wetenschap., Proc.*, C63 (1960) 318.

General reference: Chapter on Thiamine in W. H. SEBRELL AND R. S. HARRIS (Eds.), *The Vitamins*, Vol. III, Academic Press, New York, 1954, p. 403.

Chapter II

Riboflavin and Closely Related Flavins

University of Rochester Medical Center, Rochester, N.Y. (U.S.A.)

The briefness of this section necessitates reference to previous reviews which can be consulted by those interested in more historical detail. The most recent one, is written by Wagner-Jauregg[1]. It is heavily documented by citations from the literature up to the time of its appearance and its historical account is enriched by the first hand knowledge which the author can bring to the subject out of his many years of identification with the vitamin, dating from the time of its discovery.

6,7-Dimethyl-9-(1'-D-ribityl)isoalloxazine

1. Isolation

The first isolation of crystalline, pure riboflavin was accomplished by Kuhn, György and Wagner-Jauregg[2], as a direct result of their interest in the water-soluble, growth promoting vitamin B_2. They named the substance "ovoflavin", because its origin had been egg-white, and showed that it stimulated the growth of rats fed diets deficient in vitamin B_2. Ellinger and Koschara[3] isolated an impure preparation of riboflavin from milk and while they were unaware of the vitamin nature of their product, they did introduce this source material from which riboflavin could be readily isolated by the procedures perfected by Wagner-Jauregg. The possibility that these materials might be related to Warburg and Christian's[4] yellow enzyme was suggested by both groups of workers. Shortly after the appearance of these two papers, Booher[5] reported the preparation of a concentrate from whey powder which certainly was largely riboflavin and which stimulated the growth of vitamin B_2-deficient rats.

2. General chemical and physical properties

Riboflavin crystallizes from a variety of solvents as fine orange needles. The decomposition point is about 280° but values found in the literature may differ several degrees from this. It is very soluble in alkali and in 36% hydrochloric acid in the cold, and in 18% hydrochloric acid when heated. The vitamin is unstable in alkali while relatively stable toward acid. The water solution is yellow in color and shows an intense yellowish-green fluorescence (maximum 565 mμ) which is useful for quantitative determination.

The fluorescence is maximal between pH 4 and 8 but vanishes on the addition of more acid or alkali. The absorption spectrum of an aqueous solution shows maxima at 447, 373, 267 and 223 mμ. Riboflavin has an amphoteric character with dissociation constants[6] of $K_a = 63 \cdot 10^{-12}$ and $K_b = 0.5 \cdot 10^{-12}$; its isoelectric point is at pH 6 which is approximately the pH of a saturated (12 mg/100 ml at 26°) aqueous solution. In alkaline solution riboflavin shows strong optical rotation[7] which is dependent on concentration, $[\alpha]_D^{21} = -117°(c = 0.5\%; 0.1\ N\ \text{NaOH})$.

Crystalline riboflavin is relatively stable when protected from light. Exposure to light slowly destroys the activity of the crystalline material; it is rapidly destroyed in alkaline solution to produce lumiflavin while the rate is far slower in neutral or acid solution, in which case lumichrome is formed. In oxygen free, neutral, aqueous solutions, light causes the loss of the yellow color but not the biological activity. The colorless form is dihydroriboflavin. Riboflavin is relatively stable to both dry and moist heat.

Riboflavin is stable in the presence of acids, air, and mild oxidizing agents. An elegant procedure for the purification of synthetic flavins involves their solution in 6 N or stronger hydrochloric acid and the oxidation of impurities by the addition of hydrogen peroxide or nitric acid, for example[8]. The compound can be reduced to dihydroriboflavin (leucoflavin) by a number of reducing agents, the most practical of which is sodium hydrosulfite. The oxidized form can be regained by shaking with air. The redox-potential[9] of an equimolecular mixture of the oxidized and reduced form of riboflavin at pH 7.0 is −0.185 V.

Good adsorbants for riboflavin are Magnesol[10], Florisil and Frankonit. It can be eluted from these materials by dilute pyridine or acetone, for example.

3. Characterization of riboflavin

The characterization of riboflavin was only partially accomplished by degradation. Not until its total synthesis was accomplished was the true nature of the tetrahydroxypentane side chain known. The empirical formula of riboflavin is $C_{17}H_{20}N_4O_6$. Photolysis of riboflavin in alkaline solution yields a compound of empirical formula $C_{13}H_{12}N_4O_2$, called lumiflavin*, differing from riboflavin by the elements[11] of $C_4H_8O_4$. Acetylation of riboflavin yielded a readily hydrolyzable tetraacetate[11,12] while lumiflavin could not be acetylated. Oxidation of riboflavin by lead tetraacetate[11] yielded about one mole equivalent of formaldehyde while lumiflavin produced none. Riboflavin could be converted to a diacetone compound[7]. These data demonstrated that the elements of $C_4H_8O_4$, lost from riboflavin by photolysis, contained four hydroxyl groups which existed as vicinal pairs and that one primary hydroxyl group was alpha to a secondary hydroxyl group. Such conditions can be satisfied by only a tetrahydroxybutyl group and riboflavin must contain such a group which is lost in its conversion to lumiflavin.

Methylation of lumiflavin yielded a methylated product. When this product, lumiflavin and riboflavin were subjected to the Herzig–Meyer reaction it was found that they contained two, one and no methylimino groups respectively[13]. The presence of a methylimino group in lumiflavin not found in riboflavin fixed the position of the attachment of the tetrahydroxybutyl group. The loss of a polyhydroxy group by photolysis was novel but its occurrence was strongly supported by the finding that quinoxaline was formed by the photolysis in alkaline solution of 2-tetrahydroxybutylquinoxaline, a compound prepared specifically to test this point[14].

Both riboflavin and lumiflavin yielded urea on alkaline hydrolysis[12]; in the case of lumiflavin an additional compound $C_{12}H_{12}N_2O_3$ was produced. This alkaline hydrolysis required two mole equivalents of water which indicated the urea had come from a ring[15]. The compound $C_{12}H_{12}N_2O_3$ lost CO_2 on heating to produce a substance[15] $C_{11}H_{12}N_2O$ possessing monobasic properties. For these reasons it could be concluded that lumiflavin contained the elements of urea and two carbonyl groups, one lost in the urea and the other converted to a carboxyl group by the hydrolysis.

When the compound $C_{11}H_{12}N_2O$ was heated with alkali a new substance $C_9H_{14}N_2$ was formed[13]. When a solution of the latter material, suspected of being an o-phenylenediamine was treated with ferric chloride a bluish-green color indicated that it was a p,p-disubstituted-o-phenylenediamine and it proved to be 1,2-dimethyl-4-amino-5-methylaminobenzene. The structures of lumiflavin and riboflavin can be assembled from these data:

---

* When riboflavin is photolysed in neutral or acid solution the whole side chain is lost to form an alloxazine known as lumichrome.

$(C_9H_{14}N_2)$ $(C_{11}H_{12}N_2O)$ $(C_{12}H_{12}N_2O_3)$

$(C_{13}H_{12}N_4O_2)$ $(C_{17}H_{20}N_4O_6)$

Lumiflavin Riboflavin

Kuhn[16-18] and associates promptly established the structure of lumiflavin by its total synthesis but the identity of the polyhydroxy side chain in riboflavin was not known to be D-ribityl until the unequivocal synthesis of the vitamin had been accomplished.

4. Synthesis of riboflavin and related biologically active flavins

The synthesis of riboflavin was accomplished for the first time by Karrer[19] and his co-workers, but a successful synthesis was also reported by Kuhn[20] and his co-workers only a few weeks later.

In the brief description of procedures for the synthesis of riboflavin which follows, only a few examples can be given. There are basically two important steps in the synthesis, one is the formation of the N-(1'-D-ribityl)-2-amino-4,5-dimethylaniline, or its equivalent, and the second is the condensation of this material with alloxan, or its equivalent, to form riboflavin. To limit the number of compounds considered, only those sufficiently like riboflavin, by virtue of their containing the D-ribityl side chain, will be discussed. Special consideration will be given, however, to three exceptions, 6,7-dimethyl-9-(1'-L-arabityl)isolloxazine, 6,7-dichloro-9-(1'-D-sorbityl)isolloxazine and 6,7-dimethyl-9-(1'-L-lyxityl)-isolloxazine, because of particular chemical or biological importance. This means that most of the compounds related to riboflavin which will be discussed, will show variations only in the substituents on the benzenoid ring. In spite of these limitations those flavins covered will include nearly all the compounds which have a significant degree of either riboflavin-like activity or riboflavin inhibitor activity.

Procedure 1

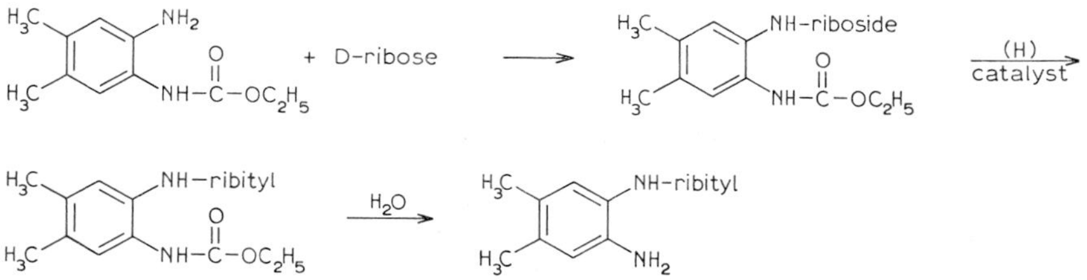

The N-(1'-D-ribityl)-2-amino-4,5-dimethylaniline has been used for the synthesis[21–23] of riboflavin. N-(1'-D-Ribityl)-2-amino-4-methylaniline[24], -2-amino-5-methylaniline[25] and -2-amino-5-ethylaniline[26] have been prepared by this method. N-(1'-D-Lyxityl)-2-amino-4,5-dimethylaniline[27] was also prepared in this way but D-ribose could not be made to condense with 2-carbethoxyamino-4-methyl-5-chloroaniline[28].

Procedure 2

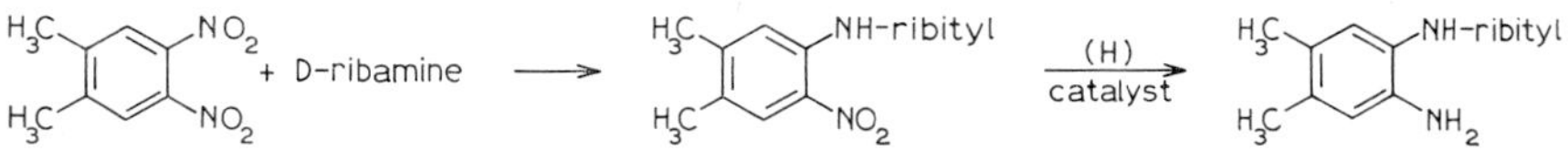

In addition to this procedure having been used for the synthesis of riboflavin[22,23], it has also been used to prepare N-(1'-D-ribityl)-2-amino-4,5-dichloroaniline[29,30], -2-amino-4,5-dibromoaniline[37], and N-(1'-D-sorbityl)-2-amino-4,5-dichloroaniline[31]. This method is useful only if the starting material is symmetrically substituted.

Procedure 3

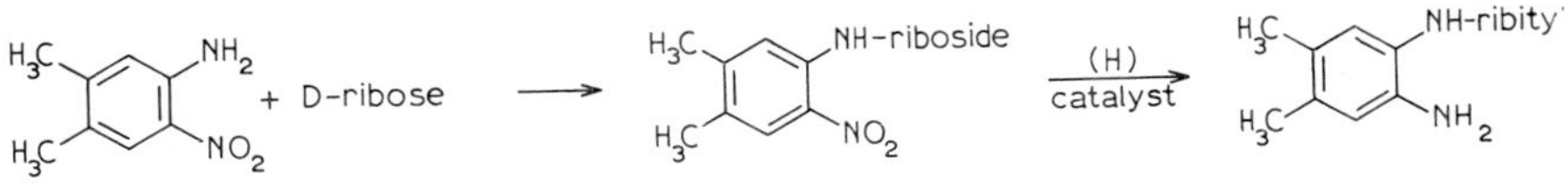

Kuhn[32,33] and co-workers prepared riboflavin in this way. The procedure has also been used to prepare N-(1'-D-ribityl)-2-amino-3,5-dimethylaniline[33], -2-amino-4,6-dimethylaniline[33], -2-amino-4,5-diethylaniline[34] and -2-amino-4-ethylaniline[35]. D-Ribose was found not to combine with 2-nitro-4-chloro-5-methylaniline and 2-nitro-4-methyl-5-chloroaniline[28].

Procedure 4

H₃C— (X), H₃C— (NO₂) ring + D-ribamine ⟶ H₃C— (NH–ribityl), H₃C— (NO₂) ring $\xrightarrow[\text{catalyst}]{\text{(H)}}$ H₃C— (NH–ribityl), H₃C— (NH₂) ring

This procedure has not been used for the synthesis of riboflavin although it was used to prepare 6,7-dimethyl-9-(1′-L-arabityl)isoalloxazine[36]. It is given here because it has been used to prepare several compounds related to riboflavin; N-(1′-D-ribityl)-2-amino-4-chloroaniline[37,38], -2-amino-4-fluoroaniline[37], -2-amino-4-chloro-5-methylaniline[28], -2-amino-4-methyl-5-chloroaniline[28], and -2-amino-4-ethylaniline[39].

The yields of product resulting from the use of D-ribamine and 2-nitro-4-methylchlorobenzene[39] and 2-nitro-4-ethylchlorobenzene are low[39].

Procedure 5

The following procedure involves the introduction of the ribityl group before the introduction of the second nitrogen *ortho* to the ribitylamino group. It is important because the industrial production methods are variations of this procedure and because several homologs and analogs of riboflavin have been prepared by its use.

H₃C— (NH₂), H₃C— ring + D-ribose ⟶ H₃C— (NH–riboside), H₃C— ring $\xrightarrow[\text{catalyst}]{\text{(H)}}$ H₃C— (NH–ribityl), H₃C— ring

Ribose can be condensed with the 3,4-dimethylaniline. The resulting N-D-riboside, can be isolated[40–42] but need not be isolated[43–45] prior to catalytic reduction to the N-(1′-D-ribityl)-4,5-dimethylaniline. N-(1′-D-Ribityl)-4-ethylaniline[35], -4-chloro-5-methylaniline[28], -4-methyl-5-chloroaniline[28], -4-ethyl-5-methylaniline[26,39], -4-methyl-5-ethylaniline[39] and -4,5-diethylaniline[39] have been made by this method.

The difficult and expensive preparation of D-ribose for the synthesis of riboflavin stimulated the search for methods which would make the D-ribityl chain available without the use of this costly sugar. Three alternative procedures are available: the condensation of 3,4-dimethylaniline with, (*a*) D-ribonolactone[46], (*b*) tetraacetyl-D-ribononitrile[47], or (*c*) tetraacetyl-D-ribose[48]. Using these materials, one to four steps are required to produce the desired N-(1′-tetraacetyl-D-ribityl)-4,5-dimethylaniline which can be converted to the N-(1′-D-ribityl)-4,5-dimethylaniline by deacetylation.

The substituted D-ribitylanilines can be converted into the *o*-phenylenediamines by the introduction* of an azo group by means of coupling with a phenyldiazonium salt[43,49]. This procedure results in mixtures of azo compounds consisting of a principal product with the azo group in the 2-position and varying small amounts of material with the azo group in the 6-position[49], depending on the R-group in the arylazo radicle.

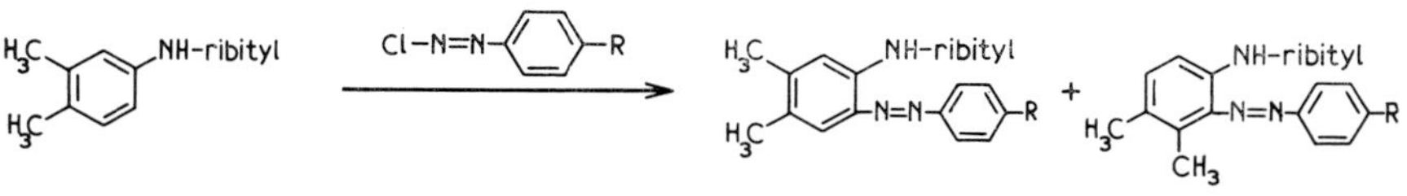

-2-azo -6-azo

N-($1'$-D-Ribityl)-2-p-tolylazo-4,5-dimethylaniline[42,49], N-($1'$-L-lyxityl)-2-phenylazo-4,5-dimethylaniline[50], N-($1'$-D-ribityl)-2-p-tolylazo-4-ethylaniline[35], -2-p-nitrophenylazo-4-chloro-5-methylaniline[28], -2-p-nitrophenylazo-4-methyl-5-chloroaniline[28], -2-phenylazo-4-ethyl-5-methylaniline[26,39], -2-phenylazo-4-methyl-5-ethylaniline[39] and -2-p-tolylazo-4,5-diethylaniline[39] have been prepared by this method. Separation of the -2- and the -6-azo compounds is very difficult[49] and if not accomplished, subsequent reduction of the azo compound to the o-phenylenediamine will lead to mixtures since the -2- and -6-isomers are reduced equally readily. For this reason, the flavins produced from such impure o-phenylenediamines will consist of mixtures of the 6,7-disubstituted** and the 5,6-disubstituted isoalloxazines[28,39,49].

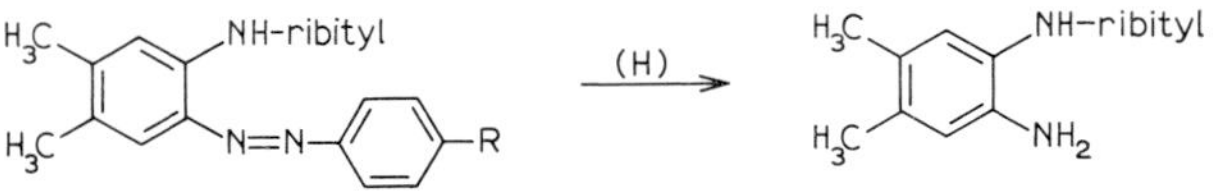

Procedure 6

The N-($1'$-D-ribityl)-2-amino-4,5-dimethylaniline can be condensed with alloxan in the presence of boric acid[51] to yield riboflavin[19,20,43].

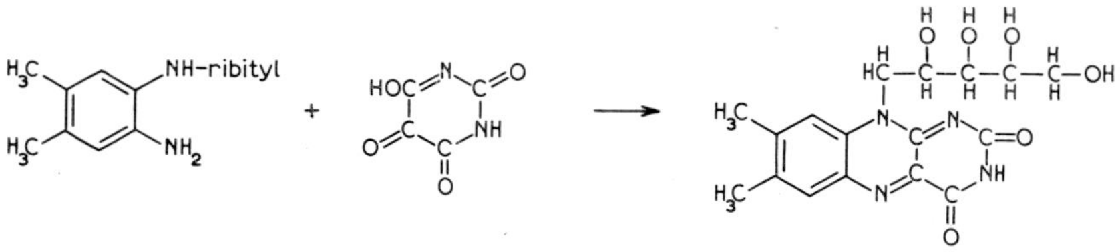

---

* N-($1'$-tetraacetyl-D-ribityl)-4,5-dimethylaniline can also be used.
** The mixture of 6-ethyl-7-methyl- and 5-methyl-6-ethyl-9-($1'$-D-ribityl)isoalloxazine referred to in ref. 39 was later purified by frequent recrystallizations from water.

References p. 34

In the synthesis of riboflavin and some related flavins, better yields are often available through the use of 5-chloro- or 5,5-dichlorobarbituric acid[52] in place of alloxan. In addition to riboflavin, 6-methyl-9-[24], 7-methyl-9-[25], 6-ethyl-9-[35], 7-ethyl-9-[26], 6,7-diethyl-9-[34], 6-ethyl-7-methyl-9-[26,39], 5,7-dimethyl-9-[33], 6,8-dimethyl-9-[33], 6,7-dichloro-9-[29,72], 6-chloro-9-[37,38], 6-fluoro-9-[37], 6,7-dibromo-9-[37], 5,6-dimethyl-9-[49], 6-chloro-7-methyl-9-[28], 6-methyl-7-chloro-9-[28], 3,6,7-trimethyl-9-(1′-D-ribityl)isoalloxazine[23] (using 2-methylalloxan), and 6,7-dichloro-9-(1′-D-sorbityl)isoalloxazine[31] have been prepared by this method.

Procedure 7

An important advance in the synthesis of riboflavin was made by Tishler[49] and associates, by the discovery that N-(1′-D-ribityl)-2-arylazo-4,5-dimethylaniline (but not the -6-arylazo isomer) would react directly with barbituric acid in a weak acid medium. Large amounts of unusually pure riboflavin can be synthesized by this procedure.

The availability of the exceptionally successful method for the purification of flavins developed by Pasternack and Brown[8] makes this method the one of choice for the synthesis of several flavins. In addition to riboflavin[49], [2-^{14}C]riboflavin[42], 6,7-dimethyl-9-(1′-L-lyxityl)isoalloxazine[50], 6-ethyl-7-methyl-9-[39], 6-methyl-7-ethyl-9-[39], 6,7-diethyl-9-[39], and 3,6,7-trimethyl-9-(1′-D-ribityl)isoalloxazine[30] (using 2-methylbarbituric acid) have been prepared by this method. N-(1′-D-Ribityl)-2-p-tolylazo-4-ethylaniline[35], -2-p-nitrophenylazo-4-chloro-5-methylaniline[28] and -2-p-nitrophenylazo-4-methyl-5-chloroaniline[28] react poorly or not at all with barbituric acid under a variety of conditions.

5. Biologically active isoalloxazines

The biological activity of several compounds showing relatively close structural similarity to riboflavin will be described in brief form. With one exception, these are the flavins whose syntheses were described in the previous section. D-Galactoflavin will be included in this group because it has considerable historical interest.

(a) Isomers of riboflavin

5,6-Dimethyl-9-(1′-D-ribityl)isoalloxazine (isoriboflavin), is a reversible antagonist of riboflavin in the nutrition of the rat with an inhibition index[53] of about 100. This material will not support the growth of *Lactolacillus casei* as the sole source of flavin[54] but it will stimulate the production of acid by this organism when suboptimal amounts of riboflavin are also present[54,55] and at no concentration tested is it inhibitory[54].

6,7-Dimethyl-9-(1′-L-lyxityl)isoalloxazine (lyxoflavin), can not serve as the sole source of flavin in the nutrition of *L. casei*[54,56], the rat[56] and the chick[57]. Small amounts of this material stimulate the production of acid by *L. casei* when suboptimal amounts of riboflavin are also present[57,59] but as the quantity of lyxoflavin is increased it inhibits the growth of this organism[54,57,59]. This compound[60] can serve as the sole source of flavin for *Lactobacillus lactis* ATCC 8000 but it has only 1/10 to 1/3 of the activity of riboflavin for this organism. Lyxoflavin stimulates a small increase in the growth rate of rats[57,59], chicks[54,59], and pigs[58] when adequate amounts of riboflavin are present in the diet. It has been suggested[56] that the compound might be an as yet unrecognized growth factor but the evidence for this is still inadequate[54,59]. Lyxoflavin is inhibitory for growth of the chick when sufficiently large quantities are added to a riboflavin containing diet[54].

(b) Homologs of riboflavin

6-Methyl-9-(1′-D-ribityl)isoalloxazine (6-methylflavin), has about 30% of the activity of riboflavin for the stimulation of the growth of the riboflavin-deficient rat when 20 μg per day are administered[24,61]. This material can serve as the sole source of flavin in the nutrition of *L. casei* and *Bacillus lactis acidi*. In both cases it stimulates the production of about 40% of the acid produced by equivalent amounts of riboflavin[62].

7-Methyl-9-(1′-D-ribityl)isoalloxazine (7-methylflavin), has about 30% of the activity of riboflavin for the stimulation of the growth of the riboflavin-deficient rat when 10 or 20 μg per day are administered[63]. This material can serve as the sole source of flavin in the nutrition of *L. casei* and *B. lactis acidi*. In the former case it stimulates the production of about 60% and in the latter case about 80% of the acid produced by equivalent amounts of riboflavin[62].

6-Ethyl-9-(1′-D-ribityl)isoalloxazine (6-ethylflavin), is a low potency antagonist of riboflavin in the nutrition of the rat with an inhibition index[64] of approximately 400. It has been found to possess about 3% of the activity of riboflavin when used as the sole flavin in the nutrition of *L. casei*[64].

7-Ethyl-9-(1′-D-ribityl)isoalloxazine (7-ethylflavin), has no vitamin-like activity for the rat when it is given as the only flavin in the diet. When it is given with suboptimal amounts of riboflavin it is said to be able to provide a small stimulus for the growth of the riboflavin-deficient rat[26].

6-Methyl-7-ethyl-9-(1'-D-ribityl)isoalloxazine (6-methyl-7-ethylflavin), has about 36% of the activity of riboflavin for the stimulation of growth of the riboflavin-deficient rat when administered in limiting quantities as the sole flavin. Animals grow to full adulthood on this flavin but they are not able to reproduce[65]. It can also serve as the sole source of flavin in the nutrition of *L. casei* for which organism it has 100% of the activity of equivalent amounts of riboflavin up to a concentration of $26.6 \cdot 10^{-11}$ moles per ml. At higher concentrations the activity levels off at about 90% of that found for equivalent amounts of riboflavin[66].

6-Ethyl-7-methyl-9-(1'-D-ribityl)isoalloxazine (6-ethyl-7-methylflavin), is active for the growth of the riboflavin-deficient rat[26] at 10 μg per day and has been found to possess about 45% of the activity of riboflavin for this purpose when administered in limiting quantities as the sole flavin[66]. Animals grow to full adulthood on this flavin but they are unable to reproduce[65]. The quantity administered influences the utilization of food for purposes of growth[66]. It can also serve as the sole source of flavin in the nutrition of *L. casei* for which organism it has 100% of the activity of equivalent amounts of riboflavin up to the concentration of $26.6 \cdot 10^{-11}$ moles per ml[66]. At higher concentrations[62,66] the activity levels off at about 90%. This material can also be utilized by *B. lactis acidi* in which case its activity is approximately 70% of that of an equivalent amount of riboflavin[62].

6,7-Diethyl-9-(1'-D-ribityl)isoalloxazine (diethylriboflavin), is a competitive antagonist of riboflavin for growth in the rat with an inhibition index[67] of about 6. When any but very small quantities are administered to the riboflavin-deficient rat, a growth response is obtained[68]. The compound does not, however, serve as a replacement of riboflavin in the nutrition of the animal because it does not permit survival[68,69]. It can serve as the sole source of flavin in the nutrition of *L. casei* for which organism it has 100% of the activity of equivalent amounts of riboflavin up to the concentration of $8.22 \cdot 10^{-11}$ moles per ml. At higher concentrations its activity[70] levels off at about 90%. It is also able to serve as the sole source of flavin for *B. lactis acidi*[68].

(c) Analogs of riboflavin

6,7-Dimethyl-9-(1'-D-dulcityl)isoalloxazine (galactoflavin), is a reversible antagonist of riboflavin in the nutrition of the rat with an inhibition index[71] of about 25. This flavin has been found to be inert for *L. casei* and *L. lactis*[54,60] but at low concentration it stimulates the acid production by *L. casei* in the presence of suboptimal quantities of riboflavin, becoming inhibitory when the ratio of galactoflavin to riboflavin becomes 500/1 or greater[54]. This material is inert for the chick[54].

6,7-Dichloro-9-(1'-D-ribityl)isoalloxazine (dichlororiboflavin), is devoid of biological activity in respect to its influence on growth in the nutrition of the rat[30]. This flavin is a reversible antagonist of riboflavin in the nutrition of *Staphylococcus aureus* and *Streptobacterium plantarum* P32 (both of which require no exogenous source of riboflavin) and *B. lactis acidi*. The inhibition is progressively released as the incubation time is increased; the inhibition index for *S. plantarum* increasing from 25 to 162 depending on whether the incubation was carried out for two or six days[29]. This material is inert for *L. casei*[30,54].

6-Chloro-7-methyl-9-(1'-D-ribityl)isoalloxazine (6-chloro-7-methylflavin), stimulates the growth of the riboflavin-deficient rat at any quantity administered from 3 μg to 2 mg per day. When small quantities are given for limited periods of time the growth response is equal to that produced by one-half the quantity of riboflavin. All quantities lead to the death of the animal in spite of this growth but the animal can be protected against the lethal effects of this flavin by the administration of adequate amounts of riboflavin. This material does not antagonize riboflavin in the classical or expected manner[72].

The compound is a potent, reversible antagonist of riboflavin in the nutrition of *L. casei* with an inhibition index of 76. When *L. casei* ATCC 7469 is incubated for several days in a medium containing a mixture of this flavin and a small amount of riboflavin a "modified" form of *L. casei* emerges. This modified form is able to utilize either riboflavin or the 6-chloro-7-methyl-flavin as its sole flavin[72,73].

6-Methyl-7-chloro-9-(1'-D-ribityl)isoalloxazine (6-methyl-7-chloroflavin), is inert in the nutrition of the riboflavin-deficient rat even when given at the level of 2 mg per day. It is a very potent, reversible antagonist of riboflavin in the nutrition of *L. casei* with an inhibition index[30] of 59. It has been found to be inert for several clinically important microorganisms[30].

6,7-Dichloro-9-(1'-D-sorbityl)isoalloxazine (dichlorosorbitylflavin), is inert as an antagonist of riboflavin in the rat in terms of its influence on growth of the animal[31]. Riboflavin deficiency, whether induced by deprivation of the vitamin or by the administration of isoriboflavin or galactoflavin causes the regression of established lymphosarcoma implants in mice[74]. Considerable interest greeted the discovery that dichloro-sorbitylflavin, a compound which appeared to be unable to produce riboflavin deficiency in the rat, caused significant regression of established lymphosarcoma implants in mice[31].

References p. 34

REFERENCES

[1] T. Wagner-Jauregg in W. H. Sebrell and R. S. Harris (Eds.), *Riboflavin, The Vitamins*, Vol. III, Academic Press, New York, 1954.

[2] R. Kuhn, P. György and T. Wagner-Jauregg, *Ber.*, 66 (1933) 576.

[3] P. Ellinger and W. Koschara, *Ber.*, 66 (1933) 315.

[4] O. Warburg and W. Christian, *Biochem. Z.*, 254 (1932) 438; 266 (1933) 377.

[5] L. E. Booher, *J. Biol. Chem.*, 102 (1933) 39; 107 (1934) 591.

[6] R. Kuhn and G. Moruzzi, *Ber.*, 67 (1934) 888.

[7] R. Kuhn, H. Rudy and F. Weygand, *Ber.*, 68 (1935) 625.

[8] P. Pasternack and E. V. Brown, *U.S. Patent 2,324,800*, July 20, 1944.

[9] R. Kuhn and P. Boulanger, *Ber.*, 69 (1936) 1557.

[10] *Magnesol, Magnesium silicate*, Waverly Chemical Co., Inc., Mamaroneck, New York; see ref. 39.

[11] R. Kuhn, H. Rudy and T. Wagner-Jauregg, *Ber.*, 66 (1933) 1950.

[12] R. Kuhn and T. Wagner-Jauregg, *Ber.*, 66 (1933) 1577.

[13] R. Kuhn and H. Rudy, *Ber.*, 67 (1934) 1125, 1298.

[14] R. Kuhn and F. Bär, *Ber.*, 67 (1934) 898.

[15] R. Kuhn and H. Rudy, *Ber.*, 67 (1934) 892.

[16] R. Kuhn, K. Reinemund and F. Weygand, *Ber.*, 67 (1934) 1460.

[17] R. Kuhn and K. Reinemund, *Ber.*, 67 (1934) 1932.

[18] R. Kuhn, H. Rudy and K. Reinemund, *Ber.*, 68 (1935) 170.

[19] P. Karrer, K. Schöpp and F. Benz, *Helv. Chim. Acta.*, 18 (1935) 426.

[20] R. Kuhn, K. Reinemund, H. Kaltschmitt, R. Ströbele and H. Trischmann, *Naturwissenschaften*, 23 (1935) 260.

[21] P. Karrer, B. Becker, F. Benz, P. Frei, H. Salomon and K. Schöpp, *Helv. Chim. Acta*, 18 (1935) 1435.

[22] R. Kuhn and F. Weygand, *Ber.*, 68 (1935) 1001.

[23] R. Kuhn, K. Reinemund, F. Weygand and R. Ströbele, *Ber.*, 68 (1935) 1765.

[24] P. Karrer and F. M. Strong, *Helv. Chim. Acta.*, 18 (1935) 1343.

[25] P. Karrer, H. Salomon, K. Schöpp and F. Benz, *Helv. Chim. Acta*, 18 (1935) 1143.

[26] P. Karrer and T. H. Quibell, *Helv. Chim. Acta*, 19 (1936) 1034.

[27] P. Karrer, H. Salomon, K. Schöpp, F. Benz and B. Becker, *Helv. Chim. Acta*, 18 (1935) 908.

[28] E. E. Haley and J. P. Lambooy, *J. Am. Chem. Soc.*, 76 (1954) 5093.

[29] R. Kuhn, F. Weygand and E. F. Möller, *Ber.*, 76 (1943) 1044.

[30] J. P. Lambooy, E. E. Haley and R. A. Scala, *J. Nutrition*, 74 (1961) 466.

[31] F. W. Holly, E. W. Peel, R. Mozingo and K. Folkers, *J. Am. Chem. Soc.*, 72 (1950) 5416.

[32] R. Kuhn and R. Ströbele, *Ber.*, 70 (1937) 773.

[33] R. Kuhn, P. Desnuelle and F. Weygand, *Ber.*, 70 (1937) 1293.

[34] J. P. Lambooy, *J. Am. Chem. Soc.*, 72 (1950) 5225.

[35] H. V. Aposhian and J. P. Lambooy, *J. Am. Chem. Soc.*, 76 (1954) 1307.

[36] R. Kuhn and F. Weygand, *Ber.*, 67 (1934) 1939.

[37] F. Weygand and E. F. Möller, *Chem. Ber.*, 84 (1951) 101.

[38] C. H. Shunk, F. R. Koniuszy and K. Folkers, *J. Am. Chem. Soc.*, 74 (1952) 4251.

[39] J. P. Lambooy, *J. Am. Chem. Soc.*, 80 (1958) 110.

[40] L. Berger and J. Lee, *J. Org. Chem.*, 11 (1945) 75.

[41] R. Kuhn and L. Birkofer, *Ber.*, 71 (1938) 621.

[42] E. E. Haley and J. P. Lambooy, *J. Am. Chem. Soc.*, 76 (1954) 2926.

[43] P. Karrer and H. F. Meerwein, *Helv. Chim. Acta*, 18 (1935) 1130.

[44] L. Berger and J. Lee, *J. Org. Chem.*, 11 (1945) 84.

[45] W. Wisansky and S. Ansbacher, *J. Am. Chem. Soc.*, 63 (1941) 2532.

[46] M. Tishler, N. L. Wendler, K. Ladenburg and J. W. Wellman, *J. Am. Chem. Soc.*, 66 (1944) 1328.

[47] K. Ladenburg, M. Tishler, J. W. Wellman and R. D. Babson, *J. Am. Chem. Soc.*, 66 (1944) 1217.

[48] Chas. Pfizer and Co., *Brit. Patents*, *545,360*, May 21, 1942; *551,491*, Feb. 25, 1943; *585,212*, Feb. 2, 1947.
[49] M. TISHLER, K. PFISTER, R. D. BABSON, K. LADENBURG AND A. J. FLEMING, *J. Am. Chem. Soc.*, 69 (1947) 1487.
[50] D. HEYL, E. C. CHASE, F. KONIUSZY AND K. FOLKERS, *J. Am. Chem. Soc.*, 73 (1951) 3826.
[51] R. KUHN AND F. WEYGAND, *Ber.*, 68 (1935) 1282.
[52] M. TISHLER, J. W. WELLMAN AND K. LADENBURG, *J. Am. Chem. Soc.*, 67 (1945) 2165.
[53] G. A. EMERSON AND M. TISHLER, *Proc. Soc. Exptl. Biol. Med.*, 55 (1944) 184.
[54] E. E. SNELL, O. A. KLATT, H. W. BRUINS AND W. W. CRAVENS, *Proc. Soc. Exptl. Biol. Med.*, 82 (1953) 583.
[55] H. P. SARETT, *J. Biol. Chem.*, 162 (1946) 87.
[56] G. A. EMERSON AND K. FOLKERS, *J. Am. Chem. Soc.*, 73 (1951) 2398,5383.
[57] H. W. BRUINS, M. L. SUNDE, W. W. CRAVENS AND E. E. SNELL, *Proc. Soc. Exptl. Biol. Med.*, 78 (1951) 535.
[58] R. WAHLSTROM AND B. C. JOHNSON, *J. Animal Sci.*, 10 (1951) 1065.
[59] J. M. COOPERMAN, W. L. MARUSICH, J. SCHEINER, L. DREKTER, E. DeRITTER AND S. H. RUBIN, *Proc. Soc. Exptl. Biol. Med.*, 81 (1952) 57.
[60] M. S. SHORB, *Proc. Soc. Exptl. Biol. Med.*, 79 (1952) 611.
[61] R. KUHN, H. VETTER AND H. W. RZEPPA, *Ber.*, 70 (1937) 1302.
[62] E. E. SNELL AND F. M. STRONG, *Enzymologia*, 6 (1939) 186.
[63] P. KARRER, H. VON EULER, M. MALMBERG AND K. SCHÖPP, *Svensk Kem. Tidskr.*, 47 (1935) 153.
[64] J. P. LAMBOOY AND H. V. APOSHIAN, *J. Nutrition*, 71 (1960) 182.
[65] J. P. LAMBOOY, *Biochim. Biophys. Acta*, 29 (1958) 221.
[66] J. P. LAMBOOY, *Federation Proc.*, 16 (1957) 208.
[67] H. V. APOSHIAN, J. P. LAMBOOY AND M. M. APOSHIAN, *Federation Proc.*, 12 (1953) 170.
[68] J. P. LAMBOOY AND H. V. APOSHIAN, *J. Nutrition*, 47 (1952) 539.
[69] J. P. LAMBOOY, *Am. J. Clin. Nutrition*, 3 (1955) 282.
[70] J. P. LAMBOOY, *J. Biol. Chem.*, 188 (1951) 459.
[71] G. A. EMERSON, E. WURTZ AND O. H. JOHNSON, *J. Biol. Chem.*, 160 (1945) 165.
[72] J. P. LAMBOOY AND E. E. HALEY, *J. Nutrition*, 72 (1960) 169.
[73] R. A. SCALA AND J. P. LAMBOOY, *Arch. Biochem. Biophys.*, 78 (1958) 10.
[74] H. C. STOERK AND G. A. EMERSON, *Proc. Soc. Exptl. Biol. Med.*, 70 (1949) 703.

Chapter III

Niacin

GUILLERMO ARROYAVE and RICARDO BRESSANI

*Institute of Nutrition of Central America and Panama (INCAP),
Guatemala (Central America)*

1. Nomenclature

The name niacin is often used for two compounds, namely pyridine-3-carboxylic acid and pyridine-3-carboxylic acid amide. This confusion occurs because there is no consistency in the empirical nomenclature used in nutrition literature. Harris[1] lists niacin and niacinamide as the terms preferred in the United States, and nicotinic acid and nicotinic acid amide in the British literature. A convenient solution to the problem would be to use the term niacin to refer generically to the two compounds of nutritional significance as anti-pellagra factor and adopt the names nicotinic acid and nicotinamide to refer specifically to each. Nicotinamide has been adopted by the Commission for the Reform of Nomenclature in Biological Chemistry of the International Union of Pure and Applied Chemistry, and nicotinic acid is already in current use in most British, United States and other scientific literature in English.

Other names which apply to both compounds and refer to their nutritional role, but are now seldom used, are vitamin PP, PP factor, pellagra preventive factor, and pellagramine.

2. History

Nicotinic acid was isolated for the first time from natural materials by Suzuki et al.[2] in Japan and Funk[3] in Europe, during their investigations of the factor present in rice bran responsible for its curative and preventive action against polyneuritis. At the time, these investigators did not recognize the nutritional essentiality of the compound. The structure of nicotinic acid had been known for around 40 years as a laboratory isolate from the oxidation products of nicotine.

The next step of great significance was the discovery of Warburg and his group[4] that the amide of nicotinic acid was part of coenzyme II (TPN, NADP) and functionally essential for the hydrogen-transporting role of this coenzyme, shortly followed by a parallel finding by Von Euler et al.[5] in coenzyme I (DPN, NAD).

Its previous discovery in yeast, as well as its presence in heart muscle extracts, emphasized the metabolic significance of nicotinamide. The emergence of nicotinic acid or nicotinamide as a nutritional essential came from the demonstration by Elvehjem et al.[6] that black tongue in dogs could be cured and prevented by its addition to the deficient diet. Simultaneously, Fouts et al.[7], Smith et al.[8] and Spies et al.[9] reported the successful treatment of pellagra in human subjects. Its universal occurrence in living tissue and its fundamental role in cellular respiration are now well established[10].

3. Chemistry, determination of structure and properties

(a) Nicotinic acid

Nicotinic acid and nicotinamide are pyridine-3-carboxylic acid and its amide respectively; their structural formulas are:

Nicotinic acid   Nicotinamide

The isolation of nicotinic acid among the products of chromic acid oxidation of nicotine[11,12] lead to the determination of its structure. The basic pyridinic ring structure was determined by the formation of free pyridine upon distilling the compound with calcium hydroxide and removal of CO_2. The presence of the —COOH group was demonstrated through the preparation of specific derivatives including salts of copper and silver, esters and the acyl chloride. The basic character of its nitrogen was determined by the formation of the hydrobromide, the hydrochloride or quarternary ammonium derivatives.

The actual location of the —COOH group at carbon 3 was established by Skraup and Cobenzl[13] by physical and chemical criteria. Through a series of steps 3-phenylpyridine is prepared from p-naphthylamine and glycerine, and upon oxidation it yields nicotinic acid. Skraup and Vortmann[14], also prepared nicotinic acid from synthetic dipyridyl of known m-structure. The three position isomers have very different melting points: picolinic acid (o-, or 1,2) around 136°; nicotinic acid (m- or 1,3-) around 236°; and isonicotinic acid[15] (p- or 1,4-) around 319°.

Nicotinic acid has a molecular weight of 123.11. From water or alcohol it crystallizes in white, odorless needles with a tart taste. It melts[15] at 236.6° (234–237° as cited in reference[10]) and sublimes without decomposition. In aqueous solution it has an absorption maximum in the ultraviolet region at 261.5 mμ. The molecular extinction coefficient at this point is pH-dependent, decreasing with increase in pH from 1.28 to 13.0. By two methods involving successive approximations K_a, the thermodynamic acid dissociation constant, was found to be $1.12 \cdot 10^{-5}$ and $1.23 \cdot 10^{-5}$, while K_b, the basic dissociation constant was $3.55 \cdot 10^{-11}$ by both methods[16] (22°). At 25°, Ostwald[17] found the acid dissociation constant to be $1.4 \cdot 10^{-5}$, that is between propionic and butyric acids. Nicotinic acid is not in amphoteric ion form in solution[16].

Nicotinic acid is very stable in air and non-hygroscopic and in water solution resists autoclaving at 120° for 20 min without decomposing. It is also stable in acid and alkaline solutions even with heat. Slobodin and Goldman[18] give the following solubilities in grams per 100 ml for nicotinic acid at 0°, 15°, 38°, 61°, 78° and 100°: in distilled water, 0.86, 1.3, 2.47, 4.06, 6.0, 9.76; in 96% alcohol 0.57, 0.92, 2.1, 4.2, 7.06, —. Nicotinic acid hydrochloride, and to a greater extent, sodium nicotinate, are more soluble in water. Nicotinic acid is also soluble in propylene glycol and insoluble in ether.

Its nitrogen readily becomes pentavalent, forming quaternary ammonium salts. Some derivatives of known properties, useful for qualitative identification are: the hydrochloride, white crystals melting at 272° with decomposition; the nitrate, m.p. 184–185°; the picrate, yellow rhombic prisms (from absolute alcohol) melting at 221–222° to a red oil[19]; the p-toluidine, m.p. 150° and the anilide[20], m.p. 85°. Alkyl iodides readily react with it to form water-soluble compounds. The carboxylic group of nicotinic acid behaves typically, forming salts with alkalies, alkaline earth hydroxides or heavy metals; the latter salts are quite insoluble and their preparation is useful to separate nicotinic acid from mixtures.

Ester derivatives may be prepared using regular procedures such as heating the acid with an alcohol in the presence of hydrogen ions or starting with the nicotinyl chloride and an alcohol. The preparation of the amide derivative (nicotinamide) is described below.

(b) Nicotinamide

Nicotinamide has a molecular weight of 122.12 and occurs as odorless, bitter-tasting white crystals, which melt[10] at 129–131°. It distills at 150–160° under a vacuum of $5 \cdot 10^{-4}$ mm Hg and is very soluble in water (1 g in about 1 ml) and alcohol (1 g in about 1.5 ml of ethanol). It also dissolves in butanol, amyl alcohol, ethylene glycol, acetone and chloroform, and is slightly soluble in benzene and ethyl ether. It is stable in dry form at temperatures below 50°.

In water solution it may be heated in the autoclave for 20 min at 120° with no destruction, but in acid or alkaline medium it hydrolyzes to nicotinic acid[15,21].

The crystalline forms of nicotinamide have been described by several investigators. Wright and King[22] give data on the morphological, optical and structural characteristics of the compound. When crystallized from ethylene glycol it forms monoclinic units of prismatic habit, predominant form [110] and from water, acetone, benzene, glycerol and aqueous ethylene glycol it gives lath-shaped monoclinic units, predominant form [010].

Jellinek and Wayne[23] reported the ultraviolet absorption for nicotinamide at pH values of 5.7 to 1.06 with a $3 \cdot 10^{-4}$ M solution giving a maximum at 261.5 mμ, that is, the same as for nicotinic acid. From this work, a pK value of 10.6 was calculated for the H$^+$RCONH$_2$ form and 13.5 for the H$^+$RCONH$_3$$^+$ form. They found the thermodynamic dissociation constants of $2.24 \cdot 10^{-11}$ for the ring nitrogen and $3.16 \cdot 10^{-14}$ for the amide group.

The chemical reactions of nicotinamide at the ring nitrogen site are typical, combining with alkyl halides and acids to form quaternary ammonium compounds. Knox and Grossman[24] have reported that ring carbon 6 is the reactive position of the quaternary nicotinamide ring, as evidenced by studies in which oxidation of N^1-methylnicotinamide chloride by a quinine-oxidizing enzyme resulted in 1-methyl-3-carboxylamide-6-pyridone.

4. Isolation

(a) Nicotinic acid

The technique for the isolation of nicotinic acid depends on the starting material. In most cases, a preliminary hydrolysis is required either with acids or alkalies. The extractions are more complete if the material is rendered free of lipids, a necessary step when working with animal products. The free acid is extracted from the hydrolysate with organic solvents such as hot alcohol. It may then be separated as such from the organic solvent extract or in the form of an ester or as the copper salt; the free acid can be recovered from the copper salt by H$_2$S treatment. Purification is carried out by crystallization from concentrated water or alcohol solutions. Nyc et al.[25] extracted nicotinic acid from the mycelium of Neurospora with acetone. Subsequent purification steps included the formation of the barium salt, acidification with H$_2$SO$_4$ and adsorption of the free nicotinic acid on charcoal. Elution was accomplished with 4% aqueous aniline and the final purification step involves recrystallization from a 1:4 mixture of acetic acid and benzene. Leifer et al.[26] have applied paper chromatography with n-butanol saturated with ammonia to separate nicotinic acid from contaminating materials.

(b) Nicotinamide

Nicotinamide can be isolated from natural materials by water extraction, followed by partial hydrolysis with $0.1 N$ H_2SO_4 to liberate it from the combined form in which it exists. The amide is then extracted with butanol or chloroform. The chloroform solution may be subjected to fractional distillation at $150°-160°$ under $5 \cdot 10^{-4}$ mm Hg. It can be recrystallized from chloroform, benzene or ethylene glycol. Methods have been described by Warburg and Christian and by Elvehjem and coworkers to isolate the compound from red blood cells and liver tissue[21].

The separation of nicotinic acid from its amide can be accomplished by extraction of a water solution with ether, chloroform or benzene. Nicotinamide dissolves in the organic solvents while nicotinic acid remains in the aqueous phase. The two compounds can also be separated by paper chromatography[26,28].

5. Synthesis[21,29]

(a) Nicotinic acid

(i) From quinoline

The stability of the pyridinic ring surpasses that of benzene[30], therefore, oxidation results in destruction of the benzene ring.

Oxidation may be accomplished by heating at $300°$ with sulfuric acid, nitric acid with mercuric oxide as catalyst, or by treatment with hydrogen peroxide. Selenium oxide has also been used as catalyst. Nicotinic acid in high yield is usually recovered as the copper salt[21].

(ii) From p-substituted pyridines

The same stability principle applies to the historical synthesis of nicotinic acid from nicotine which, for example, upon oxidation with permanganate[31], chromic acid[11] or fuming nitric acid[12], loses four carbons and the N of the 5-membered ring.

Similar reaction mechanisms are the bases for the synthesis of nicotinic acid from 3-methyl pyridine, 3-ethyl pyridine, 3-phenyl pyridine, and 3,3'-

dipyridyl. Appropriate oxidation is carried out with phosphoric–nitric acid mixture and vanadium pentoxide with small amounts of ferric oxide, or even electrochemically[21].

(iii) From pyridine

Treatment of pyridine with fuming sulfuric acid yields pyridine-3-sulfonic acid which is converted to 3-cyanopyridine by distillation of its sodium salt with potassium cyanide[32]. Better yields are claimed by initial bromination of pyridine in the 3-position and subsequent treatment with cuprous cyanide[33]. The 3-cyanopyridine is then hydrolyzed to nicotinic acid.

(iv) Labeled nicotinic acid

By halogen–metal interconversion, Murray et al.[34] prepared nicotinic acid labeled with ^{13}C (82% yield) or ^{14}C (62% yield) on the carboxylic radical. Using n-butyl lithium and 3-bromopyridine, 3-pyridyl lithium was prepared and carbonation of this compound was carried out with $^{13}CO_2$ or $^{14}CO_2$ generated from the respective labeled barium carbonates with acid.

The ^{14}C-labeled material had a specific activity of around 8 $\mu C/mg$. Deuterization of nicotinic acid has been effected by direct exchange with deuterosulfuric acid, with 83% yield, of a product containing approximately 55% of hydrogen replaced by deuterium[35].

(b) Nicotinamide

This compound can be synthesized by passing ammonia gas into nicotinic acid or by treating it with molten urea[36,37] at 230°. The methyl or ethyl esters of nicotinic acid also undergo amidation upon reaction with ammonia in aqueous or alcoholic media[38].

References p. 46

6. Properties and synthesis of some related compounds of biochemical importance[15,21,39]

N^1-*methylnicotinamide* has a molecular weight of 172.5 and crystallizes from alcohol in white rosettes or prismatic bars, m.p. 233–234°. It is soluble in water and ethanol and can be prepared by treating nicotinamide with methyl (or other alkyl) iodides which are then converted to the chloride. The picrate melts at 189.5°.

6-Pyridone of N^1-methylnicotinamide forms white crystals from acetone with a molecular weight of 152.15; it melts at 212–214° and is soluble in water and ethanol. It may be prepared from coumalic acid by ring closure with methyl amine. It is the sole product of the enzymatic oxidation of N^1-methylnicotinamide with a quinine-oxidizing enzyme, and is also obtained from N^1-methylnicotinamide or the N^1-methylbetaine of nicotinic acid by oxidation with alkaline ferricyanide and subsequent treatment with $SOCl_2$ and NH_3.

| N^1-methylnicotinamide | 6-Pyridone of N^1-methylnicotinamide | Trigonelline |

Trigonelline has a molecular weight of 137.13; it crystallizes from alcohol in hygroscopic prisms with one molecule of water, becomes anhydrous at 100° and melts at 218° with decomposition. It is very soluble in water, soluble in alcohol and slightly soluble in ether or chloroform. It is prepared in the laboratory from nicotinic acid by heating with CH_3I and treatment with silver oxide.

Nicotinuric acid has a molecular weight of 180.15, melts at 240–242° and crystallizes from dilute hydrochloric acid in white crystals which are very soluble in water and ethanol.

| Nicotinuric acid | 3-Acetyl-pyridine | Pyridine-3-sulfonic acid |

3-Acetyl pyridine. The free base has a molecular weight of 121, is liquid at room temperature, melting at 13–14° and boiling at 90–92° under 5 mm Hg. The hydrochloride (molecular weight 157.5) forms a white crystalline powder melting at 176–177.5°, and is soluble in water and ethanol. It may be prepared by condensation of the ethyl esters of nicotinic and acetic acids in the presence of sodium ethoxide followed by hydrolysis of the condensation product to 3-acetyl-pyridine.

Pyridine-3-sulfonic acid is a crystalline compound with a molecular weight of 159.11; m.p.[40] 357°; its ammonium salt melts at 243°. It is prepared by sulfonation of pyridine with fuming sulfuric acid at temperatures above 200°. The reaction at 225° with mercuric sulfate as catalyst yields only pyridine-3-sulfonic acid.

6-Amino nicotinic acid has a molecular weight of 138.12 and crystallizes with two molecules of water from dilute acetic acid. It decomposes above 300° and is slightly soluble in most solvents. The potassium salt is freely soluble in water as is the hydrochloride. The picrate crystallizes in yellow needles which melt at 248°. This compound is prepared by treating 6-chloronicotinic acid with ammonia.

Nicotinic acid hydrazide has a molecular weight of 137.14, crystallizes from dilute alcohol or from benzene in white needles. It melts at 158–159°, is very soluble in water and alcohol, and only slightly soluble in benzene. It is synthesized by treatment of ethyl nicotinate with hydrazine hydrate.

6–Amino nicotinic acid   Nicotinic acid hydrazide   Isonicotinic acid hydrazide

Isonicotinic acid hydrazide with a molecular weight of 137.14 forms white crystals, melting at 171°. It is soluble in water (14% at 25°) and alcohol (2% at 25°). It is slightly soluble in chloroform and insoluble in ether or benzene. It may be heated in aqueous solution at 120° for 30 min with no apparent destruction and is prepared by condensation of ethyl isonicotinate with hydrazine.

7. Methods of determination

The methods for the determination of nicotinic acid and nicotinamide can be classified as: (a) chemical, (b) bacteriological, and (c) biological.

References p. 46

(a) Chemical methods[10,29,41-44]

(i) Cyanogen bromide method

This is based on the reaction of derivatives of pyridine with cyanogen bromide in the presence of an aromatic amine giving specific colors. Amines commonly used are 2-naphthylamine-1-sulfonic acid, *p*-aminoacetophenone, *N*-methyl-aminophenol sulphate, aniline and *p*-naphthylamine. The reaction gives a yellowish-green color which is measured photometrically. The color is soluble in amyl alcohol which can be used to extract it from water solutions, but is not stable unless a phosphate buffer of pH 6.1 is used. This method is not specific for nicotinic acid since other pyridine derivatives and derivatives of nicotinic acid such as trigonelline, nicotinuric acid and nicotine give a similar color.

(ii) 2,4-Dinitrochlorobenzene method

This compound reacts only with free nicotinic acid or its amide. The dry material is fused with 2,4-dinitrochlorobenzene and the reaction product is dissolved in ethyl alcohol. Potassium hydroxide is then added to develop the color which is measured colorimetrically.

This method also lacks specificity since many other pyridine derivatives give the same color test. For example, in the determination of the nicotinic acid content of several plant and animal materials, especially cereal grains, the intensity of the color reactions is usually in excess of the amounts of nicotinic acid actually present, as determined by other methods.

Both nicotinic acid and its amide can be determined by the above methods. If the determination of either one alone is desired, the two compounds can be separated by extracting the amide derivative with ether from an aqueous solution.

(iii) Chromatographic separation of nicotinic acid and related compounds[27]

A mixture of nicotinic acid, nicotinamide, trigonelline and tryptophan can be separated chromatographically, using as solvent a 5:1 mixture of *n*-butanol and concentrated hydrochloric acid, saturated with water. Tryptophan is revealed by ninhydrin, while nicotinic acid, nicotinamide and trigonelline are detected with phosphomolybdic acid reagent and the color developed with stannous chloride, which reduces the phosphomolybdic acid to give a blue spot. The R_F values for the butanol–HCl solvent are: nicotinic acid, 0.37; nicotinamide, 0.28; trigonelline, 0.38 and tryptophan, 0.62.

(b) Biological methods

Several experimental animals have been used for the biological determination of nicotinic acid and derivatives. These are: chicks[45,46], growing niacin-depleted rats[47], dogs[6,48,49], and pigs[50,51].

The animal assays offer little opportunity for the quantitative determination of nicotinic acid because of interfering factors, mainly the fact that tryptophan is metabolized partly into nicotinic acid in most aninals. Biological tests offer possibilities, however, in assessing the over-all pellagra preventive potency of the foods tested. Nicotinic acid-free rations for chicks are available for the assay of the vitamin using this experimental animal and the growth response is satisfactory for biological testing. Nicotinic acid-depleted rats also respond satisfactorily to niacin feeding. The cat does not convert tryptophan into nicotinic acid, offering special opportunities for the assay of nicotinic acid, as well as the study of its metabolism.

(c) Bacteriological methods[52-56]

Niacin is required by several micro-organisms for growth and this fact is useful in determining nicotinic acid by microbiological methods. The organism commonly used is *Lactobacillus arabinosus*, which responds almost linearly to varying concentrations of nicotinic acid. The concentration is estimated either by measuring the turbidity of the media after 18 h of incubation or by titrating the lactic acid produced after 72 h of incubation at 38°. The yeast *Torulopsis utilis* has been used particularly for differentiations between related compounds such as nicotinic acid, nicotinamide and trigonelline.

(d) Hydrolysis of the samples[57-59]

For the successful application of all chemical and bacteriological methods for the determination of nicotinic acid, it is necessary to hydrolyze the sample under study, with either an acid or an alkaline reagent. Some materials of vegetable origin, particularly cereal grains, contain nicotinic acid in a form which is not biologically available to the organism. This so called "bound" form of nicotinic acid[47,60] is present in the seed coat of corn and other cereal grains. In order to liberate nicotinic acid from its bound form, it is necessary to hydrolyze the samples with dilute H_2SO_4 or, as advocated by several workers, with NaOH. The pellagragenic effect of corn has been attributed to the "bound" form of nicotinic acid in this cereal grain, which, as mentioned above, is not available to the organism.

REFERENCES

1 R. S. Harris in W. H. Sebrell Jr. and R. S. Harris (Eds.), *The Vitamins*, Vol. II, Academic Press, New York, 1954, p. 452.
2 H. Suzuki, T. Shimamura and S. Odake, *Biochem. Z.*, 43 (1912) 89.
3 C. Funk, *J. Physiol. (London)*, 43 (1911–12) 395; 46 (1913) 173.
4 O. Warburg, W. Christian and A. Griese, *Biochem. Z.*, 279 (1935) 143.
5 H. von Euler, H. Albers and F. Schlenk, *Z. physiol. Chem., Hoppe-Seyler's*, 240 (1936) 113.
6 C. A. Elvehjem, R. J. Madden, F. M. Strong and D. W. Woolley, *J. Am. Chem. Soc.*, 59 (1937) 1767.
7 P. J. Fouts, O. M. Helmer, S. Lepkovsky and T. H. Jukes, *Proc. Soc. Exptl. Biol. Med.*, 37 (1937) 405.
8 D. T. Smith, J. M. Ruffin and S. G. Smith, *J. Am. Med. Assoc.*, 109 (1937) 2054.
9 T. D. Spies, C. Cooper and M. A. Blankenhorn, *J. Am. Med. Assoc.*, 110 (1938) 622.
10 W. H. Sebrell Jr. and R. S. Harris (Eds.), *The Vitamins*, Vol. II, Academic Press, New York, 1954, p. 449.
11 C. Huber, *Ber. deut. chem. Ges.*, 3 (1870) 849; *Ann. Chem., Liebigs*, 141 (1867) 271.
12 H. Weidel, *Ann. Chem., Liebigs*, 165 (1873) 328.
13 Z. H. Skraup, *Monatsh. Chem.*, 1 (1880) 800; Z. H. Skraup and A. Cobenzl, *Monatsh. Chem.*, 4 (1883) 436.
14 Z. H. Skraup and J. Vortmann, *Monatsh. Chem.*, 4 (1883) 569.
15 Merck and Co., Inc., *The Merck Index of Chemicals and Drugs*, 7th ed., Rahway, New Jersey, 1960.
16 E. B. Hughes, H. H. G. Jellinek and B. A. Ambrose, *J. Phys. & Colloid Chem.*, 53 (1949) 414.
17 W. Ostwald, *Z. physik. Chem.*, 3 (1889) 369. Cited by J. M. Hundley in W. H. Sebrell Jr. and R. S. Harris (Eds.), *The Vitamins*, Vol. II, Academic Press, New York, 1954, p. 464.
18 Y. M. Slobodin and M. M. Gol'dman, *Zhur. Priklad. Khim.*, 21 (1948) 859; *Chem. Abstr.*, 43 (1949) 6207f.
19 H. B. Vickery, *J. Biol. Chem.*, 68 (1926) 585.
20 N. D. Cheronis and J. B. Entrikin, *Semimicro Qualitative Organic Analysis*, Thomas Y. Crowell, New York, 1947, p. 364.
21 J. M. Hundley in W. H. Sebrell Jr. and R. S. Harris (Eds.), *The Vitamins*, Vol. II, Academic Press, New York, 1954, p. 452.
22 W. B. Wright and G. S. D. King, *Acta Cryst.*, 3 (1950) 31; *Chem. Abstr.*, 44 (1950) 4775i.
23 H. H. G. Jellinek and Margaret G. Wayne, *J. Phys. & Colloid Chem.*, 55 (1951) 173; *Chem. Abstr.*, 45 (1951) 6055a.
24 W. E. Knox and W. I. Grossman, *J. Am. Chem. Soc.*, 70 (1948) 2172.
25 J. F. Nyc, H. K. Mitchell, E. Leifer and W. H. Langham, *J. Biol. Chem.*, 179 (1949) 783.
26 E. Leifer, W. H. Langham, J. F. Nyc and H. K. Mitchell, *J. Biol. Chem.*, 184 (1950) 589.
27 R. H. Block, E. L. Durrum and G. Zweig, *A Manual of Paper Chromatography and Paper Electrophoresis*, Academic Press, New York, 1955.
28 C. Yanofsky and D. M. Bonner, *J. Biol. Chem.*, 190 (1951) 211.
29 H. R. Rosenberg, *Chemistry and Physiology of the Vitamins*, Interscience, New York, 1945, p. 219.
30 L. F. Fieser and Mary Fieser, *Organic Chemistry*, 2nd ed., Heath and Co., Boston, 1950, p. 854.
31 R. Laiblin, *Ber. deut. chem. Ges.*, 10 (1877) 2136.
32 O. Fisher, *Ber. deut. chem. Ges.*, 15 (1882) 62.
33 S. M. McElvain and M. A. Goese, *J. Am. Chem. Soc.*, 63 (1941) 2283.
34 A. Murray, III, W. W. Foreman and W. Langham, *Science*, 106 (1947) 277.
35 N. R. Trenner, R. W. Walker, B. Arison and C. Trumbauer, *Anal. Chem.*, 23 (1951) 487.

[36] S. Keimatsu, K. Yokota and I. Satoda, *J. Pharm. Soc. Japan*, 53 (1933) 994; *Chem. Abstr.*, 29 (1935) 7300⁹.

[37] E. Cherbuliez and F. Landolt, *Helv. Chim. Acta*, 29 (1946) 1438.

[38] F. B. La Forge, *J. Am. Chem. Soc.*, 50 (1928) 2477.

[39] Chemical Rubber Publishing Co., *Handbook of Chemistry and Physics*, 37th ed., Cleveland, Ohio, 1955.

[40] A. J. P. van Gastel and J. P. Wibaut, *Rec. trav. chim.*, 53 (1934) 1031; *Chem. Abstr.*, 29 (1935) 470⁹.

[41] P. György and S. H. Rubin in P. György (Ed.), *Vitamin Methods*, Vol. I, Academic Press, New York, 1950, p. 223.

[42] Association of Vitamin Chemists, Inc., *Methods of Vitamin Assay*, 2nd ed., Interscience, New York, 1951, p. 177.

[43] J. P. Sweeney, *J. Assoc. Offic. Agr. Chemists*, 34 (1951) 380.

[44] T. E. Friedemann and E. I. Frazier, *Arch. Biochem.*, 26 (1950) 361.

[45] M. E. Coates, S. K. Kon and E. E. Shepheard, *Brit. J. Nutrition*, 4 (1950) 203.

[46] M. E. Coates, J. E. Ford, G. F. Harrison, S. K. Kon, E. E. Shepheard and F. W. Wilby, *Brit. J. Nutrition*, 6 (1952) 75.

[47] E. Kodicek, *Biochem. J.*, 48 (1951) viii.

[48] W. H. Sebrell, R. H. Onstott, H. F. Fraser and F. S. Daft, *J. Nutrition*, 16 (1938) 355.

[49] W. J. Dann and G. Howard (Eds.), *Biological Symposia*, Vol. XII, Jaques Cattel Press, Lancaster, Pa., 1947, p. 181.

[50] E. H. Hughes, *J. Animal Sci.*, 2 (1943) 23.

[51] R. Braude, S. K. Kon and E. G. White, *Biochem. J.*, 40 (1947) 843.

[52] *The Pharmacopoeia of the United States of America*, XIV rev., Mack Publishing Co., Easton, Pa., 1950, p. 737.

[53] E. E. Snell and L. D. Wright, *J. Biol. Chem.*, 139 (1941) 675.

[54] D. Melnick, *Cereal Chem.*, 19 (1942) 553.

[55] B. C. Johnson, *J. Biol. Chem.*, 159 (1945) 227.

[56] W. L. Williams, *J. Biol. Chem.*, 166 (1946) 397.

[57] J. P. Sweeney and W. P. Parrish, *J. Assoc. Offic. Agr. Chemists*, 37 (1954) 771.

[58] K. Sohonie and U. C. Misra, *Brit. J. Nutrition*, 4 (1950) 134.

[59] V. H. Cheldelin and R. R. Williams, *Ind. Eng. Chem. Anal. Ed.*, 14 (1942) 671.

[60] E. Kodicek, R. Braude, S. K. Kon and K. G. Mitchell, *Brit. J. Nutrition*, 10 (1956) 51.

Chapter IV

Vitamin B_6

ESMOND E. SNELL

Department of Biochemistry, The University of California, Berkeley, Calif. (U.S.A.)

1. Discovery and structure

Even before the general availability of thiamine and riboflavin in pure form, it became evident that addition of concentrates of these two vitamins to a ration deficient in the vitamin B complex failed to permit normal growth and development of rats. After several weeks on such rations, these animals showed poor growth and developed a type of dermatitis (termed "acrodynia") characterized by redness and swelling of the tips of the ears, nose and paws which eventually led to necrosis of these parts. These symptoms were prevented by feeding yeast or other sources of the vitamin B complex; that portion of these materials that prevented these symptoms was termed "vitamin B_6" by György[1,2] in 1934. These observations provided a crude means of assay for the new vitamin. During the next few years this procedure was refined and within a period of four months during 1938 five different laboratories announced isolation, from rice bran or from yeast, of a crystalline compound possessing vitamin B_6 activity[2,3]. The isolation procedures made use of the fact that the active compound was stable to acid and alkaline hydrolysis, was adsorbed on fuller's earth and eluted with barium hydroxide, failed to form insoluble salts with heavy metals but did form an insoluble phosphotungstate. It also formed esters on acetylation with enhanced solubility in organic solvents, from which the parent compound could be regenerated by saponification.

The structure of the isolated compound was determined by degradation and synthesis[2,3] to be 2-methyl-3-hydroxy-4,5-bis(hydroxymethyl)pyridine (I, Fig. 1); this compound was named pyridoxine by György[2]. This latter term largely displaced the name "vitamin B_6" from the literature during the period between 1939 and 1942. By use of certain lactic acid bacteria for assay of vitamin B_6, Snell[4] showed in 1942 that compounds other than pyridoxine contributed to the vitamin B_6 activity of natural materials, that rats formed such compounds from ingested pyridoxine, and that similar compounds could be formed from pyridoxine by partial oxidation or by amination to yield an aldehyde or amine, respectively. Synthesis[2,3] and bio-assay of his suggested structures showed that 2-methyl-3-hydroxy-4-formyl-5-hydroxymethylpyridine (pyridoxal, II, Fig. 1) and 2-methyl-3-hydroxy-4-aminomethyl-5-hydroxymethylpyridine (pyridoxamine, III, Fig. 1) showed the expected vitamin activity for both lactic acid bacteria and animals[4,5]. Pyridoxal and pyridoxamine have been shown subsequently to comprise most of the vitamin B_6 of natural materials[6]. These three compounds are interchangeable and approximately equally active in supporting growth of rats, dog, and chicks fed vitamin B_6-deficient rations and in supporting growth of vitamin B_6-dependent fungi and some bacteria; for other bacteria and some protozoa, however, pyridoxal and pyridoxamine are the only forms that show significant activity[5].

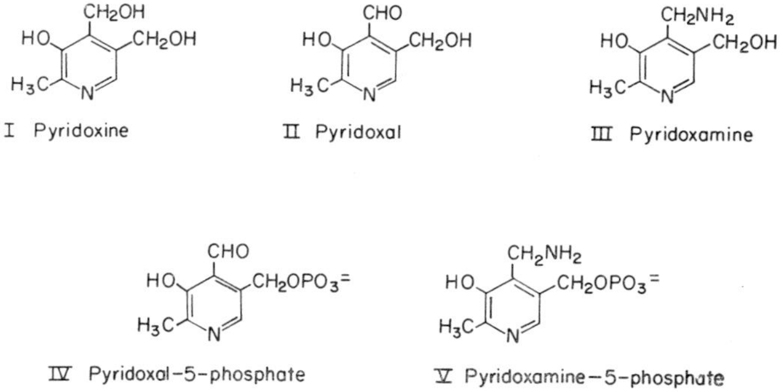

I Pyridoxine   II Pyridoxal   III Pyridoxamine

IV Pyridoxal–5–phosphate   V Pyridoxamine–5–phosphate

Fig. 1. Naturally occurring free and combined forms of vitamin B_6 of known structure.

Most of the vitamin B_6 in natural materials is present as phosphorylated derivatives of compounds I–III. Pyridoxal-5-phosphate (IV, Fig. 1) was discovered in 1944 by Gale and Epps[7] as an unidentified compound required for enzymatic decarboxylation of amino acids; Gunsalus and co-workers[8] subsequently showed it to be a phosphorylated pyridoxal[2,4]. Pyridoxamine-5-phosphate (V, Fig. 1) was discovered by Rabinowitz and Snell[9] by virtue of its differential activity in promoting growth of certain lactic acid bacteria. It is probable that pyridoxine-5-phosphate also occurs naturally, since it is both formed and oxidized to pyridoxal-5-phosphate by tissue enzymes[10,11]. An unidentified conjugate of pyridoxine also occurs in cereal grains[12].

2. Synthesis

A variety of different synthetic procedures leading to pyridoxine has been described in the chemical and patent literature[2,3]. One such synthesis from

References p. 58

the acyclic precursors, cyanoacetamide and α-acetyl-α'-ethoxyacetone, is summarized in Fig. 2. The hydroxymethyl group in the 4-position of pyridoxine is oxidized much more readily than that in the 5-position; selective oxidation with manganese dioxide in acid solutions or careful treatment with potassium permanganate yields pyridoxal. This is conveniently isolated from the oxidation mixture as the oxime, from which pyridoxamine is readily formed by reduction, or pyridoxal can be regenerated by treatment with nitrous acid (Fig. 3). An alternative route to pyridoxamine is by amina-

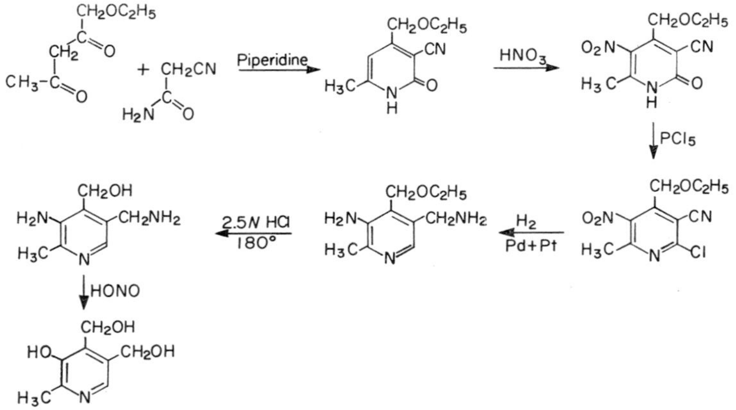

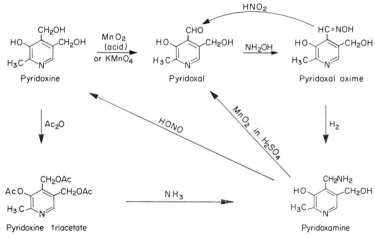

Fig. 2. Synthesis of pyridoxine from acyclic precursors[13].

Fig. 3. Synthesis of pyridoxal and pyridoxamine from pyridoxine and some inter conversions of these products.

tion of various esters or 4-ethers of pyridoxine. These reactions (Fig. 3) were of initial importance in pointing to the structures of pyridoxal and pyridox-amine[14], and were later developed as synthetic procedures for these vita-mins[3].

Direct phosphorylation of pyridoxal with phosphorus oxychloride gives very low yields of pyridoxal-5-phosphate, presumably because pyridoxal exists largely in its cyclic hemiacetal form (IIc, Fig. 4), in which the 5-hydroxymethyl group is not available for phosphorylation. A much better preparative route lies in phosphorylation of pyridoxamine to yield pyridox-amine-5-phosphate, which is readily oxidized to pyridoxal phosphate with manganese dioxide[3,15]. Alternatively, an appropriate hydrazone of pyridoxal such as the N,N-dimethylglycylhydrazone, in which the 5-hydroxymethyl group is not masked by ring formation, can be phosphorylated, and free pyridoxal phosphate regenerated from the resulting hydrazone by treat-ment with nitrous acid[3]. Mild reduction of pyridoxal phosphate with sodium borohydride yields pyridoxine-5-phosphate, which is also obtained among other products on direct treatment of pyridoxine with phosphorus oxychloride.

3. Properties

(a) Ionic forms and spectra

In aqueous solutions each of the three forms of vitamin B_6 exists in a variety of ionic forms, depending on the pH, temperature, and other factors[4]. Pyridoxine, for example, exists largely as the cation Ia (Fig. 4) in acidic solutions, as a mixture of unionized (I) and zwitterionic (Ib) forms — pre-dominantly the latter — in neutral solution, and as the anion, Ic, in alkaline solutions. These forms have detectably different spectra which can be used to follow the changes in ionic form[16]. Pyridoxamine and pyridoxal resemble pyridoxine with respect to ionization of the phenolic group and the pyridi-nium nitrogen. Pyridoxamine, however, carries a net positive charge in neutral solutions due to the basic 4-aminomethyl group. The situation with pyridoxal is especially complex, for the various ionic forms of this compound can be derived from the free aldehyde (IIa), its hydrate (IIb), or the pre-dominant hemiacetal (IIc), all of which coexist in aqueous solution. Both pyridoxal and its phosphate have some quininoid character, made possible by a resonant shift of electrons to yield structures[4,16] such as IId (Fig. 4). In pyridoxal phosphate, hemiacetal formation is no longer possible; con-sequently this compound shows more pronounced aldehydic properties than does free pyridoxal. Save for this change, ionic properties of the 5-phosphate esters resemble those of parent compounds, but with ionizations of the esterified phosphate grouping superimposed.

pK values and ultraviolet absorption maxima of the various forms of vitamin B$_6$ are summarized in Table I.

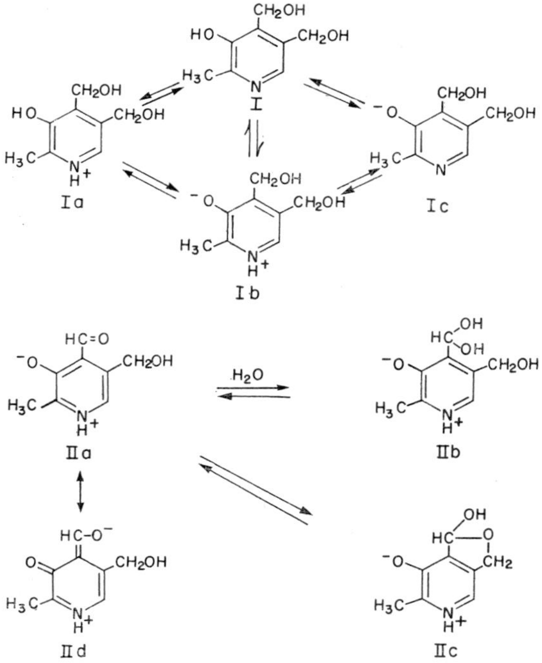

Fig. 4. Ionic forms of pyridoxine and zwitterionic forms of pyridoxal in aqueous solution.

TABLE I

pK VALUES* AND SPECTRAL PROPERTIES** OF VARIOUS
FORMS OF VITAMIN B$_6$

Compound	pK_1	pK_2	pK_3	pK_4	Absorption maxima	
					pH	λ_{max} mμ
Pyridoxal	4.20–4.23[a]	8.66–8.70[b]	13		6.9	317, 252
Pyridoxamine	3.31–3.54[a]	7.90–8.21[b]	10.4–10.63[e]		6.7	326, 252
Pyridoxine	5.00[a]	8.96–8.97[b]			6.8	324, 254
Pyridoxal-5-phosphate	<2.5[c]	4.14[a]	6.20[d]	8.69[b]	7.0	388, 330
Pyridoxamine-5-phosphate	<2.5[c]	3.25–3.69[a]	5.76[d]	8.61[b]	7.2	327, 254

* For references, see[4]. ** For references, see[15,16].
[a] Principally due to dissociation of the phenolic hydrogen.
[b] Principally due to dissociation of pyridinium hydrogen.
[c,d] Correspond principally to dissociations of phosphate grouping.
[e] Principally due to dissociation of aminomethyl group of pyridoxamine; pyridoxamine phosphate shows a pK_5 in this general pH region.

(b) Stability and chemical properties

All three forms of vitamin B_6 are white, crystalline, optically inactive compounds, freely soluble in water both as the free bases and as the commonly available hydrochlorides. In dilute aqueous solutions, pyridoxine and pyridoxamine are stable to hot dilute mineral acids or alkalis; pyridoxal is stable in acid but slowly destroyed in alkali. In dilute solutions, all three compounds are rapidly destroyed by light[2]. Although generally stable in air, the compounds are readily destroyed by stronger oxidizing agents which lead to the formation, via pyridoxal, of 4-pyridoxic acid (Fig. 5) and further

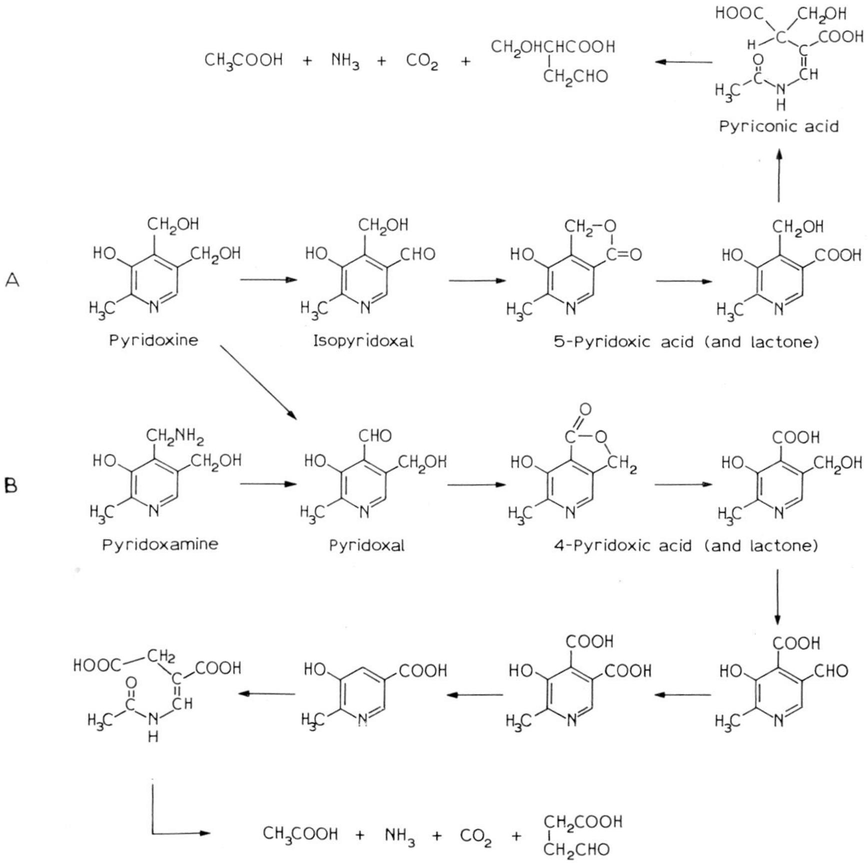

Fig. 5. Intermediate compounds in the oxidation of pyridoxine and pyridoxamine to CO_2 and water by two soil pseudomonads, IA (pathway A) and MA (pathway B).

degradation products. Each of the three compounds contains a reactive phenolic group and one or more alcoholic groups and consequently readily forms esters on treatment with appropriate acylating reagents. In addition, pyridoxamine shows reactions typical of a reactive primary amine, and pyridoxal those of an aromatic aldehyde. When moderately concentrated aqueous solutions of pyridoxine are heated near pH 7.0, substantial amounts of the vitamin activity are lost; one of the inactive compounds[17,18] formed is the pyridoxine dimer, VI.

Pyridoxine dimer, VI

Pyridoxal, pyridoxamine and pyridoxine all show the typical reactions of an aromatic phenol unsubstituted *para* to the phenolic group. In sufficient concentration they thus show reddish colors on addition of ferric chloride, couple with diazotized sulfanilic acid to yield orange to red-colored products, and with 2,6-dichloroquinone chlorimide to yield blue indophenols. The latter two reactions have been used for the quantitative estimation[2] of vitamin B_6; unfortunately, other phenols occur in many products and the three forms of the vitamin do not, in general, yield equal color values.

(c) Special reactions of pyridoxal[3,4]

Although, as noted above, pyridoxal is relatively stable in solutions that contain only the pure compound, this aldehyde is much less stable in its natural environment, or in aqueous solutions of amino acids, with which it may undergo a variety of reactions. Some of these reactions are of practical interest because of their relationship to stability of the vitamin in foodstuffs; others are of theoretical interest because they serve as models of reactions catalyzed *in vivo* by pyridoxal-dependent enzymes. A prominent example is the transamination reaction (eqn. 1) which occurs slowly at

$$RCHNH_2COOH + \text{Pyridoxal} \rightleftharpoons \text{Pyridoxamine} + RCOCOOH \qquad (1)$$

room temperature, more rapidly at elevated temperatures, and is catalyzed by certain divalent metal ions. In the uncomplicated reaction, no destruction of vitamin B_6 occurs, but only a transformation in its form. Heated with tryptophan or with histidine, a portion of the pyridoxal undergoes trans-amination to pyridoxamine, but much of it is irreversibly destroyed through condensation with these amino acids[19]; the compound formed with histidine[20] has structure VII.

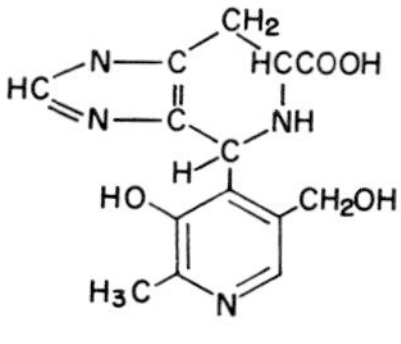

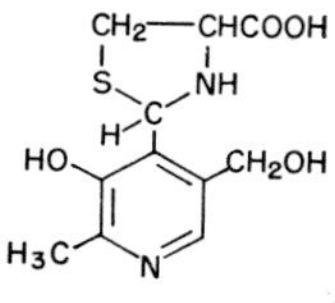

Cysteine readily forms a thiazolidine, VIII, with pyridoxal[20]; in aqueous solution this dissociates sufficiently so that all of the vitamin is available for growth[21]; however, oral administration of L-penicillamine to rats pro-duces vitamin B_6 deficiency apparently due to formation *in vivo* of an analo-gous but less dissociable thiazolidine derivative of pyridoxal that is excreted in the urine[22]. Heat processing of some food products, especially evaporated milk products, can lead to serious losses in vitamin B_6 activity for animals through another type of interaction of pyridoxal and cysteine that leads to the disulfide of compound IX, a mercapto analogue of pyridoxine[23]. Even glycine reacts with aqueous pyridoxal under mild conditions in the presence of Fe^{3+} or Al^{3+} to yield a readily isolated chelate of a Schiff's base of β-pyridoxylserine with pyridoxal, from which the latter amino acid (com-pound X) is readily obtained by acid hydrolysis[24].

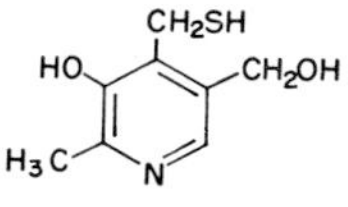

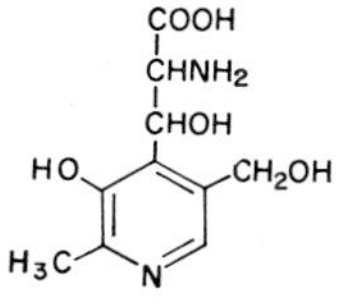

In each of these reactions, pyridoxal undergoes chemical alteration, some-times with loss of its vitamin activity. In addition, pyridoxal in aqueous systems catalyzes a whole series of non-enzymatic reactions of amino acids in which pyridoxal itself is unchanged. These reactions are as follow:

(*i*) Transamination between α-amino and α-keto acids. This reaction pro-ceeds by summation of two half reactions of the type shown in eqn. 1, leading to eqn. 2:

$$RCOCOOH + R'CHNH_2COOH \xrightarrow{\text{pyridoxal}} RCHNH_2COOH + R'COCOOH \qquad (2)$$

(*ii*) Racemization of amino acids at the α-carbon atom.

(*iii*) α,β-Elimination reactions, a great many of which are known, *e.g.*

$$\text{Serine} \rightarrow NH_3 + CH_3COCOOH \qquad (3)$$

$$\text{Tryptophan} + H_2O \rightarrow \text{Indole} + NH_3 + CH_3COCOOH \tag{4}$$

$$\text{Threonine} \rightarrow \alpha\text{-Ketobutyrate} + NH_3 \tag{5}$$

(*iv*) Synthetic reactions related to α,β-elimination reactions, *e.g.*

$$\text{Serine} + \text{Indole} \rightarrow \text{Tryptophan} + H_2O \tag{6}$$

$$\text{Serine} + H_2S \rightarrow \text{Cysteine} + H_2O \tag{7}$$

(*v*) Aldol-type reactions, *e.g.*

$$\text{HCHO} + \text{Glycine} \rightleftharpoons \text{Serine} \tag{8}$$

$$\text{CH}_3\text{CHO} + \text{Glycine} \rightleftharpoons \text{Threonine } (+ \text{ allothreonine}) \tag{9}$$

(*vi*) Decarboxylation reactions, *e.g.*

$$\text{Histidine} \rightarrow CO_2 + \text{Histamine} \tag{10}$$

$$\alpha\text{-Methylalanine} \rightarrow CO_2 + \text{Isopropylamine} \tag{11}$$

With the exception of the decarboxylation reactions, each of these reactions
is further catalyzed by appropriate metal ions. Each of them appears to
proceed through the initial formation of a Schiff base between amino acid
and pyridoxal, formation of which is readily observed spectrophotometrically
in aqueous solutions and is a freely reversible reaction. Such Schiff bases
are stabilized by hydrogen bonding, as in XI, or by chelate formation, as
in XII. Because of the special properties of pyridoxal, each of the bonds to
the α-carbon atom of such structures (1, 2 and 3 in XI and XII) is weakened.

XI   XII

Reactions of type $(i)-(iv)$ above result as a consequence of labilization of bond 1, aldol-type reactions from labilization of bond 2, and decarboxylation reactions from labilization of bond 3. Studies of these non-enzymatic reactions, which have been summarized in detail elsewhere[4,25], provide the principal experimental basis for current views of the mechanism of action of pyridoxal phosphate-dependent enzymes, which catalyze closely similar reactions in living tissues[4].

In general, pyridoxal phosphate resembles pyridoxal in each of the above systems but is somewhat more effective than pyridoxal in many of the catalytic systems.

4. Metabolic degradation

Pyridoxal, pyridoxamine and pyridoxine are interconvertible in animal tissues, and all are converted to the functional forms, pyridoxal phosphate and pyridoxamine phosphate. Excessive amounts of the vitamin over and above tissue requirements are excreted, in part unchanged and in part after oxidation to 4-pyridoxic acid[2]. Several soil micro-organisms, chiefly pseudomonads, have been isolated that grow on various forms of vitamin B_6 as a sole source of carbon, nitrogen and energy. Compounds listed in pathways A and B, Fig. 5, have been isolated as intermediates formed during oxidation of the vitamin to CO_2 and water by two different species of these organisms[18,26].

REFERENCES

1 P. GYÖRGY, *Nature*, 133 (1951) 498.
2 F. A. ROBINSON, *The Vitamin B Complex*, John Wiley and Sons, New York, 1951, p. 296.
3 A. F. WAGNER AND K. FOLKERS in A. BURGER (Ed.), *Medicinal Chemistry*, 2nd ed., Interscience, New York, 1960, p. 238.
4 E. E. SNELL, *Vitamins and Hormones*, 16 (1958) 77.
5 E. E. SNELL AND A. N. RANNEFELD, *J. Biol. Chem.*, 157 (1945) 475.
6 E. E. SNELL AND C. S. KEEVIL JR. AND R. S. HARRIS (Eds.), *The Vitamins*, Vol. III, Academic Press, New York, 1954, p. 255.
7 E. F. GALE AND H. M. R. EPPS, *Biochem. J.*, 38 (1944) 232.
8 I. C. GUNSALUS, W. D. BELLAMY AND W. W. UMBREIT, *J. Biol. Chem.*, 155 (1944) 685.
9 J. C. RABINOWITZ AND E. E. SNELL, *J. Biol. Chem.*, 169 (1947) 643.
10 D. B. McCORMICK, M. E. GREGORY AND E. E. SNELL, *J. Biol. Chem.*, 236 (1961) 2076.
11 H. WADA AND E. E. SNELL, *J. Biol. Chem.*, 236 (1961) 2089.
12 J. V. SCUDI, R. B. BUHS AND D. B. HOOD, *J. Biol. Chem.*, 142 (1942) 323.
13 S. A. HARRIS AND K. FOLKERS, *J. Am. Chem. Soc.*, 61 (1939) 3307.
14 E. E. SNELL, *J. Am. Chem. Soc.*, 66 (1944) 2082.
15 E. A. PETERSON, H. A. SOBER AND A. MEISTER, *Biochem. Preparations*, 3 (1953) 29, 34.
16 D. E. METZLER AND E. E. SNELL, *J. Am. Chem. Soc.*, 77 (1955) 2431.
17 S. A. HARRIS, *J. Am. Chem. Soc.*, 63 (1941) 3363.
18 V. W. RODWELL, B. E. VOLCANI, M. IKAWA AND E. E. SNELL, *J. Biol. Chem.*, 233 (1958) 1548.
19 E. E. SNELL, *J. Am. Chem. Soc.*, 67 (1945) 194.
20 D. HEYL, S. A. HARRIS AND K. FOLKERS, *J. Am. Chem. Soc.*, 70 (1948) 3429.
21 J. C. RABINOWITZ AND E. E. SNELL, *J. Am. Chem. Soc.*, 70 (1948) 3432.
22 E. J. KUSCHINSKAS, A. HORVATH AND V. DU VIGNEAUD, *Arch. Biochem. Biophys.*, 68 (1957) 69.
23 G. WENDT AND F. W. BERNHART, *Arch. Biochem. Biophys.*, 88 (1960) 270.
24 D. E. METZLER, J. B. LONGENECKER AND E. E. SNELL, *J. Am. Chem. Soc.*, 76 (1954) 639.
25 D. E. METZLER, M. IKAWA AND E. E. SNELL, *J. Am. Chem. Soc.*, 76 (1954) 648.
26 R. W. BURG, V. W. RODWELL AND E. E. SNELL, *J. Biol. Chem.*, 235 (1960) 1164.

Chapter V

Pantothenic Acid

*Department of Chemistry and the Clayton Foundation Biochemical Institute,
The University of Texas, Austin, Texas (U.S.A.)*

Probably the first hint as to the existence of the substance which has been designated pantothenic acid arose in 1901 from the work of a premedical student working under the supervision of Professor Ide of Louvain[1,2]. This classical work presenting evidence for the existence of the yeast growth substance "bios" was, for reasons which are irrelevant to our discussion, published under the sole authorship of the student and has borne his name (Wildiers), and not that of the man who instigated and directed the investigation. If these early investigators had been furnished a sample of pantothenic acid they would have designated it "bios" because of its high potency (without other supplements) in stimulating the yeast under investigation[3]. The total "bios" effect for different yeasts involves, of course, several other factors[4].

The first evidence that a substance answering to the general description of pantothenic acid is necessary for higher animals was probably gained by Williams and Waterman[5] who presented clear "evidence of a third factor of vitamin B" in 1928. Their factor found in yeast was not adsorbed by fuller's earth, was destroyed by dry heat and by 6 h autoclaving, and caused notably an improvement in feathers, appetite and general activity of pigeons. If pantothenic acid had been available to these investigators they would probably have recognized it immediately as the third factor. Though the B_3 designation has only occasionally been used, there is some justification for popular reference to pantothenic acid as "vitamin B_3".

Pantothenic acid stands out uniquely as a substance the structure of which was largely determined, making use of a highly quantitative biological test, long before it was obtained even in highly concentrated form. Actually its complete "isolation" was not accomplished until it was synthesized.

In 1932, eight years before its complete structure was known and confirmed, Williams and co-workers[6] reported its widespread existence as a single esterifiable acid, molecular weight by diffusion about 200 (correct 219), containing hydroxyl groups, lacking primary or secondary amino groups (or any group with substantial basic properties) or any sulfhydryl, olefinic, aldehydic or ketonic group. Two years later by an electrolytic determination of the ionization constant of the physiologically active principle[7] it was ascertained that it could not be an α-hydroxy acid, but must be a carboxylic acid with more remote hydroxyl groups.

For use in pantothenic acid investigations four new tools for dealing with minute amounts of substances were developed: a turbidimetric method for the determination of the amount of yeast or other microorganism in suspension[8], fractional electrical transport[9], oxidation equivalent analysis[10-12], and micro determination of hydroxyl groups using hydriodic acid[13]. The first two tools were used in the study of crude as well as more highly refined concentrates; the latter two could be applied only when material approaching purity was obtained.

A substantial advance in the more definitive determination of structure came in 1935 when β-alanine, under certain testing conditions, was found to be a powerful yeast growth substance[14] and later to be produced from pantothenic acid concentrates by cleavage[15].

The purification of pantothenic acid in the form of its calcium salt was eventually accomplished; only, however, to the extent of obtaining about 10 mg of material of estimated 90% purity and larger amounts of material with less potency[16]. Autolyzed beef liver was the source material and a prominent procedure involved a fractional distribution of brucine salts between water and chloroform. The extremely hydrophilic nature of the active compound was a serious drawback in its isolation; even the brucine salt was a thousand times more soluble in water than in chloroform.

At the time this degree of purification was accomplished, the writer moved his laboratory and sought the collaboration of Merck and Company so as not to incur delay in the solution of the problem. Pantothenic acid was then known to be the product of the condensation of a non-nitrogenous α-hydroxy-lactone and β-alanine[17]. On the basis of the molecular weight by diffusion and the analysis of non-crystalline calcium pantothenate known to be slightly impure, the lactone was judged to have the formula $C_5H_8O_3$ instead of the homologous correct one $C_6H_{10}O_3$. A partial synthesis of pantothenic acid[18,19] had been accomplished in June 1938 by condensation of the lactone obtained by degrading impure pantothenic acid with synthetic β-alanine ester, followed by mild hydrolysis of the ester linkage. In retrospect a simple solution to the structural problem would have involved a synthesis of all possible α-hydroxylactones with approximately the right molecular weight, and the condensation of each with β-alanine until the physiologically active agent was found. The desired "pantoic" lactone (racemic) was a known compound having been made by Glaser[20] in 1904.

Stiller and associates[21,22] in the Merck laboratories a little less than a year after the collaboration began isolated the lactone from concentrates, and determined its structure by classical methods to be α-hydroxy-β,β-dimethyl-γ-butyrolactone. This was synthesized and resolved into its optical isomers. The levo-rotatory lactone when condensed with β-alanine by various procedures[19,22,23] yields dextro-rotatory pantothenic acid with full biological activity. The antipode was found to be inactive. The biologically active form has, according to Hudson's amide rule, the D-configuration[24,25].

$$HO-CH_2-\underset{\underset{H_3C}{|}}{\overset{\overset{H_3C}{|}}{C}}-\underset{\underset{OH}{|}}{\overset{\overset{H}{|}}{C}}-\overset{\overset{O}{||}}{C}-NH-CH_2-CH_2-COOH$$

Pantothenic acid

All methods that have been used for the determination of pantothenic acid in natural sources have been biological methods. One chemical method has been used for concentrates[26].

During the final stages of these extended pantothenic acid studies Snell, Strong and Peterson[27] at Wisconsin had made progress in the concentration of the same substance using lactic acid bacteria for testing. At the same time the "filtrate factor", the "rat growth factor", and the "chick antidermatitis factor" were being investigated in various laboratories[28]. The identity of pantothenic acid with the "chick antidermatitis factor" was made highly probable when relatively crude and highly potent concentrates furnished by Williams proved correspondingly active in chick tests[29,30]. Woolley and co-workers[31] also showed that biological activity for chicks could be regenerated from concentrates which had been rendered inactive by acid or alkali treatment, by suitable condensation with β-alanine ester, subsequently followed by mild hydrolysis.

Concurrent and subsequent investigations have shown that pantothenic acid is a dietary essential for chickens, ducks, turkeys, rats, mice, dogs, foxes, pigs, monkeys, cattle and horses, as well as protozoa and insect larvae. While it can be synthesized by green plants and many bacteria, it was early shown to stimulate markedly the growth of alfalfa seedlings[32], a liverwort *Ricciocarpus natans*[33] and pea embryos[34]. Some microorganisms, including yeasts (but not lactic acid bacteria) synthesize it readily when β-alanine is furnished[35]. Some respond to pantoic acid alone[36]. Some can couple the two moieties only if they are both furnished. Deficient animals are not able to couple the two parts of the molecule, when they are fed simultaneously. The intact molecule is obviously not digested into its two components in the gastrointestinal tracts of animals.

Pantothenol[37], structurally like pantothenic acid except for the replacement of the carboxyl by a primary alcohol group, appears to be approximately the nutritional equivalent for animals[37,38] of the acid itself, indicating that *in vivo* oxidation takes place readily. In humans the alcohol appears to be converted into pantothenic acid readily[39].

Hydroxypantothenic acid[40] (*N*-(α-hydroxy-β,β′-dimethylolbutyryl)-β-alanine) has up to about 20% of the activity of pantothenic acid for some microorganisms. Several other related lactones yielded products with appreciable activity[17,41].

Pantoyltaurine[42] is one of many pantothenic acid antagonists which block competitively the utilization of the vitamin by microorganisms. Shive has discussed many antagonistic analogues in a thorough manner[43]. One of the most widely used antagonists is ω-methylpantothenic acid which has been used to induce pantothenic acid deficiencies in animals[44] and human beings[45].

One of the first findings which gave a definite clue to the functioning of pantothenic acid in biological systems was the discovery of its presence as a fundamental constituent of coenzyme A. Initially preparations of this coenzyme failed to yield pantothenic acid, but in the author's laboratory a sample of coenzyme submitted by Dr. Lipmann was found to yield on acid hydrolysis a substantial amount of β-alanine[46], a fact strongly suggesting the presence of pantothenic acid, which was itself later released by enzymatic action[46,47]. A further link in the chain was revealed in the discovery of pantothiene[48] (the *Lactobacillus bulgaricus* factor) which has the formula indicated:

$$HO-CH_2-\underset{\underset{H_3C}{|}}{\overset{\overset{H_3C}{|}}{C}}-\underset{\underset{OH}{|}}{\overset{\overset{H}{|}}{C}}-\overset{\overset{O}{\|}}{C}-NH-CH_2-CH_2-\overset{\overset{O}{\|}}{C}-NH-CH_2-CH_2-SH$$

Pantothiene

This compound when esterified at the ω-alcohol group with pyrophosphate which in turn is attached to an adenosine 3′-phosphate residue becomes coenzyme A. When the sulfhydryl group is acetylated it becomes acetyl-CoA.

The key nature of coenzyme A for synthetic processes as well as in the most important energy-yielding process in all mammalian biology (which includes the citric acid cycle) is in keeping with the early observation of Williams and co-workers[49] that pantothenic acid was found in many types of cells and tissues from widely divergent biological phyla and was concluded to be present in every type of living cell. This observation gave rise to its name pantothenic, which is from the Greek: from everywhere.

While the apparently ubiquitous occurrence of pantothenic acid was a striking fact in 1933, this is not now regarded so, because many other chemical substances, notably other B vitamins, are also widely distributed in many diverse forms of life. The widespread occurrence of pantothenic acid has led to unfortunate misconceptions. In a very recent medical journal one reads: "There is little chance of a spontaneous pantothenic acid deficiency in the human diet because of the widespread distribution of this factor in natural foods." If one were to substitute for pantothenic acid in this sentence the word thiamin or riboflavin or niacinamide or calcium or iodine, it would make just as good sense, and yet would be regarded as ridiculous. Whether or not pantothenic acid deficiency exists depends *quantitatively* upon the supply and the need. Wide distribution has nothing to do with the problem.

In medical circles the importance of pantothenic acid as a nutrient is often disregarded because of this "universal-occurrence idea" and also because it is difficult to produce in humans a specific disease condition which may be attributed specifically to its deficiency. It would appear that pantothenic acid deficiency (since it is the only organic part of coenzyme A needed nutritionally by| mammals) might well cause diffuse adverse effects comparable to those which might be expected to occur in non-osseous tissues as a result of phosphate deficiency.

There are many types of manifestations of pantothenic acid deficiency in animals: dermatitis, keratitis, ulcers throughout the gastrointestinal tract, intussusceptions, anemia, achromotrichia, depigmentation of tooth enamel, congenital malformations, bowel atony, failure to produce antibodies, hemorrhagic adrenal medulla and cortex, spinal cord lesions, dehydration, fatty liver, thymus involution, kidney damage, heart damage (and sudden death), bone marrow hypoplasia, leucocyte deficiency, spinal curvature, myelin degeneration, uncoordinated gait, etc. The close relationship of pantothenic acid to the reproductive process is suggested by the richness of "royal jelly" with respect to pantothenic acid[50], and the more recent finding that codfish ovaries[51] are several times richer than "royal jelly", previously the richest known natural source.

The artificial production of any substantial degree of pantothenic acid deficiency in humans may be questioned on humanitarian grounds and from the scientific standpoint; the findings would be scarcely more interesting than those that might be obtained by artificially producing a phosphate deficiency.

The most reasonable interpretation of the extremely diverse effects resulting from pantothenic acid deficiency in various animals (and humans) is based upon the supposition that each tissue in the body is capable of being nourished at various levels of efficiency, and that pantothenic deficiency which can potentially cause damage in every tissue, strikes sometimes here and sometimes there, depending upon many factors which reside in the species or in the afflicted individual animal. Despite the absence of any well-defined human deficiency syndrome there can be no intelligent question regarding the importance of pantothenic acid in human nutrition.

References p. 64

REFERENCES

1 E. WILDIERS, *Cellule*, 18 (1901) 313.
2 R. J. WILLIAMS, *Science*, 88 (1938) 475.
3 R. J. WILLIAMS AND D. H. SAUNDERS, *Biochem. J.*, 28 (1934) 1887.
4 R. J. WILLIAMS, *Biol. Rev.*, 16 (1941) 49.
5 R. R. WILLIAMS AMD R. E. WATERMAN, *J. Biol. Chem.*, 78 (1928) 311.
6 R. J. WILLIAMS, C. M. LYMAN, G. H. GOODYEAR AND J. H. TRUESDAIL, *J. Am. Chem. Soc.*, 54 (1932) 3462.
7 R. J. WILLIAMS AND R. MOSER, *J. Am. Chem. Soc.*, 56 (1934) 169.
8 R. J. WILLIAMS, E. D. McALISTER AND R. R. ROEHM, *J. Biol. Chem.*, 83 (1929) 315.
9 R. J. WILLIAMS, *J. Biol. Chem.*, 110 (1935) 589.
10 R. J. WILLIAMS, *J. Am. Chem. Soc.*, 59 (1937) 288.
11 R. J. WILLIAMS, E. ROHRMANN AND B. E. CHRISTENSEN, *J. Am. Chem. Soc.*, 59 (1937) 291.
12 B. E. CHRISTENSEN, R. J. WILLIAMS AND A. E. KING, *J. Am. Chem. Soc.*, 59 (1937) 293.
13 H. K. MITCHELL AND R. J. WILLIAMS, *J. Am. Chem. Soc.*, 60 (1938) 2723.
14 R. J. WILLIAMS AND E. ROHRMANN, *J. Am. Chem. Soc.*, 58 (1936) 695.
15 H. H. WEINSTOCK, H. K. MITCHELL, E. F. PRATT AND R. J. WILLIAMS, *J. Am. Chem. Soc.*, 61 (1939) 1421.
16 R. J. WILLIAMS, J. H. TRUESDAIL, H. H. WEINSTOCK, E. ROHRMANN, C. M. LYMAN AND C. H. McBURNEY, *J. Am. Chem. Soc.*, 60 (1938) 2719.
17 H. K. MITCHELL, H. H. WEINSTOCK, E. E. SNELL, S. R. STANBERRY AND R. J. WILLIAMS, *J. Am. Chem. Soc.*, 62 (1940) 1776.
18 R. J. WILLIAMS, *Science*, 89 (1939) 486.
19 R. J. WILLIAMS, H. K. MITCHELL, H. H. WEINSTOCK AND E. E. SNELL, *J. Am. Chem. Soc.*, 62 (1940) 1784.
20 E. GLASER, *Monatsh. Chem.*, 25 (1904) 46.
21 E. T. STILLER, J. C. KERESZTESY AND J. FINKELSTEIN, *J. Am. Chem. Soc.*, 62 (1940) 1779.
22 E. T. STILLER, S. A. HARRIS, J. FINKELSTEIN, J. C. KERESZTESY AND K. FOLKERS, *J. Am. Chem. Soc.*, 62 (1940) 1785.
23 R. J. WILLIAMS, H. K. MITCHELL, H. H. WEINSTOCK AND E. E. SNELL, *J. Am. Chem. Soc.*, 62 (1940) 1784.
24 A. GRÜSSNER, M. GÄTZI-FICHTER AND T. REICHSTEIN, *Helv. Chim. Acta*, 23 (1940) 1276.
25 H. C. PARKE AND E. J. LAWSON, *J. Am. Chem. Soc.*, 63 (1941) 2869.
26 C. R. SZALKOWSKI AND J. H. DAVIDSON JR., *Anal. Chem.*, 25 (1953) 1192.
27 E. E. SNELL, F. M. STRONG AND W. H. PETERSON, *J. Bacteriol.*, 38 (1939) 293.
28 S. LEPKOVSKY, *Ann. Rev. Biochem.*, 9 (1940) 400.
29 T. H. JUKES, *J. Am. Chem. Soc.*, 61 (1939) 975.
30 T. H. JUKES, *J. Biol. Chem.*, 129 (1939) 129.
31 D. W. WOOLLEY, *J. Biol. Chem.*, 129 (1939) 673.
32 C. H. McBURNEY, W. B. BOLLEN AND R. J. WILLIAMS, *Proc. Natl. Acad. Sci. U.S.*, 21 (1935) 301.
33 R. J. WILLIAMS AND E. ROHRMANN, *Plant Physiol.*, 10 (1935) 559.
34 J. BONNER AND G. AXTMAN, *Proc. Natl. Acad. Sci. U.S.*, 23 (1937) 453.
35 E. E. SNELL, *Ann. Rev. Biochem.*, 15 (1946) 375.
36 L. A. UNDERKOFLER, A. C. BANTZ AND W. H. PETERSON, *J. Bacteriol.*, 45 (1943) 183.
37 H. PFALTZ, *Z. Vitaminforsch.*, 13 (1943) 236.
38 D. M. HEGSTED, *Proc. Soc. Exptl. Biol. Med.*, 69 (1948) 571.
39 S. H. RUBIN, J. M. COOPERMAN, M. E. MOORE AND J. SCHEINER, *J. Nutrition*, 35 (1948) 499.
40 H. K. MITCHELL, E. E. SNELL AND R. J. WILLIAMS, *J. Am. Chem. Soc.*, 62 (1940) 1791.
41 R. D. LINDSAY AND V. H. CHELDELIN, *J. Am. Chem. Soc.*, 72 (1950) 828.
42 E. E. SNELL, *J. Biol. Chem.*, 144 (1941) 121.
43 W. SHIVE, *The Biochemistry of B Vitamins*, Reinhold, New York, 1950, 620.

[44] W. DRELL AND M. S. DUNN, *Arch. Biochem. Biophys.*, 33 (1951) 110.

[45] W. B. BEAN AND R. E. HODGES, *Proc. Soc. Exptl. Biol. Med.*, 86 (1954) 693.

[46] F. LIPMANN, N. O. KAPLAN, G. D. NOVELLI, L. C. TUTTLE AND B. M. GUIRARD, *J. Biol. Chem.*, 167 (1947) 869.

[47] G. D. NOVELLI, N. O. KAPLAN AND F. LIPMANN, *J. Biol. Chem.*, 177 (1949) 97.

[48] E. E. SNELL, G. M. BROWN, V. J. PETERS, J. A. CRAIG, E. L. WITTLE, J. A. MOORE, V. M. McGLOHON AND O. D. BIRD, *J. Am. Chem. Soc.*, 72 (1950) 5349.

[49] R. J. WILLIAMS, C. M. LYMAN, G. H. GOODYEAR, J. H. TRUESDAIL AND D. HOLADAY, *J. Am. Chem. Soc.*, 55 (1933) 2912.

[50] P. B. PEARSON AND C. J. BURGIN, *Proc. Soc. Exptl. Biol. Med.*, 48 (1941) 415.

[51] O. R. BRAEKKAN, *Nature*, 176 (1955) 598.

Chapter VI

Biotin

L. H. STERNBACH

*Chemical Research Department, Hoffman-La Roche, Inc.,
Nutley, N.J. (U.S.A.)*

1. Introduction

Diets containing a large percentage of egg white have a toxic effect on animals[1]. The curative effect of a number of foodstuffs such as yeast, egg yolk, or milk on this egg-white injury was ascribed by Boas[2] to the "protective factor X". This factor was called vitamin H by György[3] who found that liver was relatively rich in this vitamin. Attempts at isolation led to concentrates obtained from liver and also from yeasts, which were highly active against egg-white injury in experimental animals[4].

While the painstaking work of György and co-workers to obtain vitamin H concentrates was in progress, Kögl and co-workers[5] were concerned with the isolation from egg yolk of Bios BII, a growth factor for yeast. They succeeded in 1936 and obtained the growth factor as a crystalline methyl ester of the composition $C_{11}H_{18}O_3N_2S$ and named the corresponding acid biotin[6].

In 1940 György, Du Vigneaud and co-workers[7] obtained pure vitamin H ester from liver concentrates. The similar biological properties led them to assume that their product was identical with Kögl's biotin methyl ester. The free vitamin[8] prepared from the methyl ester by the American group had the composition $C_{10}H_{16}O_3N_2S$ and formed colorless needles melting at $230–232°$ ($[\alpha]_D^{22} = +92°$, 0.3% in 0.1 N NaOH).

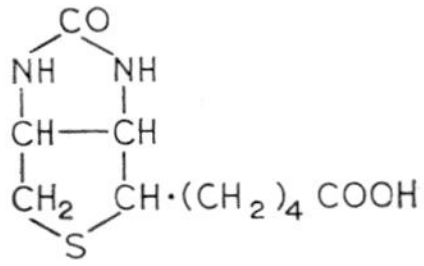

$$\begin{array}{c} \text{CO} \\ \text{NH} \quad \text{NH} \\ | \qquad | \\ \text{CH—CH} \\ | \qquad | \\ \text{CH}_2 \quad \text{CH·(CH}_2\text{)}_4\text{ COOH} \\ \text{S} \end{array}$$

(1) Biotin

The structure determination by Du Vigneaud and co-workers[9,10] was completed in 1942 and it was established that biotin (vitamin H) was *d*-2′-keto-

3,4-imidazolido-2-tetrahydrothiophenevaleric acid. This structure was confirmed by the synthesis of Harris and co-workers[11] in the Merck (U.S.A.) laboratories in 1943. Since then the name biotin is generally used in the literature[12] to designate the compound described by Du Vigneaud et al.[8].

In the meantime Kögl and co-workers continued the study of biotin isolated from egg yolk and came to the conclusion that it was not identical with the vitamin isolated from liver concentrates[13] but was an isomer of the structure (2), (ref. 14).

(2) α-biotin

They proposed the name α-biotin for their compound and β-biotin[15] for the compound first isolated by György, Du Vigneaud, and co-workers. The structure of α-biotin was, however, never confirmed by synthesis and no further chemical work has been published since. A biological comparison of α- and β-biotin was carried out again in 1948 by Krueger and Peterson[16]. The complete microbiological identity of these two compounds led the authors to the conclusion that α- and β-biotin are most probably identical.

2. Structure determination

The interesting structure determination of biotin by Du Vigneaud, Hofmann, Melville, and co-workers which involved some very fine and complicated chemical work can be discussed here only very briefly[17].

Biotin was found to have the empirical formula $C_{10}H_{16}O_3N_2S$. The electrometric titration showed that it was a simple monocarboxylic acid with a neutralization equivalent[8] of 244. The hydrolysis[18] yielded an optically active diamino-carboxylic acid which had the composition $C_9H_{18}O_2N_2S$. It contained two primary amino groups as established by the Van Slyke method and could be reconverted to biotin by treatment with phosgene[19].

These reactions (1 and 2) are best explained by the presence of a urea ring. The sulfur was present in a thioether grouping. This was proved by the oxidation of biotin with hydrogen peroxide[18] to the sulfone $C_{10}H_{16}O_5N_2S$. The empirical formula and the absence of ethylenic linkages indicated that biotin contained a bicyclic system[20], one of the rings containing the elements of urea, the other most probably the sulfur atom. Oxidation[20] of the "diamino-acid" led to the formation of adipic acid. In order to establish whether one of the carboxyl groups of the adipic acid was originally present in biotin, a transformation product was oxidized in which the carboxyl had been replaced by an amino group. This triamine was obtained by Curtius degradation[21] of biotin, followed by hydrolysis, and did *not* yield adipic acid on oxidation. This demonstrated that the carboxyl group of biotin was one of the carboxyl groups found in the adipic acid and proved the presence of the groupings (3), (4) and (5).

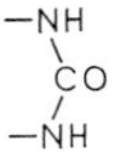

$$
\begin{array}{ccc}
\begin{array}{c} -NH \\ \backslash \\ CO \\ / \\ -NH \end{array}
&
\backslash S /
&
\backslash C-(CH_2)_4CO_2H /
\\
(3) & (4) & (5)
\end{array}
$$

The size of the urea ring for which a five- or six-membered structure was most probable was established by the reaction of the diamino-carboxylic acid with phenanthrenequinone[22].

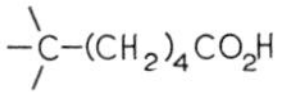

A quinoxaline derivative was formed as was shown by analysis and the ultraviolet absorption spectrum, which was almost identical with that of a related compound prepared for comparison. The isolation of a quinoxaline and not of the dihydro derivative formed originally proved in addition that each of the carbons bearing the nitrogen atoms had at least one hydrogen atom as a substituent. This indicated that the grouping (6)

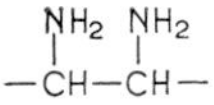

$$
\begin{array}{c}
NH_2 \quad NH_2 \\
| \qquad | \\
-CH-CH-
\end{array}
$$

(6)

was present and that the structure of biotin was most likely (7), (ref. 22). Final proof was the exhaustive methylation of the diamino-carboxylic acid (8) to the thiophene derivative (9), (ref. 10), which was identical with a synthetic sample. The following reaction sequence confirmed the structure: biotin was desulfurized with Raney nickel to desthiobiotin and the latter saponified to an optically active 7,8-diaminopelargonic acid. This was

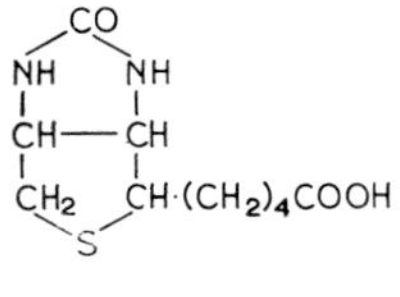

$$
\begin{array}{ccc}
\begin{array}{c}
\quad CO \\
\diagup \quad \diagdown \\
NH \qquad NH \\
| \qquad | \\
CH-\!-CH \\
| \qquad | \\
CH_2 \quad CH\cdot(CH_2)_4COOH \\
\diagdown \quad \diagup \\
\quad S
\end{array}
&
\begin{array}{c}
NH_2 \quad NH_2 \\
| \qquad | \\
\boxed{} \\
S \quad (CH_2)_4CO_2H
\end{array}
\quad\longrightarrow\quad
&
\begin{array}{c}
\boxed{} \\
S \quad (CH_2)_4CO_2H
\end{array}
\\
(7) & (8) & (9)
\end{array}
$$

reacted with phenanthrenequinone to yield an optically inactive quinoxaline which was identical with the quinoxaline prepared from synthetic 7,8-diaminopelargonic acid[9].

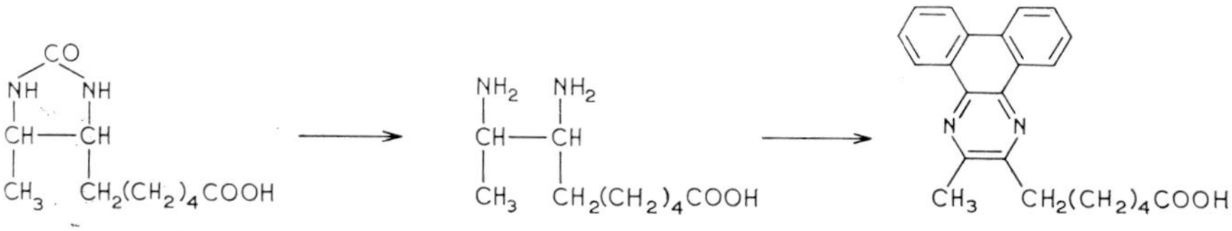

Desthiobiotin (10)

3. Synthesis of biotin

Biotin was first synthesized by Harris and co-workers[11,23] (see Fig. 1) in the Merck (U.S.A.) laboratories. The *dl*-biotin (XI) was resolved via the D(—)man-

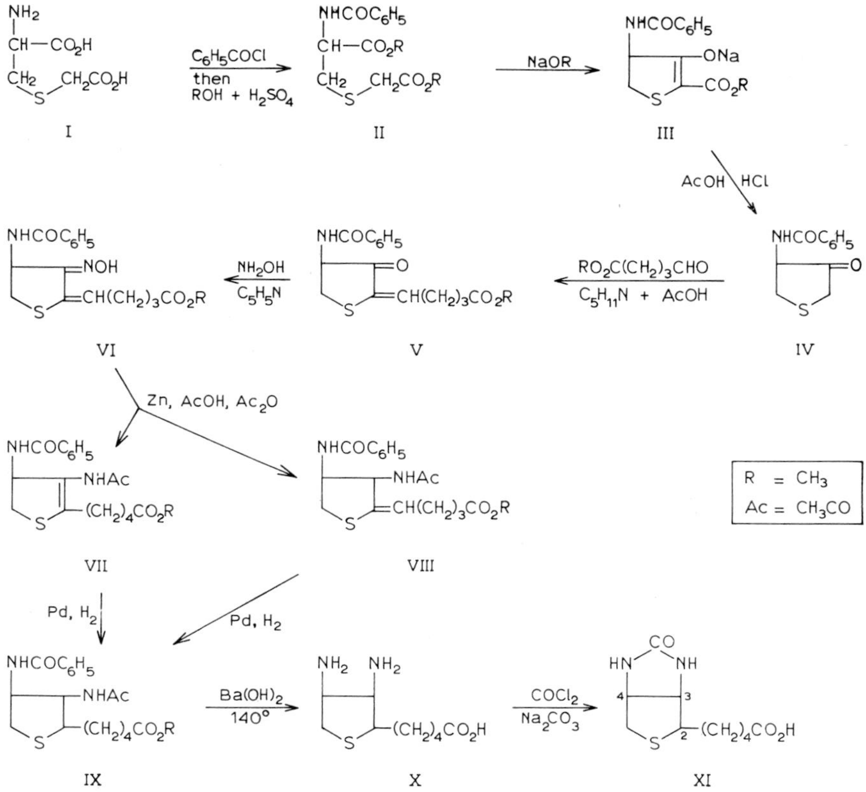

Fig. 1.

delic acid ester or via the L(+)arginine salt to produce *d*-biotin which was in every respect identical with the natural product[24],*. The synthesis was complicated by the fact that biotin (XI) has three asymmetric carbon atoms (2, 3 and 4) which would allow the formation of 8 stereoisomers or 4 racemates. In this synthesis three of these racemates were formed. Compound VII yielded two isomeric compounds of formula IX which, via isomers X, were converted into two different biotin isomers XI, namely *dl*-biotin (m.p. 232°) and *dl-allo*biotin (m.p. 194–196°). Compound VIII led after analogous transformations also to two isomers of XI, *dl-allo*- and *dl-epi-allo*-biotin (decomp. above 195°). The steric relationship[26] of these isomers was established by their conversion into desthio derivatives which eliminated the asymmetry of C-2. *dl*-Biotin yielded *dl*-desthiobiotin (m.p. 166°) which had one-half the biological activity of the desthiobiotin obtained from natural biotin**. On the other hand, the biologically inactive *allo*- and *epi-allo*-biotins yielded an isomer, the biologically inactive *dl*-desthio-*allo*-biotin. This showed that both these compounds (*allo*- and *epi-allo*-) differ from biotin by their configuration at C-3 or C-4 and from each other only by the configuration at C-2.

Allo- and *epi-allo*-biotin were formed in much lower yield from the corresponding diamines X than biotin; *allo*-biotin was also much more easily saponified to the diamine than biotin. This indicated that the two amino groups were *trans* to each other in the *allo* series, whereas they were *cis* in biotin, which therefore had the two rings connected in an unstrained bicyclic system[26].

The steric configuration of the side chain has not yet been fully elucidated. However, the interpretation of the hydrogenation results of Harris and co-workers[26] and their own experimental evidence led Grob and Sprecher[27] to assume that biotin has the all-*cis* structure (11).

(11)

A second synthesis[28] of biotin was published in 1945. The authors started with the thiophane (XII), (ref. 29) and proceeded as shown in Fig. 2. Compound XIX was separated into two crystalline isomers and an oily product. The crystalline forms led to biologically inactive compounds***

---

* *l*-Biotin was biologically inactive[25].
** In the microbiological test with *Saccharomyces cerevisiae*.
*** These compounds were not identical with *allo*- or *epi-allo*-biotin, and their structure has not been elucidated.

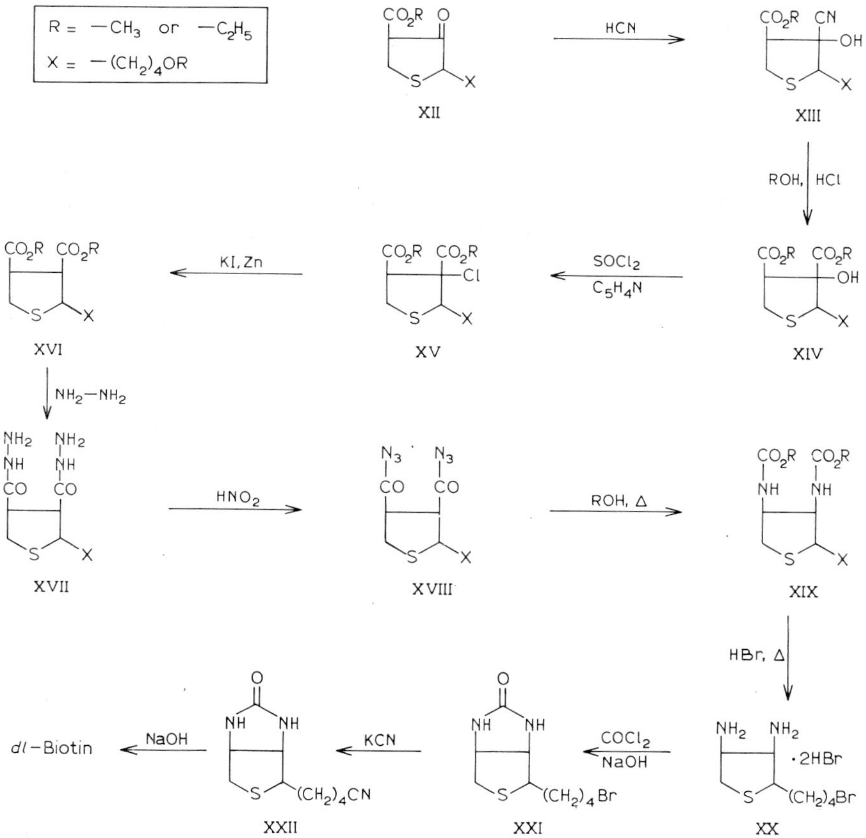

Fig. 2.

apparently isomeric with biotin which were called dl-ψ- and iso-β-biotin[30]. The non-crystalline part of XIX yielded dl-biotin.

The third synthesis[31] also started* with a substituted thiophane (XXIII), (ref. 32), and progressed in a way similar to the second synthesis[28]. However, at each step meticulous care was taken to establish the steric configuration of the substituents in positions 3 and 4. The stepwise Curtius degradation and the conversion of a *trans*-substituted thiophane (XXVI) into a derivative of the *cis* series (XXVII) led in the end to the synthesis of dl-biotin.

Analogous transformations yielded the missing fourth stereoisomer of biotin, dl-epi-biotin[33] (m.p. 190–191°). This compound was formed when the

---

* The starting material was prepared in a similar way to the thiophanedicarboxylic ester (XVI).

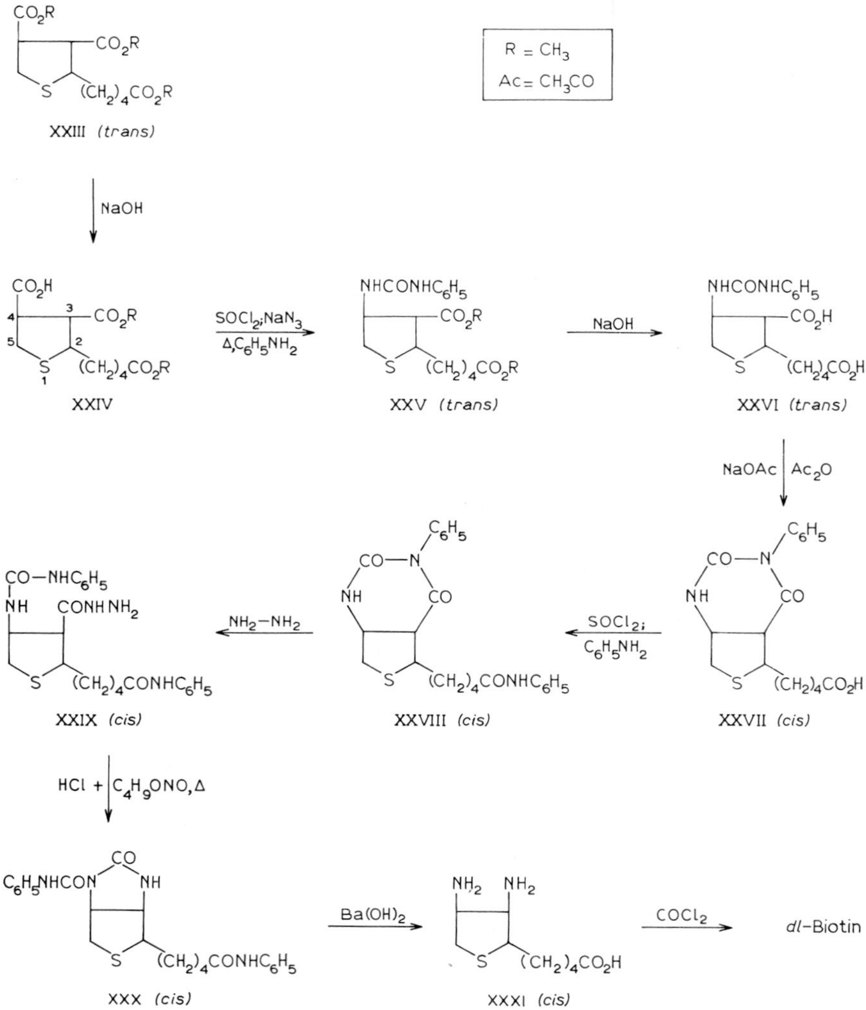

Fig. 3.

order of transformation of the carbalkoxy groups into the amino groups was reversed. The biologically inactive *dl-epi*-biotin, differing from biotin only by the steric configuration on C-2, yielded as expected on desulfuration the biologically active *dl*-desthiobiotin.

The commercial synthesis of biotin[34] developed in the laboratories of Hoffmann-La Roche, Inc., is given in Fig. 4. It differs from the other syntheses in several respects. The imidazolidone ring is formed first with the two substituents (carboxyls) *cis* to each other. The formation of the acetate of the cyclized aldehydo acid (**XXXIV**) occurs in good yield on zinc reduction of the anhydride of **XXXIII**. The introduction of the sulfur and further reduction to yield the *cis*-thiolactone (**XXXV**) is carried out without isolation of intermediates and occurs most probably via a thioaldehyde or polythioaldehyde, disulfide and the free thiol acid[35,*]. The steric configuration

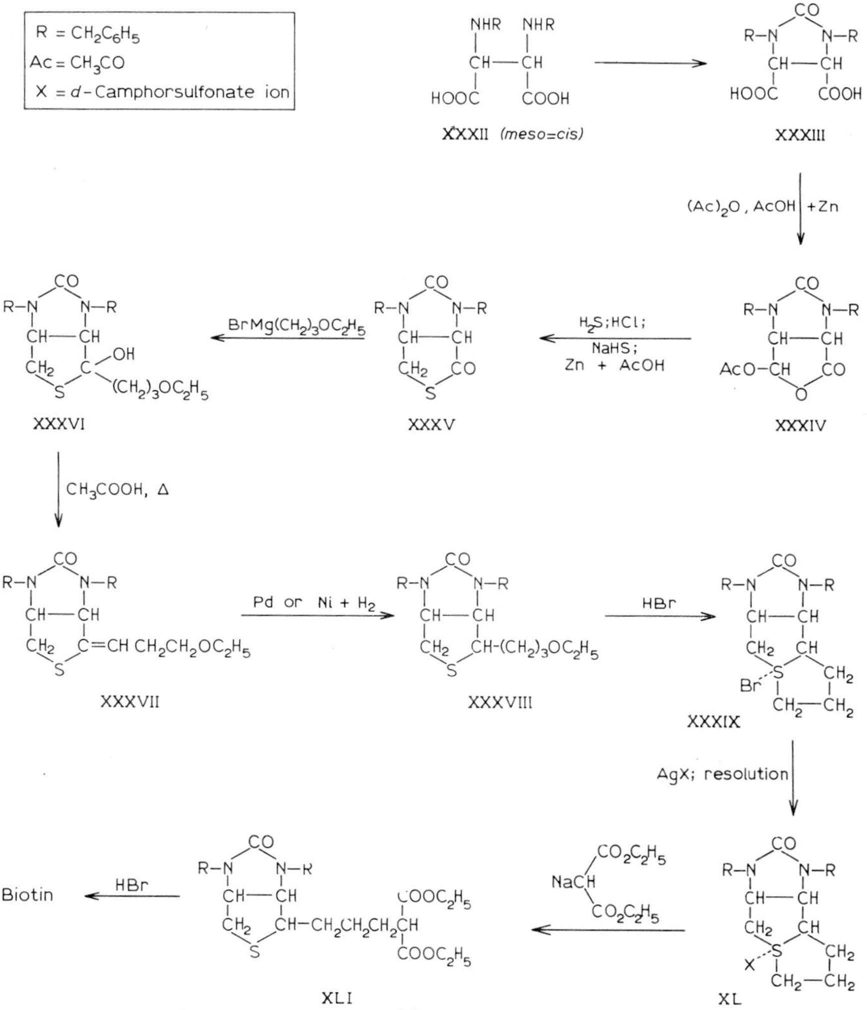

Fig. 4.

* Under different reaction conditions the *trans* thiol acid is obtained which does not form a thiolactone on acid treatment.

remains unchanged throughout the whole reaction series. This excludes the formation of *allo* compounds. The hydrogenation of XXXVII is also stereospecific and does not lead to the formation of compounds belonging to the *epi* series. The replacement of the ethoxy group in XXXVIII by bromine results in the formation of the thiophanium compound XXXIX which is resolved into its optical isomers via the *d*-camphorsulfonates. The levorotatory isomer XL is converted into a malonic ester (XLI) which on heating with hydrobromic acid is simultaneously saponified, decarboxylated, and debenzylated to yield biotin.

4. Compounds related to biotin

A number of compounds closely related to biotin can replace this vitamin as a growth factor for micro-organisms; some can also cure egg white injury in animals. Other related compounds compete with the utilization of biotin by micro-organisms and thereby inhibit their growth. A few of the more important of these compounds are discussed below.

(12)   Biocytin

(a) Biocytin

Biocytin was first isolated[36] from autolyzed yeast extracts, and has the biotin moiety bound to L-lysine. It has some of the biological properties of biotin and is probably an intermediate in the liberation of biotin from yeast or liver extracts which contain biotin bound covalently to proteins in a microbiologically inactive form. Its structure (12) was proved by degradation and by synthesis from biotin acid chloride and L-lysine[37].

(b) Desthiobiotin

Desthiobiotin was first prepared as the methyl ester by removal of sulfur from biotin methyl ester with Raney nickel[9] and also from biotin by the same method[38]. It is microbiologically as active as biotin. The racemic compound was synthesized by three groups almost simultaneously. Wood and Du Vigneaud[39] published the first synthesis (Fig. 5). Bourquin, Schnider and Grüssner[40] prepared in a somewhat simpler manner the intermediate

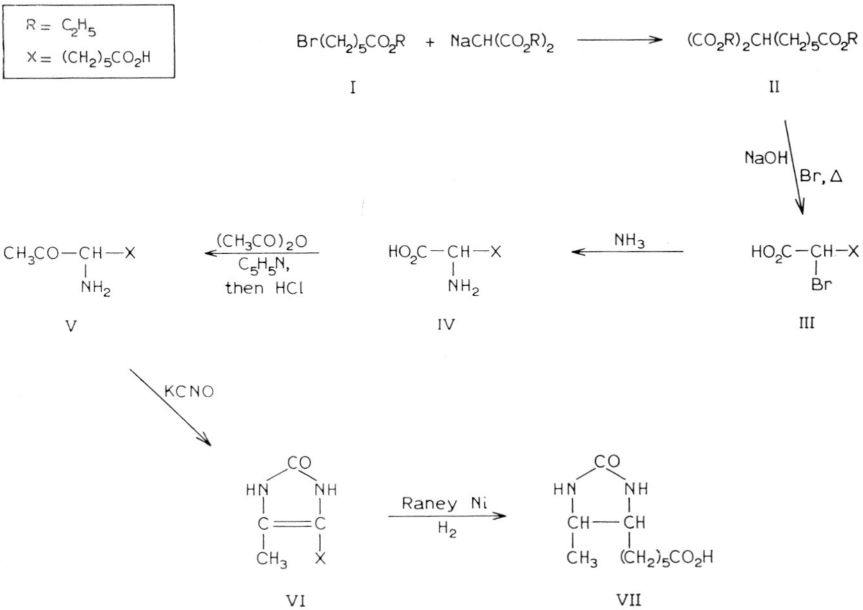

R = C_2H_5
X = $(CH_2)_5CO_2H$

$Br(CH_2)_5CO_2R + NaCH(CO_2R)_2 \longrightarrow (CO_2R)_2CH(CH_2)_5CO_2R$

I   II

NaOH, Br, Δ

$CH_3CO{-}CH{-}X$ (with NH_2)   V $\xleftarrow[\text{then HCl}]{\substack{(CH_3CO)_2O \\ C_5H_5N,}}$ $HO_2C{-}CH{-}X$ (with NH_2)   IV $\xleftarrow{NH_3}$ $HO_2C{-}CH{-}X$ (with Br)   III

KCNO

VI $\xrightarrow[\text{H}_2]{\text{Raney Ni}}$ VII

Fig. 5.

VIII $\xrightarrow[\Delta]{\text{alkali}}$ IX $\xrightarrow[\text{AlCl}_3]{\text{ClCO(CH}_2)_4\text{CO}_2\text{R}}$ X

dl-Desthiobiotin $\xleftarrow[\text{hydrolysis}]{\text{Pt, H}_2 ;}$ XI $\xleftarrow[\text{H}_2]{\text{Pt or Pd}}$

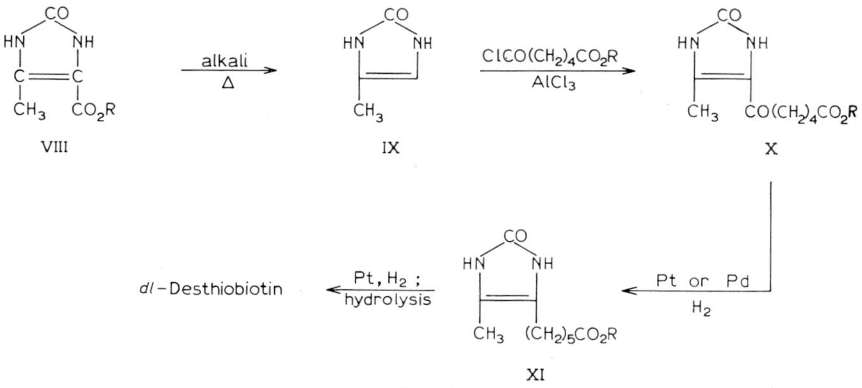

Fig. 6.

7-amino-8-keto-pelargonic acid (V), and then proceeded like Wood and Du Vigneaud. Duschinsky and Dolan[41] used a very interesting approach (see Fig. 6). A simple imidazolone (IX) was used as starting material and the side chain introduced by a Friedel–Crafts reaction (IX → X). Then the carbonyl group was reduced to CH_2 (X → XI) and the double bond hydrogenated with a noble metal catalyst. This hydrogenation was stereospecific and avoided the formation of the *allo* compound which was a by-product in the first two syntheses[39,40].

Higher and lower homologs of desthiobiotin were also synthesized[40-42];

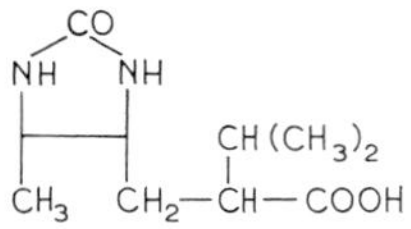

XII

some of them were weak biotin antagonists in the *Saccharomyces cerevisiae* test.

An isomer of desthiobiotin (XII) which corresponded to the postulated structure of Kögl's α-biotin was synthesized[43] by the method of Duschinsky and Dolan.

It is interesting to note that this compound was biologically completely inactive.

(c) Biotin sulfoxide

This compound was first isolated from milk concentrates in two forms differing very significantly in their optical rotation[44]. The dextrorotatory compound was found to be a highly active growth factor for *Saccharomyces cerevisiae* (as active as biotin) whereas the levorotatory isomer showed hardly any activity[44]. The oxidation of biotin with one mole of hydrogen peroxide[45] also yielded both forms which were separated by crystallization and were called *d*-biotin *l*-sulfoxide (m.p. 238–240°, $[\alpha]_D^{20} = -39.5°$) and *d*-biotin *d*-sulfoxide (m.p. 200–203°, $[\alpha]_D^{20} = +130°$). The existence of these two isomers is due to the asymmetry of the sulfoxide group.

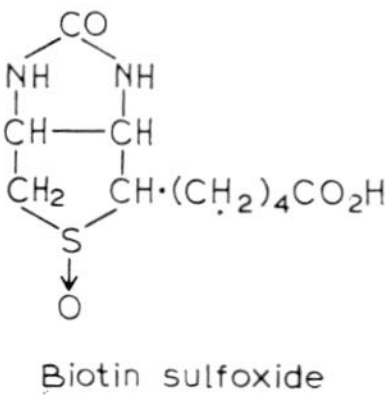

Biotin sulfoxide
(13)

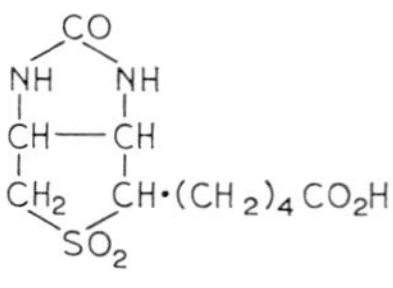

Biotin sulfone
(14)

(d) Biotin sulfone (m.p. 274–275°)

This compound is obtained by the oxidation of biotin with 2 moles of hydrogen peroxide[18]. It is a potent biotin antagonist (see second footnote on p. 70).

(e) *dl-Oxybiotin, O-heterobiotin* (m.p. 206–208°)

The synthesis of this oxygen analog of biotin was reported almost simultaneously by Hofmann[46] and by Duschinsky[47,48] and co-workers. It has biotin-like properties in micro-organisms and also in animals (3–17% of biotin). Hofmann's synthesis is given in Fig. 7. Compound XIII was prepared by

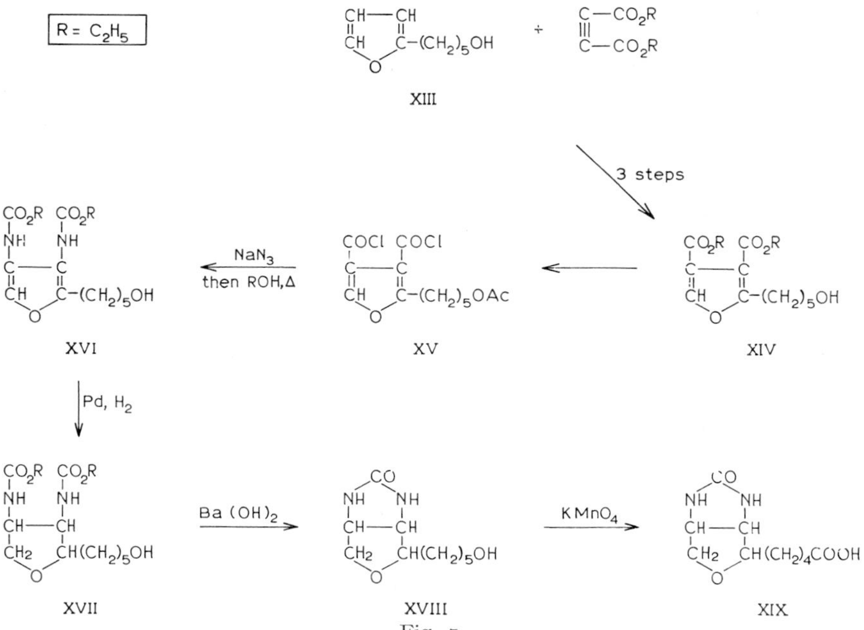

Fig. 7.

conventional methods. The Diels–Alder condensation with acetylenedicarboxylic acid ester led to an adduct which on hydrogenation followed by heating lost ethylene[49] and yielded XIV which was converted by conventional methods into XV and then as shown above into XIX. The corresponding *epi* derivative was also synthesized but had no biological activity[50]. *Trans*-diaminotetrahydrofurans[50] corresponding to XVII did not form imidazolidones on treatment with phosgene, so that no derivatives of the *allo* series could be synthesized. Homologs of oxybiotin were synthesized by Hofmann and co-workers[51] essentially via the route described above.

Duschinsky and Dolan[48] synthesized *O*-heterobiotin (Fig. 8) starting with intermediate X used in their *dl*-desthiobiotin synthesis.

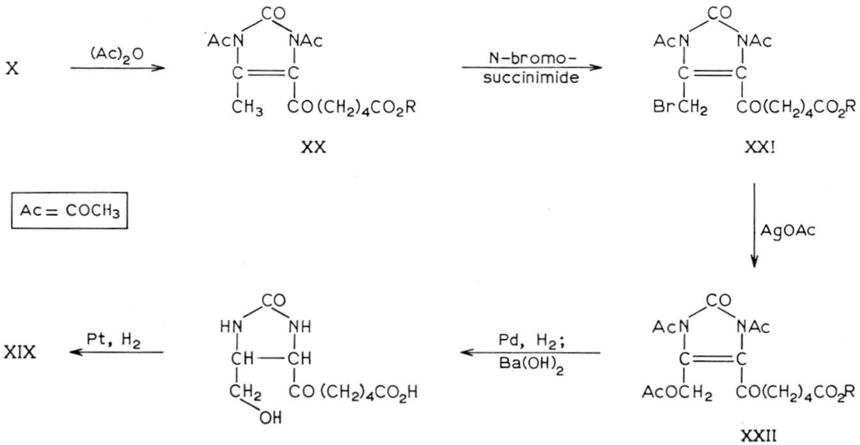

Fig. 8.

(f) d-Biotinol

d-Biotinol[52] (m.p. 174.5–175.5°, $[\alpha]_D^{25} = +84.7°$), the alcohol corresponding to biotin, was prepared from biotin methyl ester by reduction with LiAlH$_4$. It showed no biotin-like activity in micro-organisms but was as active as biotin in animals due to its enzymic oxidation to biotin[53].

(g) Preparation of homologs

Homologs of biotin were prepared as follows (Fig. 9):

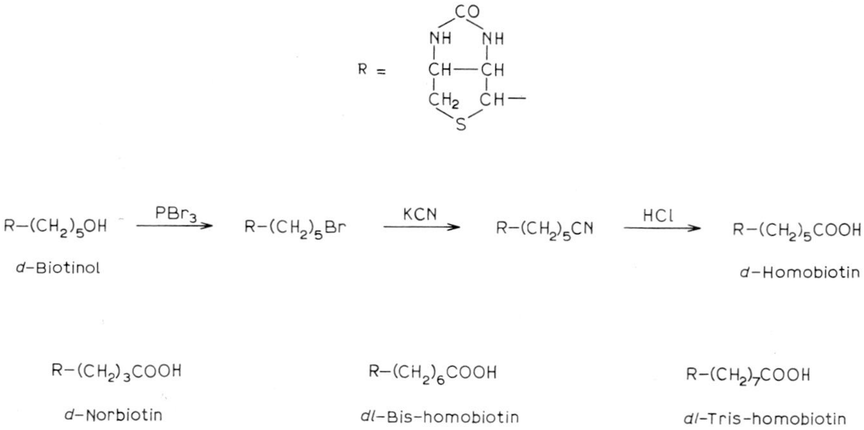

Fig. 9.

d-Norbiotin[54] (m.p. 256–257°, $[\alpha]_D^{23} = +96.4$) with 3 methylene groups in the side chain was prepared from the intermediate XL (Section 3), used in the biotin synthesis, by treatment with KCN followed by treatment with hydrobromic acid.

d-Homobiotin (m.p. 243–244°, $[\alpha]_D^{25} = +89°$) with 5 methylene groups in the side chain was prepared[54] as shown above from *d*-biotinol.

dl-Bis-homobiotin (m.p. 200.5–202.5°) and *dl-tris-homobiotin* (m.p. 216°) were prepared from the biotin intermediate XXXV (Section 3) by introducing longer side chains[55]. The corresponding sulfones[54] were prepared by oxidation with H_2O_2.

All these homologs are biotin antagonists; the most potent one is *d*-homobiotin[56,57].

ACKNOWLEDGEMENT

I wish to thank Dr. G. Berend for her valuable help.

References p. 80

REFERENCES

1 W. G. Bateman, *J. Biol. Chem.*, 26 (1916) 263.
2 M. A. Boas, *Biochem. J.*, 21 (1927) 712.
3 P. György, *Z. ärztl. Fortbild.*, 28 (1931) 377.
4 P. György, R. Kuhn and E. Lederer, *J. Biol. Chem.*, 131 (1939) 745.
5 F. Kögl, *Naturwissenschaften*, 25 (1937) 465.
6 F. Kögl and B. Tönnis, *Z. physiol. Chem., Hoppe-Seyler's*, 242 (1936) 43.
7 P. György, C. S. Rose, K. Hofmann, D. B. Melville and V. du Vigneaud, *Science*, 92 (1940) 609.
8 V. du Vigneaud, K. Hofmann, D. B. Melville and J. R. Rachele, *J. Biol. Chem.*, 140 (1941) 763.
9 V. du Vigneaud, D. B. Melville, K. Folkers, D. E. Wolf, R. Mozingo, J. C. Keresztesy and S. A. Harris, *J. Biol. Chem.*, 146 (1942) 475.
10 D. B. Melville, A. W. Moyer, K. Hofmann and V. du Vigneaud, *J. Biol. Chem.*, 146 (1942) 487.
11 S. A. Harris, D. E. Wolf, R. Mozingo and K. Folkers, *Science*, 97 (1943) 447.
12 See also IUPAC 1957 rules, *J. Am. Chem. Soc.*, 82 (1960) 5582.
13 F. Kögl and E. J. ten Ham, *Z. physiol. Chem., Hoppe-Seyler's*, 279 (1943) 140.
14 F. Kögl and W. A. J. Borg, *Z. physiol. Chem., Hoppe-Seyler's*, 281 (1944) 65.
15 F. Kögl, J. H. Verbeek, H. Erxleben and W. A. J. Borg, *Z. physiol. Chem., Hoppe-Seyler's*, 279 (1943) 121.
16 K. K. Krueger and W. H. Peterson, *J. Biol. Chem.*, 173 (1948) 497.
17 P. György in W. H. Sebrell Jr. and S. A. Harris (Eds.), *The Vitamins*, Vol. I, Academic Press, New York, 1954, p. 527.
18 K. Hofmann, D. B. Melville and V. du Vigneaud, *J. Biol. Chem.*, 141 (1941) 207.
19 D. B. Melville, K. Hofmann and V. du Vigneaud, *Science*, 94 (1941) 308.
20 K. Hofmann, D. B. Melville and V. du Vigneaud, *J. Am. Chem. Soc.*, 63 (1941) 3237.
21 V. du Vigneaud, K. Hofmann and D. B. Melville, *J. Am. Chem. Soc.*, 64 (1942) 188.
22 K. Hofmann, G. W. Kilmer, D. B. Melville, V. du Vigneaud and H. H. Darby, *J. Biol. Chem.*, 145 (1942) 503.
23 S. A. Harris, D. E. Wolf, R. Mozingo, R. C. Anderson, G. E. Arth, N. R. Easton, D. Heyl, A. N. Wilson and K. Folkers, *J. Am. Chem. Soc.*, 66 (1944) 1756.
24 D. E. Wolf, R. Mozingo, S. A. Harris, R. C. Anderson and K. Folkers, *J. Am. Chem. Soc.*, 67 (1945) 2100.
25 G. A. Emerson, *J. Biol. Chem.*, 157 (1945) 127.
26 S. A. Harris, R. Mozingo, D. E. Wolf, A. N. Wilson and K. Folkers, *J. Am. Chem. Soc.*, 67 (1945) 2102.
27 C. A. Grob and H. von Sprecher, *Helv. Chim. Acta*, 35 (1952) 885.
28 A. Grüssner, J. P. Bourquin and O. Schnider, *Helv. Chim. Acta*, 28 (1945) 517.
29 H. Schmid, *Helv. Chim. Acta*, 27 (1944) 127.
30 A. Grüssner, J. P. Bourquin and O. Schnider, *Helv. Chim. Acta*, 29 (1946) 770.
31 B. R. Baker, M. V. Querry, W. L. McEwen, S. Bernstein, S. R. Safir, L. Dorfman and Y. SubbaRow, *J. Org. Chem.*, 12 (1947) 186.
32 B. R. Baker, M. V. Querry, S. Bernstein, S. R. Safir and Y. SubbaRow, *J. Org. Chem.*, 12 (1947) 167.
33 B. R. Baker, W. L. McEwen and W. N. Kinley, *J. Org. Chem.*, 12 (1947) 322.
34 M. W. Goldberg and L. H. Sternbach, *U.S. Patents 2,489,232, 2,489,235 and 2,489,238*, 1949.
35 L. H. Sternbach, S. Kaiser and M. W. Goldberg, unpublished results.
36 L. D. Wright, E. L. Cresson, H. R. Skeggs, T. R. Wood, R. L. Peck, D. E. Wolf and K. Folkers, *J. Am. Chem. Soc.*, 72 (1950) 1048.
37 D. E. Wolf, J. Valiant, R. L. Peck and K. Folkers, *J. Am. Chem. Soc.*, 74 (1952) 2002.
38 D. B. Melville, K. Dittmer, G. B. Brown and V. du Vigneaud, *Science*, 98 (1943) 497.

[39] J. L. WOOD AND V. DU VIGNEAUD, *J. Am. Chem. Soc.*, 67 (1945) 210.

[40] J. P. BOURQUIN, O. SCHNIDER AND A. GRÜSSNER, *Helv. Chim. Acta*, 28 (1945) 528.

[41] R. DUSCHINSKY AND L. A. DOLAN, *J. Am. Chem. Soc.*, 67 (1945) 2079.

[42] H. MCKINNIS JR. AND V. DU VIGNEAUD, *J. Am. Chem. Soc.*, 68 (1946) 832; K. DITT-MER AND V. DU VIGNEAUD, *Science*, 100 (1944) 129.

[43] G. B. BROWN AND M. F. FERGER, *J. Am. Chem. Soc.*, 68 (1946) 1507.

[44] D. B. MELVILLE, D. S. GENGHOF AND J. M. LEE, *Federation Proc.*, 9 (1950) 204; *J. Biol. Chem.*, 208 (1954) 503.

[45] D. B. MELVILLE, *J. Biol. Chem.*, 208 (1954) 495.

[46] K. HOFMANN, *J. Am. Chem. Soc.*, 67 (1945) 694, 1459.

[47] R. DUSCHINSKY, L. A. DOLAN, D. FLOWER AND S. H. RUBIN, *Arch. Biochem.*, 6 (1945) 480.

[48] R. DUSCHINSKY AND L. A. DOLAN, *Jubilee Volume Emil Barell 1946*, Reinhardt, Basel, 1946, p. 164.

[49] K. ALDER AND H. F. RICKERT, *Ber.*, 70 (1937) 1354.

[50] K. HOFMANN, *J. Am. Chem. Soc.*, 71 (1949) 164.

[51] K. HOFMANN, C. CHEN, A. BRIDGEWATER AND A. E. AXELROD, *J. Am. Chem. Soc.*, 69 (1947) 191.

[52] M. W. GOLDBERG AND L. H. STERNBACH, *U.S. Patent*, 2,489,237, 1949.

[53] L. DREKTER, J. SCHEINER, E. DERITTER AND S. H. RUBIN, *Proc. Soc. Exptl. Biol. Med.*, 78 (1951) 381.

[54] L. H. STERNBACH, S. KAISER AND M. W. GOLDBERG, unpublished results.

[55] M. W. GOLDBERG AND L. H. STERNBACH, *U.S. Patent*, 2,489,236, 1949.

[56] S. H. RUBIN AND J. SCHEINER, *Arch. Biochem. Biophys.*, 23 (1949) 400.

[57] M. W. GOLDBERG, L. H. STERNBACH, S. KAISER, S. D. HEINEMAN, J. SCHEINER AND S. H. RUBIN, *Arch. Biochem.*, 14 (1947) 480.

Chapter VII

Folic Acid and Pteridines

WILLIAM SHIVE

*Clayton Foundation Biochemical Institute and the Department of Chemistry,
The University of Texas, Austin, Texas (U.S.A.)*

1. Pterins

Beginning in 1889, the isolation and characterization of pigments in wings of butterflies[1] initiated a study of a group of compounds now known as pterins which possess a previously unknown heterocyclic ring system, pyrimido[4,5-b]pyrazine, which has been given the name pteridine[2].

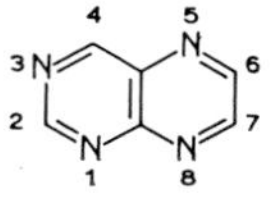

I   II

Pteridine

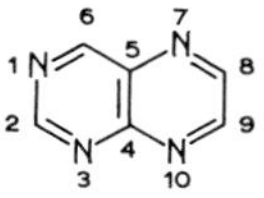

The numbering of the ring atoms indicated in formula I is used by *Chemical Abstracts*; however, a system indicated in formula II and corresponding to that for purines has also been used.

For a long time before the ring structure of pterins was known, compounds containing the pteridine ring were being prepared. In 1895, 2,4-dihydroxypteridine was prepared by oxidation of togalloxazine and decarboxylation of the resulting 2,4-dihydroxypteridine-6,7-dicarboxylic acid[3], and the same compound was prepared in 1907 by the action of hypobromite on pyrazine-2,3-dicarboxamide[4]. The condensation of 4,5-diaminopyrimidine and benzil[5] to form 6,7-diphenylpteridine reported in 1906 was the first example of the most versatile general method of pteridine synthesis.

Of a number of pterins studied[1], the white wing pigment of European cabbage butterflies was the first to be isolated in crystalline form. Subsequently, the yellow pigment of the English brimstone butterfly was isolated in crystalline form and given the name xanthopterin[6]. The white pigment, previously thought to be uric acid, was found to be a new substance which was given the name leucopterin[7]. Many other pterin pigments were studied during the early work. However, the structural studies on these pigments were difficult because pteridines do not burn readily, which results in errors in ultimate analyses, particularly nitrogen. Also, pterins give difficulty in purification and molecular weight determinations because of their limited solubility. A 2-aminopyrimidine structural unit in the pterins was indicated by the formation of guanidine upon the treatment of leucopterin with aqueous chlorine followed by hydrolysis[8], and by the formation of both oxalyl-guanidine and guanidine by treatment of xanthopterin with chloric acid[9]. Oxidation of xanthopterin with hydrogen peroxide, or catalytically with oxygen and platinum, to form leucopterin indicated a close relationship between the pterins[10]; but even the synthesis of leucopterin, which was formed by heating 2,4,5-triamino-6-hydroxypyrimidine with oxalic acid, did not establish the structure of leucopterin[11] because of difficulties in molecular weight determination. This problem was not resolved until trimethylleuco-pterin, synthesized from leucopterin by the action of diazomethane in meth-anol, was found to give in phenol a reliable molecular weight determina-tion[12]. The structure of xanthopterin was established in 1940 by synthesis[13] from triaminohydroxypyrimidine as indicated in the equations. The 5-acylamino structure was assigned to the dichloracetyl intermediate because of the known reactivity of the 5-amino group; and the formation of the pteridine ring rather than a purine-8-carboxylic acid was established by conversion of 4,5-diamino-2,6-dihydroxy-3-methylpyrimidine by the same process to a stable compound in contrast to easily decarboxylated 3-methyl-8-xanthinecarboxylic acid.

Another wing pterin[8] was found to be an isomer of xanthopterin and given the name isoxanthopterin[14]. The synthesis of this colorless pterin was accomplished by condensation of ethyl mesoxalate with 2,4,5-triamino-6-hydroxypyrimidine followed by decarboxylation of the intermediate as indicated in the above equations[15]. A small amount of xanthopterin-7-carboxylic acid was also formed in the initial step, but in the presence of sulfuric acid, the products consist of 42% xanthopterin-7-carboxylic acid and 29% isoxanthopterin-6-carboxylic acid. Xanthopterincarboxylic acid could not be decarboxylated but conversion to a dihydro derivative, decarboxylation of the dihydro derivative, and catalytic oxidation gave xanthopterin. Leucopterin can be reduced to a dihydroxanthopterin and reoxidized to xanthopterin. On the basis of absorption spectra of related derivatives, leucopterin and isoxanthopterin appear to have structures in which all of the hydroxyl groups indicated are in the lactam configuration[15a].

In a search for new pterins which were then defined as the colored or colorless pigments occurring beneath the chitin in insects, a yellow pigment, chrysopterin, and a red pigment, erythropterin, were isolated[16] along with other pterins. Following the original procedure for the separation of chrysopterin, the wings of 4400 female moths (*Gonepteryx rhamni*) were processed to obtain a chrysopterin fraction which on the basis of paper chromatographs appeared to contain mainly 7-methylxanthopterin and a small amount of xanthopterin[17]. Synthesis of 7-methylxanthopterin had been previously accomplished by condensation of pyruvic acid with 2,4,5-triamino-6-hydroxypyrimidine[18]; the isomeric 6-methylisoxanthopterin can be obtained in small yields along with 7-methylxanthopterin by carrying out the condensation in acetic acid.

Erythtropterin, on the basis of its oxidation to xanthopterin-7-carboxylic

acid, analytical data and chemical properties, was postulated to be a substituted xanthopterin[19,20] with a group, $-C(OH)=C(OH)-CH_2OH$, in the

7-position which had cyclized[21]. However, data obtained from erythropterin isolated in pure form for the first time has since demonstrated that erythropterin is xanthopterin-7-pyruvic acid[19a]. Erythropterin treated with diazomethane forms a product identical with that formed by the condensation of methyl oxalate and 3,5,7-trimethylxanthopterin.

Ekapterin, a pterin which has been isolated from the flour moth, *Ephestia kühniella*, has been identified as xanthopterin-7-lactic acid and can be synthesized by reduction of erythropterin followed by air-oxidation of the reduced product, 7,8-dihydroxyxanthopterin-7-lactic acid[20a].

The formation of a violet-red substance called rhodopterin[22] or pterorhodin[23] which results from aerobic oxidation of acidic solutions of crude butterfly wing pigments has been demonstrated to occur with a mixture of xanthopterin and 7-methylxanthopterin either upon aerobic or peroxide oxidation in acidic solution[24]. The structure was earlier suggested primarily on the basis of the formation of leucopterin and xanthopterin-7-carboxylic acid as oxidation products.

Pterorhodin (Rhodopterin)

While the wing pigments of butterflies were the initial pterins, it was soon discovered that these compounds were of broader significance and occurrence. For example, xanthopterin was found to occur in human urine[25], and was found to be hematopoietically active in anemic fingerling salmon[26]; and urothione, a sulfur-containing pteridine was isolated from human urine[27] and more recently has been assigned a tentative structure[28]. The discovery of a pteridine structural unit in the B-vitamin, folic acid, demonstrated the universal importance of this type of compound, and the naturally occurring pteridine derivatives regardless of origin have since been included in a now more broadly defined group of compounds called pterins.

2. Folic acid and related compounds

Nutritional studies with *Lactobacillus casei*[29] and *Streptococcus faecalis* R[30] resulted in the discovery of new growth factors given the names norite eluate factor and folic acid, respectively. Assay methods using these two organisms were employed in the isolation of folic acid and related compounds from natural extracts. However, a number of previously reported biological responses to natural extracts may now be attributed to the folic acid group.

References p. 99

These earlier effects include the alleviation of nutritional anemia of pregnancy[31], and the prevention of dietary deficiency symptoms in monkeys (vitamin M)[32,33] and chicks[34,35] (Factor U and vitamin B_c), and in addition the response of pernicious anemia patients to oral administration of large amounts of liver[36] may have been due to folic acid rather than to vitamin B_{12}.

Because of its acidic characteristics and its abundant occurrence in green leaves, the growth factor for *S. faecalis* R was given the name folic acid (Latin, *folium*—leaf)[30]. Folic acid was isolated in crystalline form from liver and from yeast[37,38], and its structure was established by degradation and synthesis[39,40].

Folic acid
(*N*-Pteroyl-L-glutamic acid)

A strain of *Corynebacterium* which produces a folic acid derivative was the source of the material used for many of the structural studies on folic acid and its derivatives[41], and this fermentation factor was found to be folic acid conjugated with an additional two glutamic acid units[42,43].

N-Pteroyl-di-γ-L-glutamyl-L-glutamic acid

The fermentation factor could easily be differentiated from folic acid because it was only 4–6% as effective as folic acid for *S. faecalis* R in contrast to 60–80% for *L. casei*.

(a) Structure of the pteridine moiety[39,42]

The presence of a pteridine nucleus in folic acid was suggested by early reports indicating a biological relationship between xanthopterin and folic acid as well as by a comparison of the ultraviolet absorption spectra of concentrates of folic acid with the spectra of xanthopterin and other pteridines[44].

Anaerobic alkaline hydrolysis of the fermentation factor produced two moles of glutamic acid and one of racemized folic acid, possessing only one-half the activity of its natural L-form for the assay organisms.

Aerobic alkaline hydrolysis of either racemic folic acid or the fermentation factor produced a diazotizable amine and a dibasic fluorescent pigment. The fluorescent pigment formed guanidine upon treatment with chlorine water and was decarboxylated upon heating at 250–300° in a stream of nitrogen to form a monobasic product with an absorption spectrum similar to that of 2-amino-4-hydroxypteridine. The fluorescent pigment was finally synthesized from isoxanthopterin-6-carboxylic acid by replacement of the 7-hydroxyl group with a chloro group followed by the removal of the chloro group using hydriodic acid. The structure of the pigment was thus established to be 2-amino-4-hydroxypteridine-6-carboxylic acid.

Further evidence on the structure of the pteridine moiety was afforded by sulfite cleavage of the fermentation factor to form a product which on the basis of its properties appeared to be 2-amino-4-hydroxypteridine-6-carboxaldehyde, and on alkaline treatment was found to undergo dismutation to form the corresponding carboxylic acid and a methyl substituted pteridine. Alkaline hydrolysis of the methyl substituted pteridine gave 2-amino-5-methylpyrazine-3-carboxylic acid which upon decarboxylation formed 2-amino-5-methylpyrazine. The identification of the pyrazine confirmed the position of the methyl group and also carboxyl group in the dibasic pigment, since the methyl pteridine can be oxidized with alkaline permanganate to the corresponding 6-carboxylic acid. Although the structure for isoxanthopterin-6-carboxylic acid had been correctly postulated earlier, the structure was still open to question, and this definitive proof of the 6-position for the

* The term—G is used to represent —NH—CH(COOH)—CH₂—CH₂—COOH in this and subsequent formulas.

attachment to the pteridine ring was necessary. The methyl pteridine which is also formed on reductive cleavage of folic acid was synthesized as indicated in the following equations showing these various interrelationships[39]:

(b) Structure of the diazotizable amine moiety[42,43]

The liberation of an aromatic amine by cleavage of either folic acid or the fermentation factor with the simultaneous formation of the pteridines having a 6-carboxyl or 6-methyl substituent suggested that the pteridine was bound through this single carbon to the amino group. The necessity of oxygen for the alkaline cleavage further suggested that the linkage involved a methylene group binding the pteridine ring to the aromatic amine. The aromatic amine arising from sulfite-cleavage of the fermentation factor formed upon alkaline hydrolysis *p*-aminobenzoic and three moles of L-glutamic acid as determined microbiologically. The amine formed from aerobic alkaline hydrolysis of folic acid contained one mole each of glutamic acid and *p*-aminobenzoic acid. On the basis of these data, it was possible to assign to folic acid the structure, *N*-[4-{[(2-amino-4-hydroxy-6-pteridyl)-methyl]-amino}-benzoyl]-L-glutamic acid, as previously indicated.

An early indication of an interrelationship of *p*-aminobenzoic acid and folic acid was the report of the inhibitory effect of sulfonamides upon the synthesis of microbiologically active forms of folic acid in *Escherichia coli*[45], and many other biological studies confirmed such a relationship. Glutamic acid was also implicated in studies with *Streptobacterium plantarum* 10 S for which *N*-(*p*-aminobenzoyl)-L-glutamic acid was found to be ten times as effective as *p*-aminobenzoic acid in reversing sulfonamide toxicity[46]. In addition, a *p*-aminobenzoyl derivative of a polyglutamyl peptide containing 10 or 11 L-glutamic acid units, an amide group, and a terminal unidentified amino acid was isolated from yeast[47]. Thus, biological studies, prior to the chemical elucidation of the structure of folic acid, had implicated *p*-aminobenzoic acid, glutamic acid and a pteridine as possible components of folic acid.

A *folic acid conjugate* (*vitamin B_c conjugate*), which was effective in preventing anemia in chicks, was isolated from yeast[48] and found not to be appreciably effective for *L. casei* or *S. faecalis* R. By microbiological determination of glutamate in an acidic hydrolysate of this conjugate, the derivative was found to be *N*-pteroylhexaglutamylglutamic acid[49].

(c) Synthesis of folic acid and related compounds

The synthesis of folic acid was accomplished by the interaction of 2,4,5-triamino-6-hydroxypyrimidine and *N*-(*p*-aminobenzoyl)-L-glutamic acid in aqueous solution maintained at about pH 4 with α,β-dibromopropionaldehyde

added in an organic solvent[40]. The reaction involves an oxidative condensation with dihydrofolic acid as the probable intermediate and gives crude material containing 10–25% folic acid from which the crystalline product can be obtained. Attempts to interact the dibromopropionaldehyde with either of the other reactants before adding the third resulted in poorer yields.

This method of synthesis has been widely used in the preparation of folic acid derivatives, pteroic acid[40] and related compounds. The fermentation factor (*N*-pteroyl-di-γ-L-glutamyl-L-glutamic acid) as well as *N*-pteroyl-γ-L-glutamyl-L-glutamic acid and other glutamyl conjugates of folic acid have

Pteroic acid

N-Pteroyl–γ–L–glutamyl–L–glutamic acid

References p. 99

been prepared by this procedure using the appropriate *p*-aminobenzoyl derivative[50,51]. Among the synthetic derivatives, pteroic acid, because it is effective in replacing folic acid for *S. faecalis* R but not for *L. casei*, and the pteroyldiglutamate, which is 60–70% as active as folic acid for both organisms, are of biological interest.

The versatility of this synthetic procedure is further indicated by representative metabolic antagonists of folic acid listed below which were prepared[52–54] by this method with substitution of appropriate analogous intermediates.

4-Aminopteroyl-L-glutamic acid
(Aminopterin)

N^{10}-Methyl-4-aminopteroyl-L-glutamic acid
(A-methopterin, Methotrexate)

N^{10}-Methylpteroyl-L-glutamic acid

N-Pteroylaspartic acid

These analogs represent modifications in both the pyrimidine and *p*-aminobenzoylglutamic acid moieties. The 4-aminopteroyl derivatives are noncompetitive antagonists of folic acid in contrast to competitive inhibitions exerted by the other analogs. In addition, a competitive antagonist of folic acid was prepared in crude form using this method of synthesis with α,β-dibromobutyraldehyde and was designated without structural studies as 7-methylfolic acid[55] and as X-methylfolic acid[56].

In the above method of synthesis of folic acid and its derivatives, any of a variety of three carbon compounds can be used to replace the dibromopropionaldehyde. In general, these include di- or tri-halo or haloketo derivatives of propionaldehyde or acetone[57], or similar negatively substituted derivatives. In several cases the addition of sulfite appears to be beneficial[58].

In addition to the condensation of the three components, stepwise syntheses have also been successful. For example, dibromopropionaldehyde was condensed with pyridine to form *N*-(2-formyl-2-bromoethyl)pyridinium bromide which upon reaction with the triaminohydroxypyrimidine formed *N*-(2-amino-4-hydroxy-6-pteridyl)-methylpyridinium bromide[59]. Also, dihydroxyacetone was condensed directly with the pyrimidine to form 2-amino-4-hydroxy-6-hydroxymethylpteridine[60]. Either of these pteridines can be condensed with p-aminobenzoylglutamic acid to form folic acid. A similar synthesis of folic acid from the 6-bromomethyl derivative (prepared by direct bromination of 2-amino-4-hydroxy-6-methylpteridine) has been reported[61], and 2-amino-4-hydroxypteridine-6-carboxaldehyde (prepared by periodate or lead tetracetate oxidation of 4-hydroxy-2-amino-6(D-arabo-tetrahydroxybutyl)pteridine) can be condensed with p-aminobenzoylglutamic acid to form a product which can be reduced to folic acid[62].

Reductone (HOCH=COH—CHO) has been condensed with ethyl N-(p-aminobenzoyl)glutamate to form ethyl N-[p-(2,3-dihydroxy-2-ene-propylidene-amino)-benzoyl]glutamate which can be condensed with 2,4,5-triamino-6-hydroxypyrimidine to form folic acid[63]. Another procedure for folic acid synthesis involves the alkylation of N-tosyl-p-aminobenzoylglutamate with a substituted propylene oxide such as 2,3-oxidopropionaldehyde diethyl acetal, oxidation of the product to a ketone, condensation of the ketone derivative with 2,4,5-triamino-6-hydroxypyrimidine and finally removal of the tosyl group[64]. Other three carbon unit reactants, such as α-haloacrolein, have also been condensed with p-aminobenzoyl glutamic acid to give useful intermediates for folic acid synthesis[65].

(d) Formyl derivatives of pteroic acid and folic acid

Biological studies had indicated a role of folic acid and p-aminobenzoic acid in the transfer of single carbon units[66], and the isolation and proof of structure of a factor having folic acid activity for S. faecalis R (S. lactis R) but not for L. casei gave chemical evidence for such a role[67,68]. This factor was named rhizopterin because it was isolated from Rhizopus nigricans fumaric acid fermentation liquors[67]. The structure of rhizopterin was established as

Rhizopterin (N^{10}-formylpteroic acid)

N^{10}-formylpteroic acid by hydrolysis to pteroic acid and formic acid and by synthesis upon heating pteroic acid with 98% formic acid[68]. The corresponding formyl derivative of folic acid prepared by treating folic acid with 98% formic acid was found to be ten times as effective as folic acid in reversing a competitive antagonist[69] of folic acid for S. faecalis R.

References p. 99

(e) Folinic acid and reduced folic acid derivatives

An agent exceeding the activity of folic acid in competitively reversing the toxicity of a folic acid antagonist for *L. casei* was given the name folinic acid[70] and was found to be an essential growth factor for *Pediococcus cerevisiae* 8081 (classified as *Leuconostoc citrovorum* at that time)[71,72]. Since N^{10}-formyl-folic acid had been shown to possess similar enhanced activity over folic acid in reversing a folic antagonist[69] for *S. faecalis* R, formylfolic acid was chemically treated in various ways in an attempt to produce folinic acid. Reduction, preferably catalytic hydrogenation, of N^{10}-formylfolic acid followed by heating the reduced N^{10}-formylfolic acid was found to give a derivative which replaced natural folinic acid in the microbiological assays[73]. This synthetic folinic acid (leucovorin) was shown to be N^5-formyl-5,6,7,8-tetra-hydrofolic acid and its chemical relationship to folic acid is indicated by the following equations[74-80]:

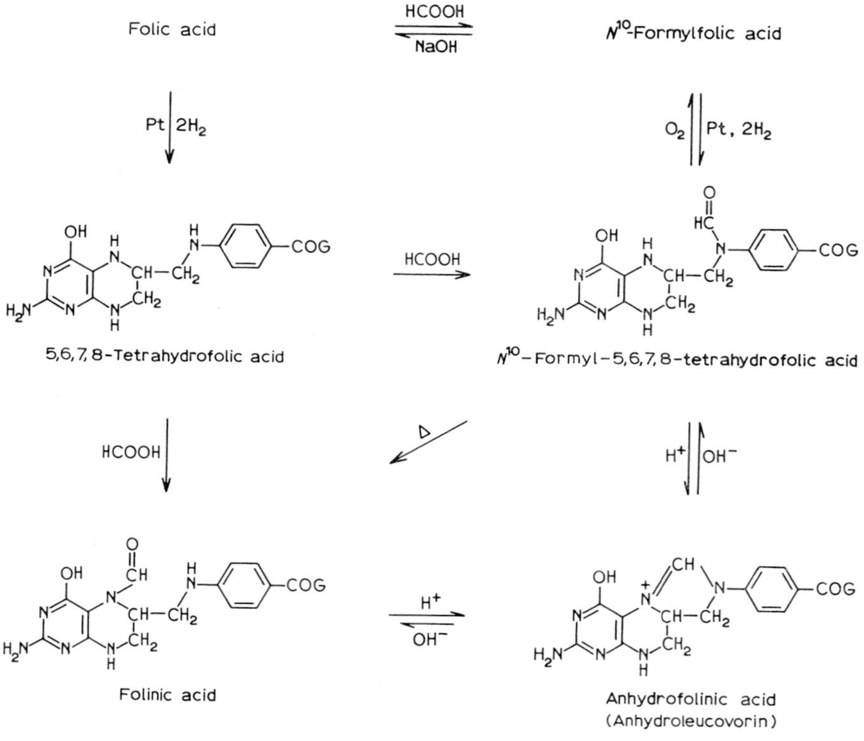

Folinic acid can be formed along with N^{10}-formyltetrahydrofolic acid by direct formylation of 5,6,7,8-tetrahydrofolic acid. Both tetra- and di-hydrofolic acid were first synthesized in a study of hydrogenation of pterins and folic acid. Acid destruction of folinic acid forms anhydrofolinic acid (anhydroleucovorin), the imidazolinium ring of which is opened with alkali sufficiently rapidly that it can be titrated giving an apparent pK_a of 8.6. Under anaerobic conditions, the primary product of ring opening, N^{10}-formyltetrahydrofolic acid, can be converted again to the ring structure in acid solution; opening of the ring forms only a trace of folinic acid directly. N^{10}-Formyltetrahydrofolic acid is oxidized rapidly in air to a dihydro derivative and more slowly to N^{10}-formylfolic acid which can be hydrolyzed to folic acid. Folinic acid can itself be formylated, and the formylfolic acid can be hydrolyzed to reform folinic acid. This reaction coupled with the ability of the compound to form a nitroso derivative indicates that folinic acid is not substituted in the N^{10}-position. The preparation and properties of the 5-formyl derivatives of model compounds such as 2-amino-4-hydroxy-6,7-dimethyl-5,6,7,8-tetrahydropteridine and 2-amino-4-hydroxy-6,7-diphenyl-8-ethyl-5,6,7,8-tetrahydropteridine, as well as the reactivity of the 5-amino group of pyrimidines toward formylation (in contrast to the inactivity of the 4- and 6-amino groups) gave added evidence that the formyl group of folinic acid is in the 5-position.

The synthesis of folinic acid from folic acid creates a new asymmetric center at the 6-carbon, and both diastereoisomeric forms tend to crystallize together. Crystallization of the calcium salt[77] from water gives the lL-form[81] which is about twice as active biologically as the original mixed crystals, and upon conversion to formylfolic acid it does not increase in folic-like activity for *L. casei* as does the diastereoisomeric mixture. This lL-diastereoisomeric form appears to be identical with natural folinic acid[82].

It is of interest that many of the reduced folic derivatives prepared as a result of chemical studies of growth factors have subsequently been found to serve directly as coenzymes in the transfer of single carbon units. Reversible enzymatic transfer of the single carbon unit from anhydrofolinic acid to glycineamide ribotide, from N^{10}-formyltetrahydrofolic acid to 5-amino-4-imidazolecarboxamide ribotide, and from folinic acid to glutamic acid have been observed to be specific for these respective formyl donors[83,84].

Tetrahydrofolic acid which was found to be a coenzyme acceptor of a single carbon unit for the conversion of serine to glycine[85,86] also reacts with formaldehyde chemically to form a derivative which can serve as an enzymatic donor of an hydroxymethyl group[86,87]. Studies on the formaldehyde binding properties of analogs with only one of the two nitrogens available have indicated that the N^5 group exerts a stronger binding effect alone than the N^{10}, but both nitrogens are essential for the low dissociation of the tetrahydrofolic acid complex; so the reaction is proposed to involve initial addition to the N^5 of a hydroxymethyl group followed by the formation of $N^{5,10}$-methylene-5,6,7,8-tetrahydrofolic acid[88]. The methylene derivative of tetrahydrofolic acid also appears to serve as an enzymic donor not only of a single carbon unit but also of the hydrogens for methylation reactions, with the formation of dihydrofolic acid[89,90]. A methylated derivative of tetrahydrofolic acid is essential for the biological conversion of homocysteine to methionine. This active derivative, presumably N^5-methyltetrahydrofolic acid, can be prepared synthetically by reduction of $N^{5,10}$-methylenetetrahydrofolic acid with sodium or potassium borohydride[90a-d].

$N^{5,10}$-Methylenetetrahydrofolic acid N^5-Methyltetrahydrofolic acid

Tetrahydrofolic acid is also an enzymic acceptor of a formimino group from formiminoglycine or from formiminoglutamic acid. The product, 5-formimino-5,6,7,8-tetrahydrofolic acid, is converted in acidic solution to anhydrofolinic acid and ammonium ion and has a half-life of about 1 h at 37° over a pH range[91] of 5–9. Aerobic oxidation of tetrahydrofolic acid produces p-aminobenzoylglutamic acid and a number of pteridines, including xanthopterin[84,92].

As models of tetrahydrofolic acid, certain N,N'-diarylethylenediamines have been used in the non-enzymatic interaction and transfer of single carbon units[93].

(f) Folinic acid conjugates

Subjecting pteroyl-di-γ-glutamylglutamic acid and also pteroyl-γ-glutamylglutamic acid to the steps used in synthesis of folinic acid resulted in three and two active compounds, respectively. Folinic acid was formed from each pteroyl derivative, and the corresponding di- and triglutamates which were separated chromatographically account for the other factors[73].

It is of interest that folic or folinic polyglutamates are required for the conversion of serine to glycine in a cell-free enzyme preparation from a *Clostridium* strain which apparently cannot utilize monoglutamates[94], and evidence for the natural occurrence of N^5-formyltetrahydropteroyltriglutamate has been reported[95]. Other bound forms of folinic acid appear to exist[94].

3. Biopterin and related derivatives

Studies on an essential growth factor for the protozoon *Crithidia fasciculata* and on eye pigments of *Drosophila* resulted in the isolation and characterization of the same compound which has been given the name biopterin[96-98]. The growth factor isolated from either human urine or from *Drosophila* formed on alkaline permanganate oxidation 2-amino-4-hydroxypteridine-6-carboxylic acid which was identified by absorption spectra and paper chromatography. Periodate oxidation of the compound produced acetaldehyde and 2-amino-4-hydroxy-6-formylpteridine; and infrared data indicated a methyl group. The compound was accordingly assigned the structure, 2-amino-4-hydroxy-6-[1,2-dihydroxypropyl-(L-*erythro*)]-pteridine, the *erythro* configuration being assigned on the basis of synthetic work.

Biopterin

The synthesis of biopterin was accomplished by treating 5-deoxy-L-arabinose or rhamnotetrose with 2,4,5-triamino-6-hydroxypyrimidine in the presence of hydrazine. Separation of isomeric compounds in the purification of the product was necessary, since the reaction of the triaminohydroxypyrimidine with sugars gives mixtures of 6- and 7-substituted pteridines with the 7-isomer predominating[98-102]. In the presence of certain agents such as hydrazine the synthesis of the 6-isomer is favored with hexoses, but no such marked directive effect has been noted with the pentose derivatives[98,101]. The preparation by this procedure and testing of a number of 2-amino-4-hydroxy-6-polyhydroxyalkylpteridines revealed that the products derived from L-arabinose and L-rhamnose but not D-ribose and D-xylose are highly active growth factors for *C. fasciculata*. Two adjacent carbon atoms with L-configuration are present in the active compounds but are not necessarily attached directly to the pteridine ring[98]; however, a 1′-hydroxyl group appears to be required since 2-amino-6-hydroxy-8-[D-*erythro*-2′,3′,4′-trihydroxybutyl]pteridine is inactive[102]. Both folic acid and biopterin are required for growth of *C. fasciculata* indicating independent roles for biopterin and folic acid[103].

An α-glycoside of biopterin has been isolated from blue-green algae (*Anacystis nidulans*) as the sole pteridine extracted under appropriate conditions[104]. Other blue-green algae similarly yield different glycosides of biopterin[105]. A naturally occurring derivative of biopterin is postulated to be converted to the glycoside under the particular conditions of extraction but may under other conditions form 2-amino-4-hydroxypteridine[104], 2,6-diamino-4-hydroxypteridine[106], 2-amino-4-hydroxy-6-carboxypteridine[104] or a yellow pigment[107]. The yellow pigment which on oxidation forms 2-amino-4-hydroxy-6-(1'-oxopropyl)pteridine[105] has also been isolated from *Drosophila* and named isosepiapterin[108].

A related yellow fluorescent eye pigment[109] isolated from the sepia mutant of *Drosophila* was found to form 2-amino-4-hydroxypteridine-6-carboxylic acid on exposure to sunlight, to be oxidized with periodate to form acetaldehyde, and to form lactic acid upon hydrolysis. This derivative, more recently called sepiapterin[108], has been reduced with sodium borohydride and treated with oxygen to form a pteridine which appears to be identical except for optical rotation with biopterin[108].

Since the yellow eye pigments accumulate in the sepia mutant of *Drosophila* which lacks the red pigments of the parent strain[109], the red pigments apparently are also derivatives related to biopterin. Three red pigments have been isolated from *Drosophila* and given the names drosopterin, isodrosopterin and neodrosopterin[110,111]. Each of these pigments can be reduced to a dihydro derivative, and upon oxidation in air, each not only reforms the original pigment, but also forms 2-amino-4-hydroxypteridine, 2-amino-4-hydroxypteridine-6-carboxylic acid and other members of this group of biopterin-related compounds. In this last group of oxidation products, drosopterin and isodrosopterin as well as a pterin identical with biopterin except in optical rotation are formed from oxidation of dihydroneodrosopterin; neodrosopterin is formed from dihydrodrosopterin; and neodrosopterin and the biopterin-like pterin are produced upon oxidation of dihydroisodrosopterin[111]. Thus, the red pigments of *Drosophila* appear to be interconverted by reduction and oxidation reactions.

The ability of light to catalyze the formation of 2-amino-4-hydroxypteridine-6-carboxylic acid and 2-amino-4-hydroxypteridine from these various derivatives related to biopterin has suggested the possibility that these compounds isolated from various natural sources may have been derived from a more complicated pteridine derivative. Reactions which may account in part for the formation of certain pteridines during the extraction of bio-pterin derivatives from natural sources have recently been discovered. 5,6,7,8-Tetrahydro-2-amino-4-hydroxypteridine upon reoxidation in the pre-sence of ammonia forms 2,6-diamino-4-hydroxypteridine[106]. This reaction undoubtedly involves the addition of ammonia to a dihydropteridine, probably to the 7,8-dihydro derivative at the 5,6-double bond. Three differ-ent dihydro derivatives, 5,8-, 7,8- and 5,6-dihydro-2-amino-4-hydroxypteri-dine, are reported to be formed in the reoxidation of the tetrahydro deriva-tive[112], and hydroxyl and sulfonic acid group additions have been found to occur during the reoxidation with the formation of 6-substituted pteridine derivatives. Pteridine derivatives which appear to be related to the *Drosophila* pigments have also been found in other organisms.

Ichthyopterin, a blue fluorescent substance[113], occurs in fish scales or skin along with isoxanthopterin and isoxanthopterin carboxylic acid[114]. The latter two compounds appear on the basis of paper chromatography to be formed upon reduction and oxidation, respectively, of ichthyopterin[114], and periodate oxidation gives isoxanthopterincarboxaldehyde[115]. Ichthyopterin shows remarkable similarities to 7-hydroxybiopterin, synthesized from 6-acetonylisoxanthopterin by bromination, treatment of the bromo derivative with potassium acetate, hydrolysis of the resulting acetate and reduction of the hydroxy ketone to the diol[116]. On the basis of R_F values in ten different solvents, the two appear to be identical[115].

4. Pteridines related to riboflavin

Two substances, one a green fluorescent and the other a blue fluorescent compound[117-119], both of which were isolated from extracts of the yeast,

Eremothecium ashbyii, and the mold, *Ashbya gosspyii*, have been shown to be derivatives of lumazine, 2,4-dihydroxypteridine, and assigned the structures 6,7-dimethyl-8-ribityllumazine (6,7-dimethyl-8(1-D-ribityl)-2,4-dioxotetrahydropteridine) and 6-methyl-7-hydroxy-8-ribityllumazine (6-methyl-8(1-D-ribityl)-2,4,7-trioxo-hexahydropteridine). The structure of the former compound was elucidated by its conversion to riboflavin on heating with diacetyl[117] and by photolysis to 6,7-dimethyllumazine and 6,7,8-trimethyl-lumazine[118]. The synthesis of the compound[118,120] was accomplished as indicated in the equations on p. 97 in which R represents a ribityl group. The blue fluorescent compound was found to form 7-hydroxy-6-methyl-lumazine upon photolysis[121], and was synthesized by the sequence of reaction indicated for above except that pyruvate was substituted for diacetyl[120,122].

Both of these compounds are derived biologically from purines, and the dimethyl derivative but not the monomethyl derivative serves as a biological precursor of riboflavin. The latter may possibly be related to the biosynthesis of other pteridines. Until the discovery of these two pteridine derivatives, all other naturally occurring pteridine derivatives had been found to be derivatives of 2-amino-4-hydroxypteridine.

REFERENCES

1 F. G. HOPKINS, *Nature*, 40 (1889) 335; 45 (1891) 197; 45 (1892) 581; *Phil. Trans. Roy. Soc. London, Ser. B.*, 186 (1893) 661.

2 F. WEYGAND, *Österr. Chemiker Z.*, 44 (1941) 254.

3 O. KÜHLING, *Ber.*, 28 (1895) 1968.

4 S. GABRIEL AND A. SONN, *Ber.*, 40 (1907) 4850.

5 O. ISAY, *Ber.*, 39 (1906) 250.

6 H. WIELAND AND C. SCHÖPF, *Ber.*, 58 (1925) 2178.

7 C. SCHÖPF AND H. WIELAND, *Ber.*, 59 (1926) 2067.

8 H. WIELAND, H. METZGER, C. SCHÖPF AND M. BÜLOW, *Ann. Chem., Liebigs*, 507 (1933) 226.

9 C. SCHÖPF AND A. KOTTLER, *Ann. Chem., Liebigs*, 539 (1939) 128.

10 H. WIELAND AND R. PURRMANN, *Ann. Chem., Liebigs*, 544 (1940) 163.

11 R. PURRMANN, *Ann. Chem., Liebigs*, 544 (1940) 182.

12 H. WIELAND AND P. DECKER, *Ann. Chem., Liebigs*, 547 (1941) 180.

13 R. PURRMANN, *Ann. Chem., Liebigs*, 546 (1940) 98.

14 H. WIELAND, A. TARTTER AND R. PURRMANN, *Ann. Chem., Liebigs*, 545 (1940) 209.

15 R. PURRMANN, *Ann. Chem., Liebigs*, 548 (1941) 284.

15a W. PFLEIDERER AND M. RUKVIED, *Chem. Ber.*, 94 (1961) 1, 118.

16 C. SCHÖPF AND E. BECKER, *Ann. Chem., Liebigs*, 524 (1936) 49.

17 R. TSCHESCHE AND F. KORTE, *Chem. Ber.*, 84 (1951) 641.

18 G. B. ELION AND G. H. HITCHINGS, *J. Am. Chem. Soc.*, 69 (1947) 2553.

19 R. PURRMANN AND F. EULITZ, *Ann. Chem., Liebigs*, 559 (1948) 169.

19a W. PFLEIDERER, *Angew. Chem.*, 73 (1961) 581.

20 R. TSCHESCHE AND F. KORTE, *Chem. Ber.*, 84 (1951) 77.

20a M. VISCONTINI AND H. STIERLIN, *Helv. Chim. Acta*, 44 (1961) 1783.

21 R. TSCHESCHE AND H. ENDE, *Chem. Ber.*, 91 (1958) 2074.

22 F. G. HOPKINS, *Proc. Roy. Soc. (London), B*, 130 (1942) 359.

23 R. PURRMANN AND M. MAAS, *Ann. Chem., Liebigs*, 556 (1944) 186.

24 P. B. RUSSELL, R. PURRMANN, W. SCHMITT AND G. H. HITCHINGS, *J. Am. Chem. Soc.*, 71 (1949) 3412.

25 W. KOSCHARA, *Z. physiol. Chem., Hoppe-Seyler's*, 240 (1936) 127.

26 R. W. SIMMONS AND E. R. NORRIS, *J. Biol. Chem.*, 140 (1941) 679.

27 W. KOSCHARA, *Z. physiol. Chem., Hoppe-Seyler's*, 279 (1943) 44.

28 R. TSCHESCHE, F. KORTE AND G. HEUSCHKEL, *Chem. Ber.*, 88 (1955) 1251.

29 E. E. SNELL AND W. H. PETERSON, *J. Bacteriol.*, 39 (1940) 273.

30 H. K. MITCHELL, E. E. SNELL AND R. J. WILLIAMS, *J. Am. Chem. Soc.*, 63 (1941) 2284.

31 L. WILLS, *Brit. Med. J.*, 1 (1931) 1059; *Indian J. Med. Research*, 21 (1934) 669.

32 L. WILLS AND H. S. BILIMORIA, *Indian J. Med. Research*, 20 (1932) 391.

33 P. L. DAY, W. C. LANGSTON AND W. J. DARBY, *Proc. Soc. Exptl. Biol. Med.*, 38 (1938) 860.

34 E. L. R. STOKSTAD AND P. D. V. MANNING, *J. Biol. Chem.*, 125 (1938) 687.

35 A. G. HOGAN AND E. M. PARROTT, *J. Biol. Chem.*, 132 (1940) 507; B. L. O'DELL AND A. G. HOGAN, *J. Biol. Chem.*, 149 (1943) 323.

36 G. R. MINOT AND W. P. MURPHY, *J. Am. Med. Assoc.*, 87 (1926) 470.

37 J. J. PFIFFNER, S. B. BINKLEY, E. S. BLOOM AND B. L. O'DELL, *J. Am. Chem. Soc.*, 69 (1947) 1476.

38 E. L. R. STOKSTAD, B. L. HUTCHINGS AND Y. SUBBAROW, *J. Am. Chem. Soc.*, 70 (1948) 3.

39 J. H. MOWAT, J. H. BOOTHE, B. L. HUTCHINGS, E. L. R. STOKSTAD, C. W. WALLER, R. B. ANGIER, J. SEMB, D. B. COSULICH AND Y. SUBBAROW, *J. Am. Chem. Soc.*, 70 (1948) 14.

40 C. W. WALLER, B. L. HUTCHINGS, J. H. MOWAT, E. L. R. STOKSTAD, J. H. BOOTHE, R. B. ANGIER, J. SEMB, Y. SUBBAROW, D. B. COSULICH, M. J. FAHRENBACH, M. E. HULTQUIST, E. KUH, E. H. NORTHEY, D. R. SEEGER, J. P. SICKELS AND J. M. SMITH JR., *J. Am. Chem. Soc.*, 70 (1948) 19.

41 B. L. Hutchings, E. L. R. Stokstad, N. Bohonos, N. H. Sloane and Y. SubbaRow, *J. Am. Chem. Soc.*, 70 (1948) 1.
42 E. L. R. Stokstad, B. L. Hutchings, J. H. Mowat, J. H. Boothe, C. W. Waller, R. B. Angier, J. Semb and Y. SubbaRow, *J. Am. Chem. Soc.*, 70 (1948) 5.
43 B. L. Hutchings, E. L. R. Stokstad, J. H. Mowat, J. H. Boothe, C. W. Waller, R. B. Angier, J. Semb and Y. SubbaRow, *J. Am. Chem. Soc.*, 70 (1948) 10.
44 H. K. Mitchell, *J. Am. Chem. Soc.*, 66 (1944) 274.
45 A. K. Miller, *Proc. Soc. Exptl. Biol. Med.*, 57 (1944) 151.
46 E. Auhagen, *Z. physiol. Chem., Hoppe-Seyler's*, 277 (1942) 197.
47 S. Ratner, M. Blanchard and D. E. Green, *J. Biol. Chem.*, 164 (1946) 691.
48 J. J. Pfiffner, D. G. Calkins, B. L. O'Dell, E. S. Bloom, R. A. Brown, C. J. Campbell and O. D. Bird, *Science*, 102 (1945) 228.
49 J. J. Pfiffner, D. G. Calkins, E. S. Bloom and B. L. O'Dell, *J. Am. Chem. Soc.*, 68 (1946) 1392.
50 J. H. Boothe, J. H. Mowat, B. L. Hutchings, R. B. Angier, C. W. Waller, E. L. R. Stokstad, J. Semb, A. L. Gazzola and Y. SubbaRow, *J. Am. Chem. Soc.*, 70 (1948) 1099.
51 J. H. Boothe, J. Semb, C. W. Waller, R. B. Angier, J. H. Mowat, B. L. Hutchings, E. L. R. Stokstad and Y. SubbaRow, *J. Am. Chem. Soc.*, 71 (1949) 2304.
52 D. R. Seeger, D. B. Cosulich, J. M. Smith Jr. and M. E. Hultquist, *J. Am. Chem. Soc.*, 71 (1949) 1753.
53 D. B. Cosulich and J. M. Smith Jr., *J. Am. Chem. Soc.*, 70 (1948) 1922.
54 B. L. Hutchings, J. H. Mowat, J. J. Oleson, E. L. R. Stokstad, J. H. Boothe, C. W. Waller, R. B. Angier, J. Semb and Y. SubbaRow, *J. Biol. Chem.*, 170 (1947) 323.
55 G. J. Martin, L. Tolman and J. Moss, *Arch. Biochem.*, 12 (1947) 318.
56 A. L. Franklin, E. L. R. Stokstad, M. Belt and T. H. Jukes, *J. Biol. Chem.*, 169 (1947) 427.
57 M. E. Hultquist and P. F. Dreisbach, *U.S. Patent 2,443,165*, June 8, 1948; *Chem. Abstr.*, 42 (1948) 7944.
58 S. Uyeo, S. Mizukami, T. Kubota and S. Takagi, *J. Am. Chem. Soc.*, 72 (1950) 5339.
59 M. E. Hultquist, E. Kuh, D. B. Cosulich, M. J. Fahrenbach, E. H. Northey, D. R. Seeger, J. P. Sickels, J. M. Smith Jr., R. B. Angier, J. H. Boothe, B. L. Hutchings, J. H. Mowat, J. Semb, E. L. R. Stokstad, Y. SubbaRow and C. W. Waller, *J. Am. Chem. Soc.*, 70 (1948) 23.
60 P. Karrer and R. Schwyzer, *Helv. Chim. Acta*, 31 (1948) 782.
61 J. H. Boothe, C. W. Waller, E. L. R. Stokstad, B. L. Hutchings, J. H. Mowat, R. B. Angier, J. Semb, Y. SubbaRow, D. B. Cosulich, M. J. Fahrenbach, M. E. Hultquist, E. Kuh, E. H. Northey, D. R. Seeger, J. P. Sickels and J. M. Smith Jr., *J. Am. Chem. Soc.*, 70 (1948) 27.
62 F. Weygand, A. Wacker and V. Schmied-Kowarzik, *Chem. Ber.*, 82 (1949) 25.
63 R. B. Angier, E. L. R. Stokstad, J. H. Mowat, B. L. Hutchings, J. H. Boothe, C. W. Waller, J. Semb, Y. SubbaRow, D. B. Cosulich, M. J. Fahrenbach, M. E. Hultquist, E. Kuh, E. H. Northey, D. R. Seeger, J. P. Sickels and J. M. Smith Jr., *J. Am. Chem. Soc.*, 70 (1948) 25.
64 D. I. Weisblat, B. J. Magerlein, D. R. Myers, A. R. Hanze, E. I. Fairburn and S. T. Rolfson, *J. Am. Chem. Soc.*, 75 (1953) 5893.
65 L. Doub and L. L. Bambas, *U.S. Patent 2,476,360*, July 19, 1949; *Chem. Abstr.*, 44 (1950) 173.
66 W. Shive, W. W. Ackermann, M. Gordon, M. E. Getzendaner and R. E. Eakin, *J. Am. Chem. Soc.*, 69 (1947) 725.
67 E. L. Rickes, L. Chaiet and J. C. Keresztesy, *J. Am. Chem. Soc.*, 69 (1947) 2749.
68 D. E. Wolf, R. C. Anderson, E. A. Kaczka, S. A. Harris, G. E. Arth, P. L. Southwick, R. Mozingo and K. Folkers, *J. Am. Chem. Soc.*, 69 (1947) 2753.
69 M. Gordon, J. M. Ravel, R. E. Eakin and W. Shive, *J. Am. Chem. Soc.*, 70 (1948) 878.

[70] T. J. BOND, T. J. BARDOS, M. SIBLEY AND W. SHIVE, *J. Am. Chem. Soc.*, 71 (1949) 3852.

[71] H. E. SAUBERLICH AND C. A. BAUMANN, *J. Biol. Chem.*, 176 (1948) 165.

[72] T. J. BARDOS, T. J. BOND, J. HUMPHREYS AND W. SHIVE, *J. Am. Chem. Soc.*, 71 (1949) 3852.

[73] W. SHIVE, T. J. BARDOS, T. J. BOND AND L. L. ROGERS, *J. Am. Chem. Soc.*, 72 (1950) 2817.

[74] E. H. FLYNN, T. J. BOND, T. J. BARDOS AND W. SHIVE, *J. Am. Chem. Soc.*, 73 (1951) 1979.

[75] J. A. BROCKMAN JR., B. ROTH, H. P. BROQUIST, M. E. HULTQUIST, J. M. SMITH JR., M. J. FAHRENBACH, D. B. COSULICH, R. P. PARKER, E. L. R. STOKSTAD AND T. H. JUKES, *J. Am. Chem. Soc.*, 72 (1950) 4325.

[76] A. POHLAND, E. H. FLYNN, R. G. JONES AND W. SHIVE, *J. Am. Chem. Soc.*, 73 (1951) 3247.

[77] M. MAY, T. J. BARDOS, F. L. BARGER, M. LANSFORD, J. M. RAVEL, G. L. SUTHERLAND AND W. SHIVE, *J. Am. Chem. Soc.*, 73 (1951) 3067.

[78] B. ROTH, M. E. HULTQUIST, M. J. FAHRENBACH, D. B. COSULICH, H. P. BROQUIST, J. A. BROCKMAN JR., J. M. SMITH JR., R. P. PARKER, E. L. R. STOKSTAD AND T. H. JUKES, *J. Am. Chem. Soc.*, 74 (1952) 3247.

[79] D. B. COSULICH, B. ROTH, J. M. SMITH JR, M. E. HULTQUIST AND R. P. PARKER, *J. Am. Chem. Soc.*, 74 (1952) 3252.

[80] B. L. O'DELL, J. M. VANDENBELT, E. S. BLOOM AND J. J. PFIFFNER, *J. Am. Chem. Soc.*, 69 (1947) 250.

[81] D. B. COSULICH, J. M. SMITH JR. AND H. P. BROQUIST, *J. Am. Chem. Soc.*, 74 (1952) 4215.

[82] M. SILVERMAN AND J. C. KERESZTESY, *J. Am. Chem. Soc.*, 73 (1951) 1897, 5510.

[83] S. C. HARTMAN AND J. M. BUCHANAN, *J. Biol. Chem.*, 234 (1959) 1812.

[84] M. SILVERMAN, J. C. KERESZTESY, G. J. KOVAL AND R. C. GARDINER, *J. Biol. Chem.*, 226 (1957) 83.

[85] R. L. BLAKLEY, *Biochem. J.*, 58 (1954) 448.

[86] F. M. HUENNEKENS, M. J. OSBORN AND H. R. WHITELY, *Science*, 128 (1958) 120.

[87] R. L. KISLIUK, *J. Biol. Chem.*, 227 (1957) 805; R. L. KISLIUK AND W. SAKAMI, *Soc.*, 76 (1954) 1456.

[88] R. L. BLAKLEY, *Biochem. J.*, 72 (1959) 707.

[89] G. K. HUMPHREYS AND D. M. GREENBERG, *Arch. Biochem. Biophys.*, 78 (1958) 275.

[90] J. M. PETERS AND D. M. GREENBERG, *J. Am. Chem. Soc.*, 80 (1958) 6679.

[90a] A. R. LARRABEE, S. ROSENTHAL, R. E. CATHOU AND J. M. BUCHANAN, *J. Am. Chem. Soc.*, 83 (1961) 4094.

[90b] J. C. KERESZTESY AND K. O. DONALDSON, *Biochem. Biophys. Research Communs.*, 5 (1961) 286, 289.

[90c] W. SAKAMI AND I. UKSTINS, *J. Biol. Chem.*, 236 (1961) PC50.

[90d] L. JAENICKE, *Z. physiol. Chem., Hoppe-Seyler's*, 326 (1961) 168.

[91] J. C. RABINOWITZ in P. D. BOYER, H. LARDY AND K. MYRBÄCK (Eds.), *The Enzymes*, Vol. 2, Academic Press, New York, 1960, 185.

[92] S. FUTTERMAN AND M. SILVERMAN, *J. Biol. Chem.*, 224 (1957) 31.

[93] L. JAENICKE AND E. BRODE, *Ann. Chem., Liebigs*, 624 (1959) 120.

[94] B. E. WRIGHT, *J. Biol. Chem.*, 219 (1956) 873.

[95] M. T. HAKALA AND A. D. WELCH, *J. Bacteriol.*, 73 (1957) 35.

[96] E. L. PATTERSON, H. P. BROQUIST, A. M. ALBRECHT, M. H. VON SALTZA AND E. L. R. STOKSTAD, *J. Am. Chem. Soc.*, 77 (1955) 3167; E. L. PATTERSON, M. H. VON SALTZA AND E. L. R. STOKSTAD, *J. Am. Chem. Soc.*, 78 (1956) 5871.

[97] H. S. FORREST AND H. K. MITCHELL, *J. Am. Chem. Soc.*, 77 (1955) 4865.

[98] E. L. PATTERSON, R. MILSTREY AND E. L. R. STOKSTAD, *J. Am. Chem. Soc.*, 78 (1956) 5868; 80 (1958) 2018.

[99] P. KARRER, R. SCHWYZER, B. ERDEN AND A. SEIGWART, *Helv. Chim. Acta*, 30 (1947) 1031.

[100] H. S. FORREST AND J. WALKER, *J. Chem. Soc.*, (1949) 79.

[101] H. G. PETERING AND J. A. SCHMITT, *J. Am. Chem. Soc.*, 71 (1949) 3977.

[102] A. WACKER AND E. R. LOCHMANN, *Z. Naturforsch.*, *Pt. b.*, 14 (1959) 222.

[103] H. P. BROQUIST AND A. M. ALBRECHT, *Proc. Soc. Exptl. Biol. Med.*, 89 (1955) 178.

[104] H. S. FORREST, C. VAN BAALEN AND J. MYERS, *Arch. Biochem. Biophys.*, 78 (1958) 95; *Science*, 125 (1957) 699.

[105] H. FORREST, paper presented before International Union of Pure and Applied Chemistry, Munich, Sept. 1959.

[106] C. VAN BAALEN AND H. S. FORREST, *J. Am. Chem. Soc.*, 81 (1959) 1770.

[107] H. S. FORREST, D. HATFIELD AND C. VAN BAALEN, *Nature*, 183 (1959) 1269.

[108] M. VISCONTINI AND E. MOHLMANN, *Helv. Chim. Acta*, 42 (1959) 836.

[109] H. S. FORREST AND H. K. MITCHELL, *J. Am. Chem. Soc.*, 76 (1954) 5656, 5658.

[110] M. VISCONTINI, E. HADORN AND P. KARRER, *Helv. Chim. Acta*, 40 (1957) 579.

[111] M. VISCONTINI, *Helv. Chim. Acta*, 41 (1958) 922, 1299.

[112] M. VISCONTINI AND H. R. WEILENMANN, *Helv. Chim. Acta*, 42 (1959) 1854.

[113] R. HÜTTEL AND G. SPRENGLING, *Ann. Chem.*, *Liebigs*, 554 (1943) 69.

[114] S. MATSUURA, S. NAWA, M. GOTO AND Y. HIRATA, *J. Biochem.* (*Tokyo*), 42 (1955) 419.

[115] T. KAUFFMANN, *Ann. Chem.*, *Liebigs*, 625 (1959) 133.

[116] R. TSCHESCHE AND A. GLAZER, *Chem. Ber.*, 91 (1958) 2081.

[117] T. MASUDA, *Pharm. Bull.* (*Tokyo*), 4 (1956) 71, 375; 5 (1957) 136.

[118] G. W. E. PLAUT AND G. F. MALEY, *J. Biol. Chem.*, 234 (1959) 641, 3010; *Arch. Biochem. Biophys.*, 80 (1959) 219.

[119] H. S. FORREST AND W. S. McNUTT, *J. Am. Chem. Soc.*, 80 (1958) 739.

[120] T. MASUDA, T. KISHI, M. ASAI AND S. KUWADA, *Pharm. Bull.* (*Tokyo*), 7 (1959) 361, 366.

[121] T. MASUDA, T. KISHI AND M. ASAI, *Pharm. Bull.* (*Tokyo*), 6 (1958) 291.

[122] W. S. McNUTT, *J. Am. Chem. Soc.*, 82 (1960) 217.

Supplemental Reviews: M. GATES, *Chem. Revs.*, 41 (1947) 63; A. ALBERT, *Quart. Revs.* (*London*), 6 (1952) 197.

Chapter VIII

Vitamin B_{12}

ARTHUR F. WAGNER AND KARL FOLKERS

Merck Sharp & Dohme Research Laboratories, Merck & Co., Inc., Rahway, N.J. (U.S.A.)

1. Introduction

Pernicious anemia, a chronic disease characterized by megaloblastic anemia with accompanying neurologic lesions, was described over one hundred years ago. It was found that this deficiency syndrome results from a secondary or "conditioned" nutritional deficiency and not from a primary nutritional deficiency state. The specific cause is inability to absorb the vitamin B_{12} which is in the alimentary tract. After the pure crystalline vitamin was available for medical comparison, vitamin B_{12} was correlated with the "extrinsic factor". The secretory factor necessary for absorption of vitamin B_{12} is known as the "intrinsic factor". For the treatment of pernicious anemia, vitamin B_{12} is usually administered parenterally at the microgram level; if the vitamin in low dosage is administered orally, a concentrate of the gastric intrinsic factor is included in the formulation. The vitamin is also administered for the therapeutic control of other megaloblastic anemias and other neuropathies. Administration of the vitamin to humans is especially recommended in pregnancy, pediatrics and geriatrics. By virtue of its growth-promoting properties, vitamin B_{12} is used widely as an animal feed supplement. It is also important for chick hatchability and for reproduction in swine.

A major breakthrough toward the recognition of a vitamin etiology came with the observed therapeutic control of pernicious anemia by feeding whole liver. This discovery led to efforts in many laboratories to determine the principle or principles responsible for the therapeutic effect. Details of this twenty-year search have been reviewed[1]. Fractionation studies were extremely slow, and after about twenty years of effort, the activity equivalent to 400 g of whole liver could be concentrated in a 1-mg mass.

In 1948, a red crystalline compound designated vitamin B_{12} was described from the research in two laboratories[2,3]. The initial clinical studies[4] with this crystalline vitamin showed that it was active in producing hematological responses in patients with pernicious anemia at a single dose level of 3–6 μg. Vitamin B_{12} was also found to possess activity at extremely low concentrations for the growth of the micro-organism, *L. lactis* Dorner. The latter activity and the red color of the vitamin itself guided subsequent studies of vitamin B_{12} activity and related cobalt complexes in chromatographic and related purifications. Crystalline vitamin B_{12} was also obtained[5] from the fermentation source, *Streptomyces griseus*.

2. Purification and crystallization of vitamin B_{12}

Early studies for the purification of the antipernicious anemia factor used either minced liver preparations or proteolyzed liver extracts in which the concentration of the factor was of the order of one part per million. Adsorption chromatography, partition chromatography, and extraction were the methods of choice for purification. In the initial fractionation steps, the factor was adsorbed on either activated carbon or fuller's earth, and eluted with either aqueous ethanol, phenol, or pyridine. Intermediate purification steps were accomplished by partition chromatography; adsorption chromatography on either silica or alumina was also effective. At various stages of these column procedures, the activity could be removed from aqueous solution by butanol extraction or with phenol or cresol in combination with solvents such as butanol or toluene. Final purification was usually accomplished by crystallization from aqueous acetone solution.

3. Structure*

The structure of vitamin B_{12} was established as α-(5,6-dimethylbenzimidazolyl)cobamide cyanide (I) by chemical degradation and physical methods, particularly including X-ray crystallography. Details of these structural studies may be found in several reviews[6–10].

The ultraviolet absorption spectrum of the vitamin in aqueous solution is unaffected by pH and is characterized by absorption maxima at 278, 361, and 550 mμ. Early ebullioscopic measurements gave a value of 1490 $\pm$ 150 for the molecular weight of the crystalline vitamin, and a value of 1360–1575 was calculated from early crystallographic data. The first determinations of molecular formula resulted in the expression $C_{61-64}H_{86-92}N_{14}O_{13}PCo$. A molecular formula of $C_{63}H_{88}N_{14}O_{14}PCo$ and a molecular weight of 1355 correspond to the established structure I. The vitamin is optically active and behaves as a polyacidic base on electrometric titration in glacial acetic acid.

---

* The tentative nomenclature used in this section is defined in Section 4.

After the identification of cobalt in the molecule, the metal ion was established in the trivalent state by magnetic susceptibility measurements and polarographic studies.

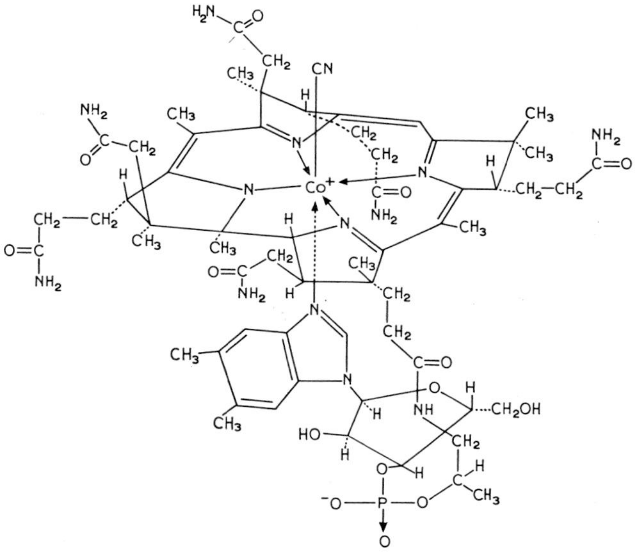

(I)

(a) The α-ribazole phosphate moiety

Varying degrees of acid hydrolysis of the crystalline vitamin yielded 5,6-dimethylbenzimidazole (II), 1-α-D-ribofuranosyl-5,6-dimethylbenzimidazole (III), which is also known as α-ribazole, and α-ribazole phosphate (IV).

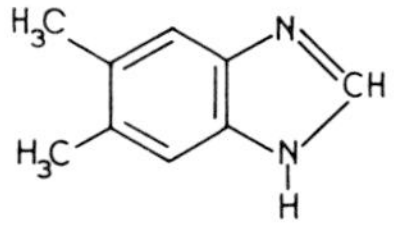

(II)

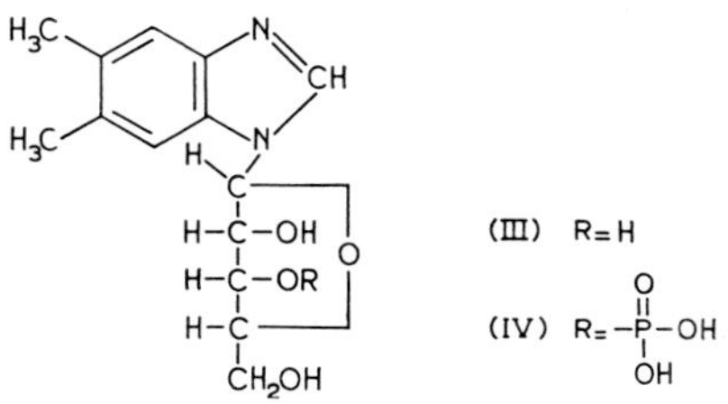

(III) R = H

(IV) R = $-\overset{\overset{\displaystyle O}{\|}}{\underset{\underset{\displaystyle OH}{|}}{P}}-OH$

(i) 5,6-Dimethylbenzimidazole

Treatment of cyanocobalamin with 6 N hydrochloric acid at 150° for 20 h yielded 5,6-dimethylbenzimidazole. Further degradation of this product with benzoyl chloride in aqueous alkali yielded the known compound, 4,5-dibenzamido-1,2-dimethylbenzene. The structure of the benzimidazole fragment was confirmed by synthesis from formic acid and 4,5-diamino-1,2-dimethyl-benzene.

(ii) α-Ribazole

Treatment of the vitamin with 6 N hydrochloric acid at 100° for 8 h yielded 1-α-D-ribofuranosyl-5,6-dimethylbenzimidazole. The glycosyl moiety of the ribazole was a pentose rather than a hexose on the basis of elemental analysis, and a pentofuranoside structure was assigned to this moiety on the basis of periodate oxidation. The conditions necessary to cleave the glycosidic link also caused extensive decomposition of the pentose. Consequently, liberation and identification of the sugar moiety was an unattractive degradative approach. Periodate oxidation of α-ribazole yielded α-(5,6-dimethylbenzimidazole-1)-α'-hydroxymethyldiglycolic aldehyde. The structure of the latter was derived by comparison with an authentic sample of an anomeric dialdehyde prepared from 1-β-D-glucopyranosyl-5,6-dimethyl-benzimidazole. The glycosidic carbon atom was established at the 1-position of the sugar moiety, and an α-configuration for the glycosidic carbon atom was deduced by comparing the oxidation products from α-ribazole and the synthetic model compound, 1-β-D-glucopyranosyl-5,6-dimethylbenzimid-azole. Final proof of structure was obtained by the synthesis of α-ribazole from 2-nitro-4,5-dimethylaniline and 5-trityl-D-ribofuranose. Reduction of the nitro group in the product, 4,5-dimethyl-2-nitro-N-(5'-trityl-D-ribofuran-osyl)-aniline (V) yielded the corresponding amino derivative which, on treat-

(V)

ment with ethyl- or isopropylformimino ether hydrochloride, yielded the 5'-trityl derivative of α-ribazole. Hydrolysis of the latter yielded α-ribazole.

(iii) α-Ribazole phosphate

When cyanocobalamin was hydrolyzed for 1–20 h with 1 N HCl at 100°, α-ribazole phosphate was isolated. This phosphate did not react with periodic acid. Hydrolysis of the phosphate yielded an *N*-substituted benzimidazole which did react with periodic acid. From these data and prior knowledge of the structure of α-ribazole, it was apparent that the phosphate group was attached to either C-2 or C-3 of the ribose moiety. The nucleotide was synthesized by the reaction of 5'-trityl-α-ribazole with diphenylphosphorochloridate followed by hydrolysis, or alternatively, by reaction with dibenzylphosphorochloridate followed by hydrogenolysis. Neither method of synthesis permitted the unambiguous assignment of the phosphate group at either the 2'- or 3'-position of the ribose moiety. Attachment of the phosphate group to the 3'-position was deduced by comparative paper chromatography of α-ribazole phosphate and the known adenosine 2'- and 3'-phosphates. X-ray crystallographic studies showed that the phosphate group was attached to the 3'-position of the ribose moiety within the vitamin B_{12} molecule.

(b) *The aminopropanol moiety*

Among the products of mild acid hydrolysis of cyanocobalamin was a ninhydrin-reacting substance, later identified as D_g-1-amino-2-propanol. Since the 1-aminopropanol and α-ribazole phosphate moieties were isolated after mild hydrolysis, it was assumed that the two moieties were linked through the phosphate group in the intact molecule. On the basis of relative stabilities of mono-, di-, and tri-substituted phosphate esters to acid hydrolysis, it was considered in early studies that the phosphate ester function in the vitamin was either a di- or tri-substituted ester. The aminopropanol moiety was assumed to be bound through its oxygen substituent to the phosphate ester group and through its amino function to the remainder of the molecule.

On the basis of all of the preceding data, the partial structure (VI) was considered for the vitamin. Later it was determined that this formulation is correct except for the tri-substituted phosphoric ester moiety. As shown in structure I, the phosphate ester is actually disubstituted.

(VI)

(c) The corrin moiety

The polyamide character of the macro-ring system of cyanocobalamin was demonstrated most clearly by paper chromatographic and electrophoretic studies of the red cobalt-containing fragments obtained after the acid hydrolysis of the vitamin. About six equivalents of ammonia are liberated for each mole of cyanocobalamin hydrolyzed. After partial hydrolysis of the vitamin with dilute acid, a mixture of red nucleotide-containing pigments was obtained which, after electrophoresis and purification of the various electrophoretic fractions by paper chromatography, yielded three monobasic acids, three dibasic acids, one tribasic acid, and one tetrabasic acid. Conversion of the mono-, di- and tri-carboxylic acids to cyanocobalamin through the intermediate formation of a mixed anhydride, followed by reaction with ammonia, was accomplished. On the basis of these observations and those presented earlier it was considered that the vitamin contained at least three primary amide groups, and in addition one secondary amide group binding the aminopropanol moiety.

Hydrolysis of cyanocobalamin for 5 min with concentrated hydrochloric acid liberated the nucleotide moiety; the aminopropanol fragment was retained and there was little effect on either the cyanide group or the amide linkages. This cobalt-containing hydrolytic fragment is identical with Factor B, a microbiologically active compound from fecal material. Further hydrolysis of Factor B yielded corresponding mono-, di-, and tri-carboxylic acids in which the nucleotide moiety was absent. These could also be converted to the parent compound, Factor B, by way of the intermediate mixed anhydride and treatment with ammonia.

Chromate oxidation of acid hydrolysates of cyanocobalamin or direct oxidation of the vitamin with sodium chromate yielded three crystalline succinamide derivatives, particularly 3,3-dimethyl-2,5-dioxopyrrolidine-4-propionamide (VII). The isolation and identification of these compounds constituted proof for a 3,3-dimethylpyrrolidine-4-propionamide-like moiety (VIII) in the vitamin and was the first detailed degradative evidence for the pyrrole-like character of the corrin system of the vitamin.

(VII)   (VIII)

(d) X-ray diffraction data

X-ray crystallographic studies on both cyanocobalamin and a hexacarboxylic acid degradation product provided clarification for the remaining structural features of the vitamin[11,12].

The molecule is compactly constructed around the cobalt atom. The benzimidazole moiety is nearly perpendicular to the almost planar macro-ring and the ribofuranose ring is almost parallel to the corrin nucleus. Six groups are linked coordinately to the cobalt atom and are about 1.9 Å from the central atom. Cobalt is in the trivalent state. Its coordination requirements are met by the contribution of one negative charge from the cyano group, one negative charge from a nitrogen atom of the corrin ring, and four neutral groups, namely the remaining three nitrogen atoms of the corrin ring and N-3 of the benzimidazole nucleus. The singly positive net charge of the fully coordinated cobalt is neutralized by the phosphate anion giving a neutral molecule.

4. Nomenclature

A nomenclature committee submitted a basic proposal[13] of "tentative" rules in 1957; these rules were subsequently improved and published[14] in 1960.

The macro-ring system of four partially reduced pyrrole nuclei joined through three bridge-carbon atoms is designated *corrin*; metal derivatives of this compound are designated *cobalto-corrin*, *cobalti-corrin*, etc.

The heptacarboxylic acid derived from cyanocobalamin by converting all amide groups to carboxyl groups is designated *cobyrinic acid* (IX).

The nucleotide-free hexacarboxylic acid in which all amide linkages except the propanolamide link are converted to carboxyl groups is designated *cobinic acid* (X). The corresponding structure with the primary amide groups intact is referred to as *cobinamide* (XI).

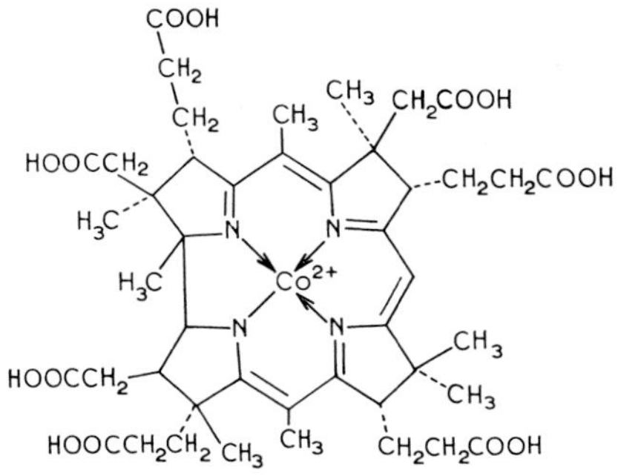

Cobyrinic acid

(IX)

The ribose 3'-phosphate-containing moiety in which the primary amide groups are hydrolyzed to carboxyl groups is designated *cobamic acid* (XII). The corresponding structure in which the primary amide groups are intact is *cobamide* (XIII).

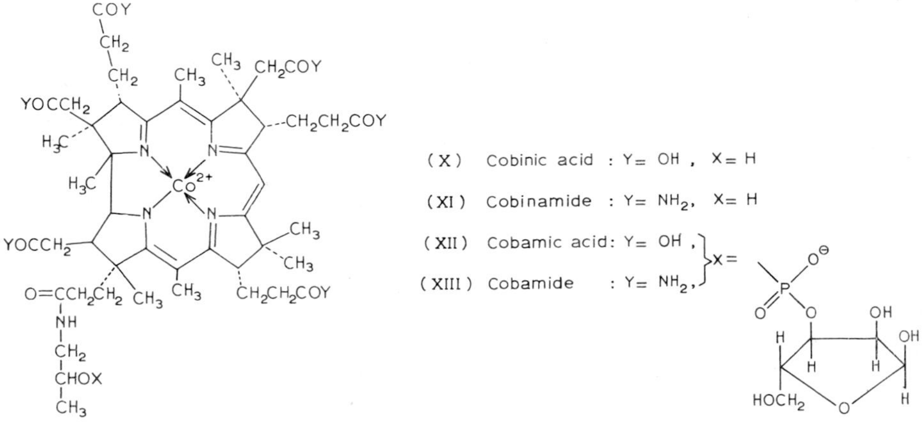

(X) Cobinic acid : Y= OH , X= H

(XI) Cobinamide : Y= NH$_2$, X= H

(XII) Cobamic acid: Y= OH ,

(XIII) Cobamide : Y= NH$_2$,

The older term cobalamin designates the moiety formally derived from cyanocobalamin by removing the cyano group.

5. Modifications of vitamin B$_{12}$

Other ions and neutral molecules can replace the cyano group in cyanocobalamin. Compounds such as hydroxocobalamin (vitamin B$_{12a}$), chlorocobalamin, cyanatocobalamin, thiocyanatocobalamin, and nitrocobalamin, are known. The microbiological activity of these compounds by the *L. lactis* and *L. leichmannii* assays is from 30–100% of the activity of cyanocobalamin, depending upon the assay conditions employed.

Several modifications of cyanocobalamin have been obtained from animal feces and from sewage sludge. In these analogs, the 5,6-dimethylbenzimidazole of the nucleotide moiety is replaced by another nitrogen-containing base. With this exception, the total structure of the modified forms has appeared to be identical with that of cyanocobalamin. Among the examples of such compounds are Factor III derived from 5-hydroxybenzimidazole, pseudovitamin B$_{12}$ derived from adenine, Factor A derived from 2-methyladenine, Factor G derived from hypoxanthine, and Factor H derived from 2-methylhypoxanthine. A guanine and 2-methylmercaptoadenine analog were recently obtained from sewage sludge. Although some of these modifications are significantly active in microbiological assays, few exhibit an activity for the growth of animals comparable to that of cyanocobalamin.

Factor III exhibits hematological activity in man and animal growth activity.

Benzimidazole analogs of cyanocobalamin are also known and were obtained mostly by biosynthetic incorporation during fermentation. Such modifications are usually prepared by the incorporation of Factor B and an appropriate benzimidazole in a medium for the growth of *E. coli* 113-3 or solely by the incorporation of the desired nucleotide base into the medium for the growth of *Streptomyces griseus*. In some instances, the new products were prepared only in microgram quantities and identified by paper chromatography. Others were prepared in crystalline form. Among the analogs prepared in this manner were those containing nucleotide base moieties from benzimidazole, 5,6-diethylbenzimidazole, 5,6-dichlorobenzimidazole, 5(6)-aminobenzimidazole, 5(6)-trifluoromethylbenzimidazole, and 2,3-naphthimidazole.

6. Coenzyme forms

The most recent significant modifications of the vitamin B_{12} molecule to be reported are the photosensitive cobamide coenzymes[15-18]. Cyanide is absent from these coenzyme forms. In addition to the macro-ring system, the molecule contains one atom of cobalt, one phosphate group, and one riboside moiety; furthermore, there is one adenine-containing moiety which is not present in the corresponding cobamide vitamin. Three such forms have been crystallized from cell-free extracts of *Clostridium tetanomorphum* and are designated adenyl cobamide coenzyme, 5,6-dimethylbenzimidazolyl cobamide coenzyme and benzimidazolyl cobamide coenzyme. These B_{12} coenzymes are cofactors for the isomerization of glutamate to β-methylaspartate. The B_{12} coenzyme participates in propionate metabolism by catalyzing the isomerization of methylmalonyl coenzyme A to succinyl coenzyme A. Coenzyme activity is lost on irradiation, hydrolysis or treatment with cyanide.

All structural features of the corresponding vitamin except the cyanide group are present in the B_{12} coenzymes (*cf.* I). The cyanide group is replaced by the 5′-deoxyadenosine moiety which was identified after aerobic and anaerobic photolysis of the coenzyme[19-22] and by X-ray crystallography[23]. The 5′-methylene group of the 5′-deoxyadenosine moiety is linked directly to the cobalt atom in the intact coenzyme.

7. Assay

The vitamin B_{12} activity of a given sample may be determined by biological, chemical, microbiological or physical methods including radioactive tracer, spectrophotometric, and partition techniques. The nature of the sample, the concentration of activity, precision, and time required will usually determine the assay of choice.

A radioisotope dilution assay and an assay based on animal growth are the most reliable methods for the determination of vitamin B$_{12}$ activity. The tracer technique is highly specific for cyanocobalamin or analogs which are convertible to cyanocobalamin. The assay is specific for cyanocobalamin if cyanide treatment of the sample is avoided; total cobalamins convertible to cyanocobalamin are determined if a given sample is first treated with cyanide. The method consists in the addition of a known amount of pure [^{60}Co]-cyanocobalamin. A series of selective extractions and adsorptions to remove interfering substances is completed and the radioactivity and color of the purified sample are measured. From these data, it is possible to calculate the amount of cobalamin present in the original sample. The isotope dilution method is accurate and precise and can be used for both relatively pure samples and for crude extracts of low potency.

The growth response of B$_{12}$-depleted chicks or weanling rats to a given sample is perhaps the most specific measure of vitamin B$_{12}$ activity but is not highly precise. The activity of a given sample is determined from a standard growth response curve of depleted animals fed known amounts of the vitamin. Satisfactory depletion of the test animals is one of the uncertainties of the procedure.

The most sensitive method for the estimation of vitamin B$_{12}$ is based on the stimulation of microbial growth. The assays are conducted in either fluid media in tubes or in agar media on plates. Among the organisms used are *Lactobacillus leichmannii, E. coli, Ochromonas malhamensis,* and *Euglena gracilis.*

Chemical assays are based either upon the liberation of cyanide or 5,6-dimethylbenzimidazole. These methods are used when the samples are moderately concentrated and relatively free of interfering substances.

For samples of relatively high purity, the cyanocobalamin content may be estimated by spectrophotometry, and also by the partition coefficient between an equilibrated water and benzyl alcohol system.

REFERENCES

1 Y. SubbaRow, A. B. Hastings and M. Elkin, *Vitamins and Hormones*, 3 (1948) 237.
2 E. L. Rickes, N. G. Brink, F. R. Koniuszy, T. R. Wood and K. Folkers, *Science*, 107 (1948) 396.
3 E. L. Smith and L. F. J. Parker, *Biochem. J.*, 43 (1948) viii.
4 R. West, *Science*, 107 (1948) 398.
5 E. L. Rickes, N. G. Brink, F. R. Koniuszy, T. R. Wood and K. Folkers, *Science*, 108 (1948) 634.
6 R. S. Harris, G. F. Marrian and K. V. Thimann (Eds.), *Vitamins and Hormones*, Vol. XII, Academic Press, New York, 1954.
7 W. H. Sebrell Jr. and R. S. Harris (Eds.), *The Vitamins: Chemistry, Physiology and Pathology*, Vol. I, Academic Press, New York, 1954, p. 395.
8 R. T. Williams (Ed.), *The Biochemistry of Vitamin B$_{12}$*, Biochem. Soc. Symposia, Cambridge, England, 1955, No. 13.
9 H. C. Heinrich (Ed.), *Vitamin B$_{12}$ und Intrinsic Factor*, Ferdinand Enke Verlag, Stuttgart, 1957.
10 E. L. Smith, *Vitamin B$_{12}$*, Methuen, London, John Wiley & Sons, New York, 1960.
11 D. C. Hodgkin, J. Kamper, M. Mackay, J. Pickworth, K. N. Trueblood and J. G. White, *Nature*, 178 (1956) 64.
12 D. C. Hodgkin, J. Pickworth, J. H. Robertson, K. N. Trueblood, R. J. Prösen, J. G. White, R. Bonnet, J. R. Cannon, A. W. Johnson, I. Sutherland, A. R. Todd and E. L. Smith, *Nature*, 176 (1955) 325.
13 E. L. Smith in H. C. Heinrich (Ed.), *Vitamin B$_{12}$ und Intrinsic Factor*, Ferdinand Enke Verlag, Stuttgart, 1957, p. 554.
14 IUPAC, Commission on the Nomenclature of Biological Chemistry, *J. Am. Chem. Soc.*, 82 (1960) 5581.
15 H. A. Barker, H. Weissbach and R. D. Smyth, *Proc. Natl. Acad. Sci. U.S.*, 44 (1958) 1093.
16 H. A. Barker, R. D. Smyth, H. Weissbach, A. Munch-Petersen, J. I. Toohey, J. N. Ladd, B. E. Volcani and R. M. Wilson, *J. Biol. Chem.*, 235 (1960) 181.
17 H. Weissbach, J. Toohey and H. A. Barker, *Proc. Natl. Acad. Sci. U.S.*, 45 (1959) 521.
18 H. A. Barker, R. D. Smyth, H. Weissbach, J. I. Toohey, J. N. Ladd and B. E. Volcani, *J. Biol. Chem.*, 235 (1960) 480.
19 J. N. Ladd, H. P. C. Hogenkamp and H. A. Barker, *Biochem. Biophys. Research Communs.*, 2 (1960) 143.
20 H. P. C. Hogenkamp and H. A. Barker, *J. Biol. Chem.*, 236 (1961) 3097.
21 A. W. Johnson and N. Shaw, *Proc. Chem. Soc.*, (1961) 447.
22 H. P. C. Hogenkamp and H. A. Barker, *Federation Proc.*, 21 (1962) 470.
23 P. G. Lenhert and D. C. Hodgkin, *Nature*, 192 (1961) 937.

Volume II

Part B

HORMONES

Chapter IX

Plant Hormones

Section a

Indole Auxins of Plants

BRUCE B. STOWE

Department of Botany, Yale University, New Haven, Conn. (U.S.A.)

1. Introduction

The demonstration that the growth of plants is under hormonal control has profoundly influenced the direction of botanical research. Among the well-established plant hormones the most studied belong to the group known as auxins. At present, all conclusively identified natural auxins are compounds chemically related to indoleacetic acid (X).

Auxins have characteristic physiological properties which can serve to define them. In addition, study of their molecular structure has revealed certain common properties which can be used to predict the biological activities of synthetic compounds. Thus many substances not known to occur in plants (and most of which are not indoles) can act as auxins. A discussion of the biochemistry of such compounds is to be found in Section b of this Chapter under the heading "Synthetic Auxins".

It is noteworthy that the synthetic auxins cannot properly be called "hormones" since a hormone is a substance *produced* in one part of an organism which in trace quantities produces characteristic biological effects when it moves to another part of the organism. The common link between synthetic and natural auxins is thus their biological effect and this then must be carefully defined. In the case of the auxins it is agreed that the most fundamental biological property is their capacity to promote plant cell elongation[1]. The most specific bioassays therefore use plant material which readily permits cell elongation to be evaluated.

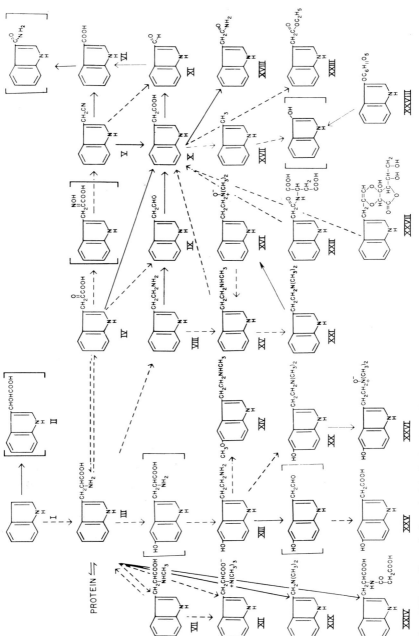

Fig. 1. Metabolism of plant indole derivatives. Transformations for which there is good evidence are indicated by solid arrows. The dotted arrows depict plausible reactions not yet conclusively established. The bracketed compounds are not known to occur naturally in plant tissues, but are likely intermediates. Details are available in ref. 8.

Like most hormones, auxins have manifold other effects. Among these at low concentrations of 10^{-5} to 10^{-8} M some are stimulatory — as in promotion of cell division, root initiation, parthenocarpy (fruit formation without fertilization), cellular water uptake, protoplasmic streaming, and in a few special cases, flowering. But as concentrations are increased above these values auxins will begin to inhibit these functions, and to show toxic effects. This latter property is the basis of the extensive use of these compounds for weed-killing. Equally typical is the inhibition — this time at the low concentrations — of other plant processes such as root elongation, the growth of lateral buds, and the abscission of leaves and fruits. Finally, one of the most unusual and specific properties of auxins is their movement in only one direction through plant tissues — from the morphological apex to the base. This polar transport of auxin is particularly evident with the natural auxins, the synthetic substances usually showing much less movement in plant tissues.

The potency of an auxin can be influenced by other factors. Among these are the availability of energy reserves to the plant tissue, the ambient pH, the presence of potassium and other inorganic ions, previous or concurrent exposure of the plant to light, certain lipids, and the synergistic effects that a number of compounds may have in increasing or decreasing the auxin response when applied simultaneously with it. Details of these problems of hormonal physiology cannot be discussed here, but may be found elsewhere[2,3].

The discovery of the auxins derives from the observation of Charles and Francis Darwin that the phototropic response of grass seedlings originates in the seedling tip but is manifested by a growth response some distance below. Analysis of this phenomenon and the development of the first reliable bioassay led Went many years later to the proof that a hormone was involved[4]. Early attempts to isolate the substance responsible were hindered by what we now know to be potent oxidizing enzymes in plant tissue. So it was that the first isolations of growth substances were not carried out with higher plant materials, but were performed on urine concentrates by Kögl, Haagen-Smit and Erxleben[5] and on a fungus culture by Thimann[6]. Both investigations resulted in the isolation of indoleacetic acid, and the former workers also showed it to be present in yeast. However, Kögl and his group isolated two other compounds at the same time, which they named auxins a and b. Presuming that the indoleacetic acid they obtained was at least in part an artefact of tryptophan degradation they named it "heteroauxin", and advanced the belief that auxins a and b were the important compounds *in situ*.

Unfortunately for this concept, and despite several attempts (including efforts by one of the initial workers), auxins a and b have never been re-isolated. Furthermore, recent studies also cast doubt on the chemical structures originally proposed for these molecules[7]. The status of auxins a and b is thus quite uncertain.

On the other hand, the position of indoleacetic acid has steadily strengthened. It has been definitively isolated by several workers from higher plant tissues, and the advent of paper chromatography has permitted at least its tentative identification throughout the plant kingdom from algae to the highest flowering plants. Furthermore, the demonstration of a number of other indole auxins and of enzymes which can convert them to indoleacetic acid has made the existence of a family of indole auxins secure.

Some lines of evidence point to other, non-indolic, natural products that may also act as auxins in plant tissues. Some are as yet unidentified chemically, others (like phenylacetic acid) act as auxins in bioassays, occur in plant tissues, but have not been shown to play a role in natural growth regulation. Also some other hormones, such as the gibberellins, have at least weak auxin activity. Interpretation of the importance of substances such as these will have to await the development of specific chemical methods of analysis which are at least as sensitive as the relatively non-specific bioassays now employed out of necessity.

In all auxin work the low concentrations of the hormone have required that heavy reliance be placed on this identification by bioassay, more recently combined with paper or column chromatography. The evidence is thus frequently insecure and interpretation of the results may vary.

Investigations of indolic auxin metabolism in plants have centered about attempts to understand plant growth regulation. As a consequence, factors which limit the concentration of indoleacetic acid in plant tissue have received the most attention. These include its synthesis, its catabolism, and its removal from the site of action by other means. This will also provide a convenient division for discussion here. Full reference to the original work has been provided elsewhere[8].

2. Auxin synthesis

As soon as he had identified indoleacetic acid as a plant growth substance, Thimann proposed that it must be derived from tryptophan (III). Since tryptophan is the most prominent indole in plant tissues, occurring both in protein and as a free amino acid, this still seems reasonable. However, numerous workers have investigated various plant tissues for their capacity to produce indoleacetic acid from tryptophan and in all cases the capacity of their systems has been feeble indeed. The best conversions obtained have fallen in the range of 0.3%, and most are less. As it is not difficult to obtain comparable amounts of indoleacetic acid from tryptophan non-enzymatically under mild conditions, the specificity of the systems investigated is still doubtful. Thus it would appear that in plants, as in animals, the limiting step (as judged from lack of demonstrable enzymes) in the production of indole hormones is the initial reaction of tryptophan.

In bacteria, some of which produce copious amounts of indoleacetic acid from the amino acid, the initial reaction is a transamination which requires pyridoxal phosphate and is specific for certain α-keto acids, in particular α-ketoglutaric acid and oxaloacetic acid. Although sought for, no comparable reaction has yet been shown in higher plants. The product of the bacterial reaction, indolepyruvic acid (IV) has been reported to occur in corn seed and probably in other plants. This compound is unstable and decomposes spontaneously in aerated aqueous solutions to indoleacetic acid and a number of other products. Study of the decomposition is complicated by the fact that indolepyruvic acid undergoes a tautomerism between its keto and its enol form when in solution. Since the enol double bond is conjugated to an aromatic ring, the reactivities and absorption spectra of the tautomers vary greatly. As a consequence, it has not yet been possible to accurately assess whether plant or bacterial enzymes exist which convert indolepyruvic acid to indoleacetic acid.

Other precursors of indoleacetic acid have been more satisfactorily studied. It has long been known that neutral auxins existed in plant tissues and the first of these was identified by the painstaking work of Larsen[9]. Working with trace quantities of materials and with bioassays, he was able to show that a neutral auxin from several plant sources was converted to an acid auxin by plant enzymes, as well as by the specific aldehyde oxidizing Schardinger enzyme of milk. The reaction was inhibited by bisulfite, and the molecular weight (by diffusion) was comparable to indoleacetaldehyde (IX). Similar results have been obtained by other investigators, and although indoleacetaldehyde has never been isolated from plants in the classical chemical sense, there is no reason to doubt its presence. Synthetic material was not available until some years later, when it was found to be very unstable in the concentrated state, and only recently has it been prepared in a form which should make it available for experimental work.

A most intriguing aspect of indoleacetaldehyde oxidase in plants is its extreme sensitivity to ionizing radiation. Gordon has shown[10] that it is very likely that a blockage of *in situ* indoleacetic acid synthesis is brought on by γ-irradiation, and that this leads to the characteristic morphological deformations observed in many plants. He was able to demonstrate that a neutral auxin with the properties of indoleacetaldehyde builds up after exposure to radiation, and that the dosage response curves indicate a remarkable radiation sensitivity of the aldehyde oxidase present.

The source of indoleacetaldehyde itself is most likely tryptamine (VIII). This decarboxylation product of tryptophan has been identified in a few plants, and even more widespread are amine oxidases which can oxidize it to the aldehyde. Evidence that this reaction can occur within plant tissues is provided by the fact that tryptamine has weak to moderate auxin activity in oat bioassays (an indication that it is being oxidized to indoleacetic acid since non-acidic substances are never in themselves active as auxins).

Amino-N-methyl tryptamine (XV), as well as amino-N,N-dimethyl tryptamine (XXI) and its N-oxide (XVI), all occurring in plants, have been shown to be oxidized to indoleacetic acid by mouse liver homogenates, but these reactions have not yet been observed with plant enzymes. It is noteworthy that these compounds might be derived from the naturally occurring amino-methylated derivatives of tryptophan, namely abrine (VII) and hypaphorine (XII).

The best characterized enzyme synthesizing indoleacetic acid is a unique nitrilase. When indoleacetonitrile (V) was isolated from crucifers, its high auxin activity on oats was a surprise. Equally puzzling was its inactivity on peas. This was resolved by the discovery of an enzyme in oats, since found in other grasses, crucifers and members of the *Musaceae*, which actively hydrolyzes the nitrile to indoleacetic acid and ammonia. This is a reaction special to biochemistry, since the enzyme does not attack indoleacetamide (XVIII), which therefore cannot be a free intermediate. The enzyme mechanism thus differs from that of the alkaline nitrile hydrolysis familiar to the organic chemist. Despite the fact that indoleacetonitrile is the only non-glycosidic nitrile known in plants, the enzyme has a broad specificity attacking a number of synthetic nitriles. Indoleacetonitrile can also be enzymatically oxidized to indolecarboxylic acid (VI), a substance of natural occurrence.

A more recently established potential precursor of indoleacetic acid is the unusual compound named ascorbigen by its Czech discoverers. This substance is found in *Cruciferae* and releases ascorbic acid on hydrolysis. When indole compounds including indoleacetic acid were also found among the products of chemical hydrolysis, a tentative structure could be formulated (XXVII). Studies of ascorbigen and indoleacetic acid levels show certain parallelisms and radioactive tryptophan labels both compounds[11]. It seems certain therefore that a biochemical linkage exists, but the nature of the intermediate steps can only be hypothesized at the present time.

Synthetic indole acids of greater chain length than indoleacetic acid when applied to plants are in some cases actively β-oxidized to indoleacetic or indolepropionic acid. This principle has been employed for the preparation of selective weed-killers, the actively β-oxidizing plants being poisoned by the high auxin concentrations they themselves create, while non-β-oxidizing plants remain unharmed. The natural occurrence of such higher chain length indole acids has yet to be conclusively proven.

Two volatile plant products, normally constituents of floral perfumes, are indole (I) and skatole (XVII). Surprisingly, the first of these has distinct growth promoting activity, although it fails to meet the well established structural requirements for an auxin. A possible explanation for this lies in the discovery that indole and glyoxylic acid will couple non-enzymatically to form indole glycolic acid (II), a weak auxin. This latter compound has not been shown to exist in plant tissues, but as glyoxylic acid is of common occurrence, the coupling with indole likely takes place in nature. The action of indole, however, might also be due to its role as a precursor of tryptophan.

5-Hydroxyindoles, some of which are important animal hormones, are also present in plants. But here, as in several other cases, the animal hormones are only weak or ineffective on plants, and the converse situation also holds. Hence 5-hydroxyindoleacetic acid (XXV) is not a powerful auxin, but hews to the structural rule that the introduction of an hydroxyl group substantially reduces the auxin activity of any active compound. Nonetheless, since the substance is found in plants and is a weak auxin, it must be kept in mind as a possible natural growth regulator. It could be produced from 5-hydroxytryptamine (XXIII) (the animal hormone serotonin), which occurs in plants (notably as one of the active irritating principles in nettle stings) and which is attacked by plant amine oxidases. Dimethyl derivatives (XIV, XX, and XXI) are also found in plants, but no information on their metabolism is yet available. Another hydroxylated indole is the 3-glucoside indican (XXVIII), which is widely found in plants and was for many years an important commercial source of the dye indigo. Its metabolism is also uninvestigated.

Thus it is established that plants have a remarkably large number of potential precursors of their principal growth hormone. This may reflect our lack of good information on the processes which are actually occurring *in vivo*, but may also be an evolutionary fact of some importance since the presence of several possible precursors in a plant might allow more flexibility in the translocation of materials needed for growth and development at different sites in the organism.

3. Indoleacetic acid catabolism

It is similarly well established that the removal of indoleacetic acid from metabolic availability may also follow more than one pathway. These include both oxidation by light and by enzymes, and conjugation to other compounds.

Photo-oxidation of auxin by light is important to plants since at least part of the phototropic response seems linked to an auxin destroying mechanism. However, the *in situ* nature of this process is far from certain. The action spectra of the most sensitive phototropic responses in both higher plants and fungi are remarkably similar, with maxima in the blue, but whether the photoreceptor is carotene[12] or riboflavin[13] remains a hotly debated but unresolved question. *In vitro*, solutions of indoleacetic acid are readily photo-oxidized and this is accelerated by many natural and synthetic pigments. The products of the photo-oxidation include indolealdehyde (XI) — known to occur in plants — as well as other unidentified products in which the indole ring has apparently been cleaved.

The enzymes involved in indoleacetic acid oxidation have been intensively studied. Tang and Bonner[14] were the first to demonstrate that a potent indoleacetic acid oxidase exists in pea tissue. Similar enzymes, very specific for this substrate, have since been shown to be widely distributed in the plant kingdom. A recent review[15] indicates that these vary as to cofactor require-ments and the nature of the products that are formed. It can be said that the enzymes bear some similarity to peroxidase in that they are inhibited by heavy metal reagents, and under some conditions show a stimulation by hydrogen peroxide. This stimulus may occur at concentrations much less than that of the substrate and thus cannot always be peroxidative in nature. The initial product of the reaction has never been satisfactorily identified, but is probably still indolic. In most systems, it further reacts (probably largely spontaneously) to predominantly non-indolic compounds including oxindoles. The expected product of the reaction, considering that a mole to mole ratio of oxygen, substrate and carbon dioxide is found, would be indole-aldehyde, but this substance does not seem to predominate in the reaction products unless cytochrome c is added to the reaction mixture.

Interest in this oxidative destruction of indoleacetic acid has been height-ened by the possibility that this reaction might be important in the natural growth regulatory processes of plants. And indeed it can be shown that extractable indoleacetic acid oxidase activity increases with decreasing growth in certain plant parts. But like so many attractive correlations, decisive evidence that these reactions do occur *in situ* and are really responsible for the decline in growth rate is still lacking and would be difficult to obtain.

Other studies of the fate of indoleacetic acid in plant tissues have concen-trated on non-oxidized products. It has been shown that indoleacetic acid can readily be esterified to its ethyl ester (XXIII) by plant enzymes, and there is some evidence this that is a naturally occurring substance. Similarly, when indoleacetic acid is applied to plant tissue it is rapidly conjugated into indoleacetamide (XVIII) and indoleacetylaspartic acid (XXII). The details of this process have been extensively studied by Andreae and his coworkers[16], but the nature of the enzymes involved remains unclarified. All three of these compounds can produce auxin effects when applied to tissue, hence they can act as indoleacetic acid precursors. However, the kinetics of the reactions which form them appear to favor the conjugated substances and they are more correctly considered as products rather than precursors of indoleacetic acid. One other indole peptide, malonyl tryptophan (XXIV), also occurs naturally in plants.

A problem of long standing concerns the absorption or release of indoleacetic acid from plant proteins. This is not easily studied at physiological concentrations, and there is some question whether the release of "bound auxin" from proteins by various means parallels in any way natural processes. Similarly, the details of the binding process are not yet known.

Finally, it must be mentioned that a large number of alkaloids in plants contain the indole structure. Most of these are of much higher molecular weight than the substances mentioned here, and only one, gramine (XIX), has been proven to be metabolically linked to well known indoles. But theoretical considerations ensure that connections do exist. Many of these indole alkaloids have potent effects on animal tissues, but virtually nothing is known of their physiological role, if any, in the plant. Potentially, they could be produced from simpler indoles and thus serve to divert materials from auxin synthesis, but this hardly seems an adequate explanation for molecules of such complexity. Their structures and chemistry are amply monographed elsewhere[17].

4. Summary

The relationships of all known simple indoles in plants to the growth hormone indoleacetic acid is indicated in Fig. 1. Although the enzymes for many steps indicated have yet to be demonstrated, the present arrangement is in reasonable accord with such evidence as is available.

Since the preparation of this diagram, two important papers have appeared. Hinman et al.[18] have shown that the initial product of indoleacetic acid oxidation probably is 3-methylene oxindole. Gmelin and Virtanen[19] have found that at pH 3–4 myrosinase produces indoleacetonitrile (V) from the mustard oil glucoside glucobrassicidin, rather than from the oxime precursor pictured here. Glucobrassicidin is believed to be 3-indoleacet-thio-(S-β-glucopyranosido)-hydroximyl-O-sulfate. When the pH is changed to 7, ascorbigen (XXVII) is produced from glucobrassicidin. This makes necessary a re-assessment of the proposed structure of ascorbigen and of its role in plant metabolism.

REFERENCES

1 H. B. TUKEY, F. W. WENT, R. M. MUIR AND J. VAN OVERBEEK, *Plant Physiol.*, 29 (1954) 307.
2 K. V. THIMANN in W. W. NOWINSKI (Ed.), *Fundamental Aspects of Normal and Malignant Growth*, Elsevier, Amsterdam, 1960, Ch. 10; A. W. GALSTON AND W. K. PURVES, *Ann. Rev. Plant Physiol.*, 11 (1960) 239.
3 L. J. AUDUS, *Plant Growth Substances*, Interscience, New York, 1959.
4 F. W. WENT AND K. V. THIMANN, *Phytohormones*, Macmillan, New York, 1937.
5 F. KÖGL, A. J. HAAGEN-SMIT AND H. ERXLEBEN, *Z. physiol. Chem., Hoppe-Seyler's*, 228 (1934) 90.
6 K. V. THIMANN, *J. Biol. Chem.*, 109 (1935) 279.
7 J. B. BROWN, H. B. HENBEST AND E. R. H. JONES, *J. Chem. Soc.*, (1950) 3634.
8 B. B. STOWE, *Fortschr. Chem. org. Naturstoffe*, 17 (1959) 248.
9 P. LARSEN, *Dansk. Bot. Ark.*, 11 (1944) 1.
10 S. A. GORDON, *Quart. Rev. Biol.*, 32 (1957) 3.
11 M. KUTAČEK, Ž. PROCHÁZKA AND D. GRÜNBERGER, *Nature*, 187 (1960) 61.
12 K. V. THIMANN AND G. M. CURRY in M. FLORKIN AND H. S. MASON (Eds.), *Comparative Biochemistry*, Vol. I, Ch. 6, Academic Press, New York, 1960.
13 A. W. GALSTON in W. RUHLAND (Ed.), *Encyclopedia of Plant Physiology*, Vol. XVII, Part 1, Springer-Verlag, Berlin, 1959, p. 492.
14 Y. W. TANG AND J. BONNER, *Arch. Biochem.*, 13 (1947) 11.
15 P. M. RAY, *Ann. Rev. Plant Physiol.*, 9 (1958) 81.
16 W. A. ANDREAE AND M. W. VAN YSSELSTEIN, *Plant Physiol.*, 35 (1960) 225.
17 J. B. HENDRICKSON in R. H. F. MANSKE (Ed.), *The Alkaloids*, Vol. VI, Ch. 6, Academic Press, New York, 1960.
   J. E. SAXTON in R. H. F. MANSKE (Ed.), *The Alkaloids*, Vol. VII, Ch. 10, Academic Press, New York, 1960.
   E. SCHLITTER AND W. I. TAYLOR, *Experientia*, 16 (1960) 244.
18 R. L. HINMAN, C. BAUMAN AND J. LANG, *Biochem. Biophys. Research Communs.*, 5 (1961) 250.
19 R. GMELIN AND A. I. VIRTANEN, *Suomen Kemistilehti*, B 34 (1961) 15.

Chapter IX

Plant Hormones

Section b

Synthetic Auxins

H. VELDSTRA

Biochemical Department, Leiden University (The Netherlands)

1. Introduction

In no other sector of biochemistry and physiology has the isolation of an ergon and the elucidation of its structure been followed by such a synthetic activity as when Kögl *et al.*[1] in 1934 found indoleacetic acid (IAA, I) to be a naturally occurring plant growth substance. Nor has the harvest of active analogues ever been so abundant, resulting in such a diversity of practical applications[2].

On the one hand this has to be attributed to the simple structure of the plant hormone and on the other hand to its functional poly-valency, *viz.* the fact that apart from promoting growth (cell elongation) this auxin acts in differentiation (initiation of root formation, control of flower initiation) too.

The initial stimulus for synthesizing analogues came mainly from the work of Zimmerman, Wilcoxon and Hitchcock[3,4] (*cf.* also Haagen-Smit and Went[5]), which showed that naphthalene-1-acetic acid (II) and 2,4-dichlorophenoxyacetic acid (2,4-D, III) in several tests come up to the level of activity of IAA, while the practical implications of the selective toxicity of 2,4-D were discerned.

From then onwards a continuous flow of synthetic compounds has been tested for activity and on account of the results obtained several attempts have been made to relate structure and activity[7-15].

As to the test methods, there exists a plentiful choice (*cf.* Linser *et al.*[16]), illustrating what has been said already about the many-sided actions of the growth substances. Whether or not these different manifestations of being active may be reduced to the same denominator still remains to be answered. One could imagine that on the (macro)molecular level the mechanism of action in essence is the same, finding different expressions depending upon the type of the respective tissue, organ etc. It has to be admitted, however, that up till now no cast from such a possibly common mold (receptor) has been obtained, which may be designated as the active form in all details, even if correctly making use of one test method only. It may be useful in this respect to stress the point that a completely unifying picture never can be expected from comparing results of different tests, in which different secondary factors determine the accessibility of the active site by the externally added compounds. In fact this is an often underestimated factor operating in all cases of physiologically active compounds, whose analyzed response is given by an intact biological system only, where the primary action cannot be isolated, as *e.g.* in studying enzymatic processes.

What has proved possible is the indication of a structural common divisor of the active compounds, though opinions are still differing on this level too.

In condensing the most important data about synthetic auxins in a short survey, for classification and arrangement we also made use to a certain extent of such a guiding principle, derived from results obtained with a restricted number of tests, *viz.* avena curvature, avena straight growth and pea test[16] in all of which cell elongation is the basis of the growth response.

As the allocated space does not allow a critical comparison of the different opinions on structure–activity relationships, the author is starting mainly from his own point of view. Though attention will be called to the most important disputed points, the reader should be constantly aware of this fact. Completeness has not been pursued, but for each group the most typical representatives are chosen to arrive at a general picture, linking the most salient features.

2. Indole derivatives

The first analysis of the structural specificity of IAA by Kögl and Kostermans[17] provided evidence, supplemented by subsequent investigations[6,18,19], that substitution in the pyrrole nucleus (1- and 2-positions) is not compatible with high activity, whereas lipophilic substitution in the benzene ring is less detrimental or may even enhance activity, especially in the case of halogens.

Indications are that the 7-position (just as the 2-position) preferably should be free, which points to a possible functioning of the —NH group in the interaction with the primary active site.

IV

Hydrophilic substituents in the indole ring drastically reduce the activity or cause inactivation, an experience gained quite generally in different series. The hydrophily (H) of the growth substances mainly resides in the COOH group and this is counterbalanced by the lipophily (L), of the rest of the molecule (the ring system with its substituents). Rather restricted limits on the H/L balance are set for optimal activity. In our opinion such an amphipatic structure (three-dimensional asymmetric distribution of hydrophilic and lipophilic parts of the molecule) represents the primitive form of each growth substance, structurally different as they may be.

With lengthening of the side-chain results were obtained which are of wider purport. Depending on the respective ring system and on the test method used, an oscillation in activity was observed in several cases, namely, generally the compounds with n = odd being (highly) active and those with n = even being less active or inactive. As an explanation Synerholm and Zimmerman[20] suggested that the higher homologues would not be active *per se*, but — being subject to a β-oxidation — would produce the highly active acetic acid for n = odd only.

This has been substantiated in a series of very elegant researches by Wain *et al.*[21-23], who clearly proved such a β-oxidation was operative with different series of growth substances, *e.g.* in wheat and pea tissues. As to the indole derivatives, on account of their results[24] it has to be concluded that β-indole-3-propionic acid is active *per se* and most probably γ-indole-3-butyric acid (IV, n = 3) too, (*cf.* also Åberg[25]) whereas the higher homologues derive their activity from a degradation to active acids, involving shortening of the side-chain.

When the attachment of the side-chain is shifted to the 2- or 4-position respectively, the activity drops rather sharply, especially in the first case.

Hydrophilic substitution in the side-chain invariably leads to the same result as *e.g.* for indoleglycollic (Va) and indolelactic acid (Vb) (*cf.* Thimann[26]).

V

R

a = CH(OH)COOH
b = CH₂CH(OH)COOH
c = CH(CH₃)—COOH
d = C(CH₃)₂—COOH

By introduction of methyl groups into the side-chain of IAA the interesting α-indole-3-propionic acid (Vc) and indole-3-isobutyric acid (Vd) are obtained. The assay of Vc in different tests led to a discussion on the importance of optical activity for growth-substance activity, which will be dealt with in Section 11.

Though Vd is considerably active in the pea-test, its main characteristic is that of a "root auxin", *viz.* its ability to promote elongation of roots and to counteract the growth-inhibitory action of IAA. In this respect it is an antiauxin, for which reason we will come back to its action under this heading (Section 12).

3. Arylalkanecarboxylic acids

One of the most simple structures, meeting the requirements for growth substance activity, is that of phenylacetic acid (PAA, VI). Its relatively low activity can be enhanced by substitution, both in the benzene nucleus and in the side-chain. As to the first, the most important data have been summarized by Pybus *et al.*[27] (*cf.* Weintraub and Norman[28]) to which we refer for details about the separate investigations.

R

a = CH_3
b = CH_2CH_3
c = $CH_2CH_2CH_3$
d = $CH_2-CH=CH_2$
e = $CH(CH_3)_2$
f = $CH_2CH_2CH_2CH_3$
g = $C(CH_3)_3$
h = $CH_2CH_2CH_2CH_2CH_3$

VI

COOH
CH_2

VII

COOH
CHR

VIII

COOH
$C-R^1$
R^2

a $R^1=R^2=H$
b $R^1=H$, $R^2=CH_3$
c $R^1=H$, $R^2=C_2H_5$
d $R^1=R^2=CH_3$

Giving an overall picture one may conclude that methyl or hydroxyl and amino substituents either do not have a significant influence or are unfavourable, whereas nitro and halogen groups may increase the activity to a different degree, depending on their positions. A NO_2 group in the 4-position causes inactivation. 2- and 3-Nitro-PAA are more active than PAA, and since 4-substituted phenylacetic acids may be quite active compounds (*e.g.* the chloro and bromo derivatives), the inactivity of 4-nitro-PAA must be related to the character of the substituent. As electromeric effects cannot be operating in this case, it may be that the size of the substituent is of importance, in which respect it is interesting to note that 4-iodo-PAA is also reported to be inactive.

Mono- and polychloro substitution has been studied rather completely, from which it appears that, as to the first, activity is enhanced to a comparable degree in all cases. For the dichloro derivatives the same is true, with the exception of 3,5-dichloro-PAA, which shows a much lower activity. In this respect it should be pointed out that also in the phenoxyacetic and in the benzoic acid series the 3,5-dichloro derivatives are weakly active only or inactive.

As to the trichlorophenylacetic acids, the 2,3,6-derivative stands out for high activity, still surpassing those of the dichloro-acids, whose level is about that of 2,4-dichlorophenoxyacetic acid.

When an α-alkyl substituent is introduced into the side-chain, as in methyl-, ethyl- and n-propyl-PAA (racemates, VII a,b,c), a somewhat increased activity is observed. α-Allyl-PAA (VII d) is more active still and by resolution of the racemate it was shown that its activity is practically wholly due to the (+) form (*cf.* also Section 11).

It was interesting in this connection to find that α-isopropyl-PAA (VII e) is an auxin antagonist[29]. This holds also for the n-butyl-, *tert.*-butyl- and n-amyl derivative (racemates, VII f,g,h). Apparently when a certain size of the α-substituent is exceeded, normal interaction at the active site is prevented (*cf.* also the discussion in Section 12). That rather subtle factors play a part here is evident if one compares the effects of the n- and iso-propyl derivatives, and this is more apparent still when analyzing the activities of alkylidenephenylacetic acids. Whereas the activity of α-methylene-PAA (VIII a) is slightly higher than that of PAA, α-isopropylidene-PAA (VIII d) is markedly more active. As indications are that the double bond is co-planar with the benzene nucleus (U.V.-spectra), one is inclined to make a comparison with the active 2-substituted 1-naphthoic acids (Section 7). The picture is not complete, however, as the ethylidene- and n-propylidene-phenylacetic acids (VIII b,c) were found to be practically inactive, for which no explanation is at hand so far.

This group provides examples of the great sensitivity of biological activity to small structural variations.

IX   X   XI   XII

Of the bicyclic acids, 1-naphthaleneacetic acid (NAA, IX) is the best known structural analogue of indoleacetic acid, also resembling the natural auxin in many aspects of its actions. The fact that the isomeric 2-naphthalene-acetic acid (X) is very weakly active only, forms one of the most intriguing questions on structure–activity relationships, especially when compared with the inverse relations found with the naphthoxyacetic acids (*cf.* Section 4).

With the higher homologues of NAA the same was found as discussed for the indole derivatives, *viz.* that the acids with an odd number of side-chain methylene groups are more active than those with an even number. Though this has not been investigated in detail in this series, one may plausibly assume that β-oxidation to active lower homologues again is underlying the observed oscillation of activities.

Data about substituted naphthaleneacetic acids are relatively scarce. It was found that alkyl or methoxy substituents in the ring cause a strong decrease of activity[30]. The effect of other ring substituents or of substitution in the side-chain has not been studied systematically. Indications are that with naphthaleneacetic acid a rather optimal structure is achieved and that enhancing of the lipophily of the molecule reduces the activity. This is also apparent from the fact that enlargement of the ring system results in weakly active (9-phenanthreneacetic acid, XI) or inactive compounds (2-, and 3-phenanthreneacetic acids, 9-fluoreneacetic acid, XII).

4. Aryloxyalkanecarboxylic acids

The comparatively great interest in synthesis has been evident in the phenoxyacetic acid series because of the practical importance of 2,4-D (XIII, $X_2 = X_4 = $ Cl, $n = $ 1). Consequently a large number of (especially chloro)

XIII   XIV   XV

derivatives has permitted a detailed study of structure–activity relationships.

Theories put forward rather early and thus based on part of this material only, have not enabled us, however, to frame all of the data into one picture (*cf.* for a critical discussion, Toothill, Wain and Wightman[31]). As to chlorine substitution in the benzene nucleus the most important results may be summarized as follows: mono-substitution enhances the activity as compared with that of the parent phenoxyacetic acid (POA), most pronouncedly in 3- and 4-positions.

The effect of di-substitution is more selective, as 3,5- or 2,6-di-substituted POA's are generally inactive or very slightly active only and the same is found for the tri-substituted acids if these positions are involved simultaneously. Methyl substituents give similar results. One would conclude that one position *ortho* to the side-chain, and 3- and 5-positions should be free. In its generality this does not hold, however, since with 3,5-acids additional substitution in the 4-position may cause activity to appear, whereas the same may be achieved with some 2,6-acids by introduction of a methyl group into the side-chain (4-substitution has no such effect with 2,6-acids, nor has methyl substitution with the 3,5-acids!).

Moreover 2,4-dichloro-6-fluoro- and 2,4-dibromo-6-fluoro-phenoxyacetic acids are highly active compounds. This might suggest that the size of the substituent is of importance and if not exceeding that of the hydrogen atom, behaves in neutral fashion. Though more indications in this direction have been obtained (*cf.* Section 7) here certainly it is too simple a representation, as *e.g.* 2- and 4-fluoro- and 2,4-difluoro-POA are distinctly more active than POA. Hence, apart from not interfering, fluorine substitution gives a positive contribution too.

Apparently substitution implies introduction of more than one variable, as it influences several properties of the molecule simultaneously, which changes may contribute to a different degree, *viz.* in a complex way, to a change in activity. This is also the reason why theories based on limited data, as *e.g.* the need for a chemical reactive function of a free *ortho*-position[32], or the requirement for two free positions *para* to each other in order to enable *para*-quinone formation[33], fail when confronted with all of the data now available (apart from the fact that they may be open to criticism for other reasons too; *cf.* Sections 7 and 10). Nor can our considerations on the importance of the H/L balance account for the differences in activity of the isomeric trichlorophenoxyacetic acids.

Of the nitrophenoxyacetic acids only the *m*-derivative is an active compound. One is inclined, also by comparing molecular models, to suppose that mesomerism in the *o*- and *p*-nitro-acids influences the spatial form of the molecule in an unfavourable way[9].

Homologous series of ω-phenoxyalkanecarboxylic acids have been studied very extensively by Wain's group[34] with respect to β-oxidation in different tissues and the influence of ring substitution thereupon. In general, the oxidation of compounds with an odd number of side-chain methylene groups results in formation of the active acetic acid, which produces their generally higher activity as compared with that of acids with an even number of methylene groups. Hindrance of this β-oxidation in the former series may occur, however, at the butyric acid stage with certain tissues when an *ortho*-substituent (chloro or methyl) is present, whereas such a hindrance sometimes is observed at the propionic acid stage with the "even" acids. This may complicate the pattern of biological activity in these series.

Introduction of an alkyl group into the side-chain of phenoxy- or substituted phenoxyacetic acids (α-substituted propionic, butyric, isobutyric or valeric acids) is interesting mainly because of the resulting optical activity and the different activities of the antipodes (*cf.* Section 9) or because of antiauxin properties of the isobutyric acids (*cf.* Section 12). The fact that di-*ortho*-substituted phenoxypropionic acids may be appreciably active compounds in contrast with the corresponding acetic acids has already been stressed. Herewith the seemingly plausible explanation of the negative effect of di-*ortho* substitution in the phenoxy series on the basis of steric influences is invalidated to a large extent.

The 1-naphthoxy- and 2-naphthoxy-acetic acids (1- and 2-NOA, XIV, XV) have attracted considerable attention as the latter proved to be far more active than the first, which is just the reverse of what has been observed with the isomeric 1- and 2-naphthaleneacetic acids.

One would expect that from such a clearcut situation decisive information about structure–activity relationships could be deduced, but no satisfactory explanation has been given so far. In this respect it is interesting, however, that on account of their effect in root growth tests, 2-naphthaleneacetic acid and 1-naphthoxyacetic acid have been characterized as antiauxins[35,36]. Together with their low activity in stem growth tests, this would indicate that these acids in their interaction with the primary active site deviate from the pattern of an auxin to a small extent only. This means that when the carboxyl groups select the same "opponent" at the active site as the auxinic isomers do, the ring system does not fit exactly as in the case of the latter; or if one assumes a good fit of the ring system, then the polar group cannot take up its position in an optimal way. This implies that the unknown receptor offers a fixed "landing-stage" to the active compounds.

Systematic investigations of substituted naphthoxyacetic acids have been carried out rather recently only and the most important data have been summarized by Luckwill and Woodcock[37]. From their work (with the tomato ovary test) it appears that chlorine substitution in 2-NOA in the 3-position only is compatible with an activity similar to that of the parent acid itself. Substitution at 1-, 4- or 5-positions results in a practically complete inactivation. This emphasizes again that substitution in bi-cyclic compounds is rather generally less effective (or even undesirable) than in the phenyl and phenoxy series. Although possibly more complicated, an overweighting of the lipophily of the molecule may play an important part.

In a series of ω-(2-naphthoxy-)alkanecarboxylic acids, activity was found for the members with an odd number of side-chain methylene groups, being indicative of a β-oxidation as already discussed for other series. In these homologues of 2-NOA, 3-chlorine substitution is inactivating.

With increasing chain length of an alkyl substituent in the side-chain of 2-NOA or 3-chloro-2-NOA, activity decreases. Resolution of a number of the racemic acids has revealed large differences in activity of the antipodes, generally the (+) form being active (less than 2-NOA) and the (—) form being inactive or even antagonistic (*cf.* Section 12).

5. Cinnamic acids and related compounds

Viewed in retrospect it has been very fortunate that Haagen-Smit and Went[5] in their early researches on the activity of synthetic compounds included also the isomeric *cis*- and *trans*-cinnamic acids. From the fact that the *cis*-acid (XVII) is a distinctly active growth substance, whereas the *trans*-isomer (XVI) is not, it was evident that the spatial form of the molecule is a decisive factor for activity.

XVI   XVII   XVIII   XIX

XX   XXI   XXII   XXIII

We have used this as a starting point for a more detailed analysis of the architecture of the active form, also by means of molecular models.

By comparing the models of the *cis*- and *trans*-cinnamic acids it is evident that the *cis*-isomer can occur in a non-flat form only, because of a steric hindrance, which limits the free rotation of the side-chain (*cf.* Fig. 1).

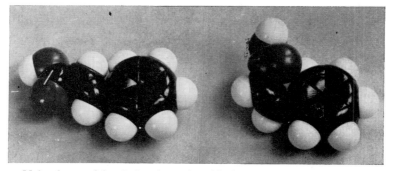

Fig. 1. Molecular models of the cinnamic acids. Left: *trans*-cinnamic acid; benzene nucleus, unsaturated side-chain and carboxyl group in one plane. Right: *cis*-cinnamic acid; coplanarity as occurring in the *trans*-form is impossible because of steric hindrance; the side-chain cannot pass the hydrogen atoms in 2- and 6-positions.

This was corroborated by spectrographic evidence: the *cis*- as compared to the *trans*-form shows a lower extinction in its ultraviolet spectrum, together with a shift of the maximum towards shorter wavelength, plausibly explained by steric hindrance of coplanarity of the benzene nucleus and the unsaturated side-chain with the carboxyl group. The higher dissociation constant of the *cis*-acid is attributable, at least partly, to the same cause. Furthermore the results of measurements of the dipole moments are compatible with the spatial structures[38,39].

The importance of this non-flat structure, thus deduced and implying that the hydrophilic (polar) group is out of the plane of the lipophilic (nonpolar) ring system, was accentuated by the fact that of different other pairs of *cis–trans* acids, only the *cis*-form proved to be active [naphthalene-1-acrylic acid (XVIII–XIX), tetralydeneacetic acid (XX–XXI), phenylcyclopropane-carboxylic acid[40] (XXII–XXIII)].

With the active *cis*-acids, the molecular form which fits on to the primary active site (receptor) is more or less pre-fixed. One can imagine that in the case of the highly active acetic acids (*e.g.* IAA) such a structural adaptation of the flexible molecule "on the spot" leads to maximal activity. Prefixation of a compound into a more rigid form, which still includes the active conformation, leads to activity as a growth substance. If, however, the form required for the primary response is excluded in this way, then inactivity results.

The insight thus obtained by studying the *cis*- and *trans*-cinnamic acids has made it possible to get an idea about the active form by comparing compounds, pre-fixed to a different degree and by different means (*cf.* the section on hydrogenated naphthoic acids and on substituted benzoic acids).

Substitution of *cis*-cinnamic acid, in the 2-, 3- or 4-position with a methyl group does not notably influence the activity, whereas chlorine in the 2- or 4-position enhances the activity considerably. Nitro groups in the same positions cause inactivation. Similar experiences were gained in the phenoxyacetic and benzoic acid series, NO_2 in the 3-position being compatible with activity, however. This suggests that electromeric effects are of decisive importance.

6. Hydronaphthoic acids

Exploring further possibilities for pre-fixation of the side-chain (—COOH group) in a position favorable for activity as derived from the relations found with the cinnamic acids, the partially hydrogenated naphthoic acids were investigated[11,41–43].

1,2,3,4-Tetrahydronaphthoic acid (XXIV) may be considered as a phenylacetic acid with fixed side-chain. In the hydroaromatic part of the molecule the carboxyl group in the main could be either in the equatorial or in the polar position, the latter of which would correspond in principle with the form of *cis*-cinnamic acid. Hydrogenation in the 1,2,3,4-positions enhances

indeed the very weak activity of the parent naphthoic acid (to be discussed with the benzoic acids) to a large extent. That this is a specific effect may be derived from the fact that hydrogenation in the 5,6,7,8-positions (XXV) has no such effect, and that the 1,2- and 1,4-dihydro derivatives (XXVI, XXVII) are active, whereas the 3,4-dihydro derivative (XXVIII) is not.

How satisfactory this result may be in judging the importance of the active spatial form, it is quite clear that this is part of the story only, since 2-naphthoic acid and all of its hydrogenated derivatives were found to be inactive. Apparently therefore the required spatial position of the polar group has to be realized in a special region of the molecule, hence experiments as discussed above cannot give a definite answer.

With the indane-, indene- and 2,3-dihydrothionaphthene-carboxylic acids (XXIX, XXX, XXXI) the same relations are found[44]; the acids with COOH in α-position to the aromatic ring being active and their β-isomers being inactive or even showing weak antiauxin (root growth-promoting) properties.

Of tricyclic acids belonging to this type, 1-acenaphthenecarboxylic acid (XXXII, to be considered as α-naphthaleneacetic acid with fixed side-chain) proved to be a highly active compound, whereas 9-fluorenecarboxylic acid (XXXIII) is weakly active only.

The partially hydrogenated naphthoic acids are interesting also in that they are optically active and thus the contribution of the antipodes to the action of the racemates (as discussed) could be analyzed.

The respective results will be dealt with in the section on optically active auxins (Section 11).

7. Substituted benzoic and naphthoic acids

Zimmerman *et al.*[4] had already included some substituted benzoic acids in their series of compounds tested for growth substance activity.

Of these, especially 2,3,5-triiodobenzoic acid (XXXIV) attracted attention because of its pronounced formative effects.

The real impulse for more extensive investigations, however, came from the work of Bentley[45], who established that 2,3,6-trichlorobenzoic acid (XXXV) is a highly active growth substance.

Thereafter a relatively large number of substituted benzoic acids were investigated[8,46–48], from which emerged the finding that lipophilic substituents only may confer activity on the resulting benzoic acid derivative, especially in the 2,6-(di-*ortho*)-positions.

This suggested to us[49] that again steric hindrance of resonance, which in the unsubstituted benzoic acid causes the carboxyl group to be coplanar with the benzene nucleus, would result in a non-flat molecule, required for activity (*cf.* Fig. 2).

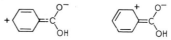

Fig. 2. Molecular models. Left, benzoic acid, the molecule tends to take a flat form as structures with an exocyclic double bond contribute to the mean state:

Right, 2,6-dichlorobenzoic acid, non-flat form as the *o*-substituents cause steric inhibition of resonance.

Comparison of the ultraviolet spectra of different dichloro benzoic acids clearly showed this effect to be operating. The *ortho*-substituents should not be larger than Cl or CH$_3$, as 2,6-dibromobenzoic acid is inactive.

This may be explained most probably by a masking of the carboxyl group which then — though sterically in active position — is not accessible enough for normal interaction with the receptor. In this connection it is interesting that mono-*ortho*-substitution with a larger group (and then preferably together with a 3-substituent) in some cases is compatible with (weak) activity, *e.g.* for 2-ethyl-3-chlorobenzoic acid (XXXVI) and 2-iodo-3-chlorobenzoic acid (XXXVII), whereas 2-isopropyl-3-chlorobenzoic acid (XXXVIII) is inactive again.

Additional substituents in 3- and/or 5-positions generally enhance the activity as compared with the di-*ortho*-substituted acids, and the restrictions as to their size are less than those for the *o*-substituents. Such restrictions are very imperative for the 4-position, where — apart from hydrogen — only fluorine substitution is compatible with activity[10].

All of these data concerning the substituents in our opinion strongly suggest that on the one hand they are essential to change the inactive flat benzoic acid into an active non-flat derivative, while on the other hand size and position must be such that no hindrance for fitting of the molecule onto its counterpart in the cell occurs.

Muir and Hansch[46] have ascribed a chemically reactive role to the 2,6-(chlorine) substituents. Apart from more general objections[8] the activity of the methyl-substituted benzoic acids in our opinion is a conclusive argument for the steric function as indicated above.

XXXIX   XL   XLI   R = CH$_3$, Cl, Br, I

When considering the weakly active 1-naphthoic acid (XXXIX) as a 2,3-disubstituted benzoic acid, one might expect that introduction of a substituent in the 2-position, leading to an analogous situation as in 2,3,6-trichlorobenzoic acid, would enhance the activity.

Indeed 2-chloro-1-naphthoic acid (XL) was found to be as active as this benzoic acid derivative.

A comparison of molecular models showed that in fact an 8-substituent is interfering with coplanarity to such a degree that the position of the COOH group practically is limited to one in which its plane is perpendicular to that of the naphthalene ring system (Fig. 3).

So it was certainly interesting to find 8-methyl-, 8-chloro-, 8-bromo- and 8-iodo-1-naphthoic acids (XLI) to be highly active compounds[10].

From the point of view presented it would follow that the forces operating in the growth substance–receptor interaction are not able to abolish the

Fig. 3. Molecular model of 8-methyl-1-naphthoic acid, showing the fixed ("active") position of the COOH group.

coplanarity of carboxyl group and ring system in the inactive benzoic and naphthoic acids, as apparently a steric hindrance is indispensable to attain an active non-flat form. This would imply that the respective forces are weak ones, which in our opinion excludes a chemically reactive type of interaction, in which for example the COOH group participates in a chemical bond[50].

It is also in this sense that the substituted benzoic acids provide basic information as to the type of interaction leading to the primary response.

8. Auxins with a heterocyclic ring system

Apart from the indole derivatives, which have been discussed separately, practically all of the active compounds possess an aromatic or partially hy-

XLII   XLIII   XLIV droaromatic ring system. As far as heterocyclic carboxylic acids have been tested, few of them appeared to be active. When *e.g.* in indoleacetic acid the NH group (possibly functioning in a rather specific way in the interaction at the receptor surface, *cf.* Section 2) is replaced by O or S (XLII, XLIII) activity drops to low values. Introduction of nitrogen has no such effect, 7-azaindoleacetic acid being considerably active[26].

That active compounds are found less frequently here may be connected with a generally increased hydrophily of the ring system as compared with that of the aromatics, but more plausibly perhaps with the possibility that hetero-atoms are more "over-particular" with respect to their counterpart on the active site than are C-atoms. This could imply that few positions of a suitable hetero-atom in the ring system are compatible with activity. Possibilities in this domain certainly are not yet fully explored.

That very interesting results may be obtained appears from the investigations of Den Hertog *et al.*[51] on pyridoxyacetic acids[10].

XLV   XLVI   XLVII

Whereas *N*-(1-pyridonyl)acetic acid (XLV) is inactive, 2-pyridoxyacetic acid (XLVI) and its 3,5-dichloro derivative (XLVII) are active. The activity of the latter is even comparable with that of IAA. It is striking that, as compared with 2,4-D, the phytotoxicity of its pyridine analogue is much lower, at least for avena and pea tissue.

For a further analysis of this series it may be useful to remember that the

$$=N-\overset{\|}{C}-O-CH_2COOH$$

structural element occurs also in the active carbamates (*cf.* Section 9).

9. Auxins without a ring system

In all of the active compounds discussed until now the carboxyl group was connected directly or via a bridge with an unsaturated ring system and the latter has generally been considered as an essential part of the active molecule.

That the polar group may be presented yet in a different way, however, was shown by Van der Kerk *et al.*[52,53], who, while analyzing fungicidal action of dithiocarbamates, found carboxymethyldithiocarbamate (XLVIII) to be distinctly active as a growth substance. Its activity is surpassed by that of the monothio analogue[10] (XLIX).

The diethyl homologue of XLVIII is very weakly active only, and replacing of C=S by C=O results in inactivation.

In a series of carboxymethyl-*O*-alkylxanthates Fawcett *et al.*[54] did not find any appreciable activity. While with this type of compound the number of active ones thus seems to be rather restricted (for which no wholly satisfactory explanation has been given), it is clear that quite different structures, bearing the polar COOH group, can assume or already possess more or less prefixed the form required for an active fitting onto the receptor.

In our opinion this strongly suggests that the ring system or its equivalent is functioning as a whole as an attaching unit, and that no reactive function can be attributed to certain localized points (*cf.* two-point attachment theory of Bonner[55]).

10. Auxins with a polar group different from —COOH

The investigations on synthetic auxins have been concerned practically exclusively with carboxylic acids. Undoubtedly this reflects the fact that IAA was the first such compound and because it has been generally believed that the undissociated acid is the active form. This would imply that acids which are completely dissociated at physiological pH are inactive.

When the sulphonic acid analogue of IAA (LI)

was shown to be clearly active, provided that high concentrations in the medium were applied, this point of view had to be abandoned[56]. The very low toxicity of indolemethanesulphonic acid (IMSA) (completely ionized) suggested already that the uptake by the tissue is poor and that the difference between the undissociated carboxylic acids and their anions is connected with a secondary factor, *viz.* penetration into the cells, as transport across membranes is much easier for the undissociated acid than for the anion. Unequivocal evidence in this respect came from a comparison of ^{14}C-labeled IAA and IMSA, by which means it was shown that at equimolar concentration the sulphonic acid enters the cells to a much less extent than the carboxylic acid[57].

Investigations were extended to phosphonic and phosphonous acids of the indole and the naphthalene series (LII, LIII, LIV). Activity was found in both cases, at high concentrations again; the indole derivatives were more active than the naphthalene derivatives. In the latter series the phosphonous acids are superior to the phosphonic acids[58-60], possibly related to the fact that the mono-basic $PO(H)(OH)$ resembles $C(O)(OH)$ more than the dibasic $P(O)(OH)_2$.

Unexplained is the observation that sulphonic and phosphonic acids of the phenoxy series are practically inactive. Retention of activity while changing to strongly acidic polar groups thus is restricted mainly to the indole and naphthalene ring system.

A parallel experience was gained when replacing the carboxyl group by a different organic group of acidic character, *viz.* the tetrazol residue. 5-(3-Indolylmethyl)tetrazol (LV) is markedly active, the 2,4-D analogue quite weak while now the naphthalene derivative is much inferior[61].

Hence introduction of these non-carboxylic polar groups involves a lot of new questions, but in our opinion the positive information gained is twofold. In the first place activity of the completely dissociated acids implies that the anion is the physiologically active form and at the moment we see no compelling reason why this should be different for the carboxylic acids.

Secondly the fact that such different polar groups as $COOH$, NO_2, $SO_2(OH)$, $PO(OH)_2$, $PO(H)(OH)$ and CN_4H attached to a ring system yield growth substances, makes it very unlikely that the primary reaction involves a chemically reactive step[46,62] as no plausible reaction common to all of these types can be envisaged.

11. Optically active auxins

It is perhaps because of the fact that an asymmetric structure, leading to optical activity, apparently is not a prerequisite for growth substance activity, that the early work of Kögl and Verkaaik[63] on α-indole-3-propionic acid

(LVI) did not initiate directly more extensive investigations in this domain.

LVI

Moreover, when it appeared that the large difference of activity between the antipodes in the avena test (proportion for (+) and (−) form = 30 : 1) was not found in the straight growth test, and most probably had to be ascribed to differences in basipetal transport, it seemed that the asymmetry had no importance for the primary activity itself.

When in about 1950 several research groups[41,64-67] took up the subject again, because different activities for antipodes were found in the straight growth and in the pea test, very interesting data were obtained. When surveying the whole of the material it is evident that the proportions of the activities of the antipodes form a sort of sliding scale: in many cases one is an auxin, the antipode may then be less active (*e.g.* the (+) form of 1,2,3,4-tetrahydronaphthoic acid and the (−) form of α-2,4-dichlorophenoxy-propionic acid), inactive (*e.g.* the (−) form of α-allyl-phenylacetic acid), or even become an auxin antagonist (*e.g.* the (−) forms of α-(naphthoxy-2)-propionic and butyric acids and of α-(naphthalene-2-methyl)propionic acid).

When the substituent in the parent acetic acid assumes a more bulky character, as for example in α-phenyl-, phenoxy- and naphthoxy-2-iso-valeric or caproic acids, the racemate and both (+) and (−) forms show antiauxin activity only, which in the first case is the same for the antipodes[68].

From these data one may plausibly deduce that the interaction under-lying the primary growth response takes place with an asymmetrically built cell component.

Quite naturally the different activities found for the antipodes have been ascribed to a "three-point attachment", an already classical characterization of this sort of problem. No satisfactory explanation can be given, however, for the sliding scale of activities indicated above. In our opinion a better approach is to assume that the whole of an active molecule has to fit onto the receptor in a definite spatial form and that introduction of an α-substituent (leading to optical activity) may be interfering on this level.

Such a hindrance may explain different activities of the antipodes and also the change to antagonistic properties, which no longer differ for both forms when with a bulky substituent the possible consequences of optical asymmetry are overshadowed.

That the spatial form "requires the greatest care" indeed, is apparent from the very elegant analyses performed by Matell and Fredga[69-71] with respect to the steric relationships between the active forms of different compounds. It was shown namely by means of the quasi-racemate method that, in all cases investigated until now, in related groups the forms with high auxin activity invariably belong to the same steric series, irrespective of the sign of rotation. For the (+)-α-phenoxy-, (—)-naphthoxy-1- and (+)-naphthoxy-2-propionic acids the absolute configuration LVII could be determined (synthetic methods); they belong to the D-series.

LVII   LVIII   LIX   LX

Moreover D-configuration could also be determined for the auxins (+)-α-allyl-phenylacetic acid, (—)-indane carboxylic acid and (—)-1,2,3,4-tetrahydro-1-naphthoic acid (LVIII, LIX, LX).

12. Auxin antagonists (Antiauxins)

When testing potential antiauxins the methods used in evaluating (stem) growth-promoting properties cannot be applied satisfactorily, since secondary inhibitory effects, not being real antiauxin actions (*e.g.* phytotoxicity), may easily confuse the issue. Root tests are to be preferred then for two reasons.

When judging antagonistic capacity from counteraction of the root growth inhibition caused by an externally added auxin, the effective concentration of the latter usually is so low that a potential antiauxin can be applied over a wide range of concentrations without appearance of toxicity phenomena. And furthermore a rather specific antiauxin activity of a compound may be discerned by establishing root growth promotion in low concentration, presumably being effected by antagonizing the natural auxin, present in the roots in supra-optimal concentration.

Using these test methods it appears that antagonists may be obtained by structural modifications of a growth substance in different ways, but that a change in the side-chain (substitution), leaving the ring system and the carboxyl group intact, has been common[66,72,73].

This is expected since the antagonist should have an affinity comparable with that of the growth substance, but without being able to cause a growth response. Such an ineffective occupation on the active site is imaginable especially for compounds with the "mooring capacity" (ring system and polar group) of the growth substance, but lacking the latter's flexibility to adjust itself into active position because of an hindrance brought about by faulty substitution.

Illustrative in this respect are the cases referred to already in the preceding section, in which of the (+) and (−) forms of an optically active compound one is an auxin and the other an auxin antagonist as *e.g.* the naphthoxy-2-propionic acids (LXI, LXII). This implies that in the action of a racemate the components may be counteracting each other.

Whereas the methyl substitution in the active acid apparently does not interfere, it does so in the antipode.

The antiauxin character rather generally established for isobutyric acids (LXIII) could also find an explanation along these lines[72–74].

Other changes in the side chain also may lead to antagonistic activity as *e.g.* for (+)-α-naphthalene-1- and (−)-α-naphthalene-2-methylpropionic acid (LXIV) and for α-naphthalene-1-methylmercaptopropionic acid (NMSP, LXV)[35].

When the α-substituent in an acetic acid becomes more bulky, a situation may arise where for each antipode a hindrance for the right attachment is present, resulting in antiauxin properties for both of them, as *e.g.* in iso-propylphenylacetic acid (LXVI), its phenoxy and naphthoxy analogues or their corresponding *n*-butyl derivatives. Diphenylacetic acid (LXVII) is an antiauxin of the same type[29].

Also in other series of growth substances indications are found that substitutions not compatible with auxin activity may lead to an antiauxin character of the respective compound, as *e.g.* for benzoic acids and phenoxy-acetic acids substituted in the 4- or 2,6-positions respectively[72,74].

Undoubtedly many important details have been omitted in this condensed summary of material on antiauxins, emphasis being centered on the central theme.

13. Auxin synergists

Antiauxin action involves a competition with the active auxin on the primary active site. The auxin molecules functioning in a biological system will, however, not be in a dynamic equilibrium with these sites exclusively, but certainly may be interacting at sites of more secondary importance for the total function, or be adsorbed on sites which result in eliminating or enzymically destroying the auxin. With respect to the auxin function, in all of these cases we might speak of "sites of loss".

When an auxin analogue has a higher affinity for these sites, it will for this reason be less active or inactive as an auxin, as the compound now reaches the primary active site to a lesser extent or not at all (apart from a possible intrinsic inactivity because of the modified structure). When such a compound is administered simultaneously with an auxin it will compete succesfully with the latter on these sites of loss, which implies that more auxin molecules are available for their proper function. This means that in combination with such a compound a smaller number of auxin molecules can effect a certain response than when applied alone. In other words the analogue is acting as a real synergist. Synergists of this type were obtained by enhancing the lipophily of the ring system, e.g. by hydrogenating (decahydronaphthalene acetic acid, LXVIII), introduction of extra lipophilic substituents (2,3,5-triiodobenzoic acid, LXIX; 2,4,6-trichlorophenoxyacetic acid, LXX; 2,4-dichloronaphthoxy-1-acetic acid, LXXI) or by enlarging the ring system (9-anthroic-acid, LXXII and its dihydro derivative[8,75,76], LXXIII).

LXVIII   LXIX   LXX   LXXI

LXXII   LXXIII   LXXIV   LXXV

It is interesting that in an open analogue of decahydronaphthalene acetic acid, viz. di-n-amylacetic acid (DNAA, LXXIV), high synergistic activity is retained. Its branched-chain isomers are equally active, whereas normal fatty acids of a comparable molecular weight are weak synergists. This could suggest that the effect of this type of synergists is that of a wetting agent, which might favour the uptake of the growth substance.

Structurally unrelated, but physico-chemically related wetting agents, and also the amino analogue of DNAA, *viz.* 6-amino-undecane (LXXV), proved to be inactive as a synergist. Since it could be shown by comparing the uptake of ^{14}C-labeled indoleacetic and indolemethanesulphonic acid, with and without DNAA, that the uptake is not influenced by the latter, it is clear that the synergistic effect must imply a redistribution of the growth substance inside the cell[57].

This concept of synergism applies more generally to pharmacologically and physiologically active compounds[77].

14. Summary

When the large number of compounds, active as auxins, and at first sight of quite different structures, is analyzed for a common denominator, the following picture emerges.

An anionic polar group is attached to a ring system (or in a few cases to an open equivalent), either via a side-chain or directly.

Indications are that the hydrophily (H) of the polar group has to be in balance with the lipophily (L) of the carrier. Generally hydrophilic substitution in the latter is not compatible with activity, which means that an asymmetric distribution of H- and L-parts in the molecule is essential (amphypatic structure). This structure has to be able (*e.g.* in the flexible acetic acids) to take a special, non-flat, configuration (conformation) which may be present already in a more or less pre-fixed form, brought about by steric hindrance (cinnamic and benzoic acids).

Details about the effect of lipophilic substitution in the ring system do not find an explanation within this frame, however. For that purpose we shall need more information on the structure of the active site.

From a physico-chemical point of view the three-dimensional architecture of an auxin strongly suggests that its action is exerted at a surface (boundary layer) (*cf.* the proportionality of activity with the logarithm of the concentration in those tests where transport is restricted to a minimum).

All efforts to locate such a primary active site inside the cell have failed until now, however[10,78].

In this sense the synthetic auxins permit only a one-sided story. We are rather well informed as to the active structure, but what is at the base of the observed responses is completely unknown. This forms the main challenge of future auxin research.

REFERENCES

[1] F. KÖGL, A. J. HAAGEN-SMIT AND H. ERXLEBEN, Z. physiol. Chem., Hoppe-Seyler's, 228 (1934) 90.

[2] L. J. AUDUS, Plant Growth Substances, Leonard Hill, London, 1959.

[3] P. W. ZIMMERMAN AND F. WILCOXON, Contrib. Boyce Thompson Inst., 7 (1935) 209.

[4] P. W. ZIMMERMAN AND A. E. HITCHCOCK, Contrib. Boyce Thompson Inst., 12 (1942) 321.

[5] A. J. HAAGEN-SMIT AND F. W. WENT, Proc. Koninkl. Akad. Wetenschap. Amsterdam, 38 (1935) 852.

[6] J. B. KOEPFLI, K. V. THIMANN AND F. W. WENT, J. Biol. Chem., 122 (1938) 763.

[7] H. VELDSTRA, Enzymologia, 11 (1944) 97, 137.

[8] H. VELDSTRA, Ann. Rev. Plant Physiol., 4 (1953) 151.

[9] H. VELDSTRA, Proc. 2nd Intern. Congr. Crop Protection, London, 1949.

[10] H. VELDSTRA, in R. L. WAIN AND F. WIGHTMAN (Eds.), The Chemistry and Mode of Action of Plant Growth Substances, Butterworth, London, 1956, p. 117.

[11] R. L. WAIN, The Royal Institute of Chemistry, Monograph No. 2, 1953.

[12] A. JÖNSSON, Svensk Kem. Tidskr., 67 (1955) 166.

[13] H. LINSER, in R. L. WAIN AND F. WIGHTMAN (Eds.), The Chemistry and Mode of Action of Plant Growth Substances, Butterworth, London, 1956, p. 141.

[14] M. B. PYBUS, Ph.D., Thesis, University of London, 1958.

[15] J. VAN OVERBEEK, Botan. Rev., 25 (1959) 271.

[16] H. LINSER AND O. KIERMAYER, Methoden zur Bestimmung Pflanzlicher Wuchsstoffe, Springer Verlag, Wien, 1957.

[17] F. KÖGL AND D. G. F. R. KOSTERMANS, Z. physiol. Chem., Hoppe-Seyler's, 235 (1935) 201.

[18] S. P. FINDLAY AND G. DOUGHERTY, J. Biol. Chem., 183 (1950) 361.

[19] O. L. HOFFMANN, S. W. FOX AND M. W. BULLOCK, J. Biol. Chem., 196 (1952) 437.

[20] M. E. SYNERHOLM AND P. W. ZIMMERMAN, Contrib. Boyce Thompson Inst., 14 (1947) 369.

[21] C. H. FAWCETT, J. M. A. INGRAM AND R. L. WAIN, Nature, 170 (1952) 887; Proc. Roy. Soc. (London), B, 142 (1954) 60.

[22] R. L. WAIN AND F. WIGHTMAN, Proc. Roy. Soc. (London), B, 142 (1954) 525.

[23] C. H. FAWCETT, H. F. TAYLOR, R. L. WAIN AND F. WIGHTMAN, Proc. Roy. Soc. (London), B, 148 (1958) 543.

[24] C. H. FAWCETT, R. L. WAIN AND F. WIGHTMAN, Nature, 181 (1958) 1387.

[25] B. ÅBERG, Kgl. Lantbruks-Högskol. Ann., 24 (1958) 375.

[26] K. V. THIMANN, Plant Physiol., 33 (1958) 311.

[27] M. B. PYBUS, R. L. WAIN AND F. WIGHTMAN, Ann. Appl. Biol., 47 (1959) 593.

[28] R. L. WEINTRAUB AND A. C. NORMAN, Econ. Botany, 3 (1949) 289.

[29] H. VELDSTRA AND B. ÅBERG, Biochim. Biophys. Acta, 12 (1953) 593.

[30] N. N. MELNIKOV, R. K. TURETSKAYA, Y. A. BASKAKOV, A. N. BOYARKIN AND M. S. KUZNETSOVA, Doklady Akad. Nauk S.S.S.R., 89 (1953) 953; cf. C.A., 48 (1954) 6398.

[31] J. TOOTHILL, R. L. WAIN AND F. WIGHTMAN, Ann. Appl. Biol., 44 (1956) 547.

[32] R. M. MUIR AND C. HANSCH, Plant Physiol., 28 (1953) 218.

[33] J. M. F. LEAPER AND J. R. BISHOP, Botan. Gaz., 112 (1951) 250.

[34] C. H. FAWCETT, R. M. PASCAL, M. B. PYBUS, H. F. TAYLOR, R. I. WAIN AND F. WIGHTMANN, Proc. Roy. Soc. (London), B, 150 (1959) 95.

[35] B. ÅBERG, Physiol. Plantarum, 4 (1951) 627.

[36] H. BURSTRÖM, Physiol. Plantarum, 8 (1955) 174.

[37] L. C. LUCKWILL AND D. WOODCOCK, in R. L. WAIN AND F. WIGHTMAN (Eds.), The Chemistry and Mode of Action of Plant Growth Substances, Butterworth, London, 1956, p. 195.

[38] E. HAVINGA AND R. J. F. NIVARD, Rec. trav. chim., 67 (1948) 846.

[39] O. J. MATRAY, Thesis, University of Leyden, 1956.

[40] H. VELDSTRA AND C. VAN DE WESTERINGH, Rec. trav. chim,. 70 (1951) 1127.

[41] H. VELDSTRA AND C. VAN DE WESTERINGH, Rec. trav. chim., 70 (1951) 1113.

[42] T. MITSUI AND A. TAMURA, J. Agr. Chem. Soc. Japan, 25 (1951) 17.

[43] M. INABA AND T. MITSUI, Bull. Agr. Chem. Soc. Japan, 20 (1956) 42.

[44] R. A. HEACOCK, R. L. WAIN AND F. WIGHTMAN, Ann. Appl. Biol., 46 (1958) 352.

45 J. A. BENTLEY, *Nature*, 165 (1950) 449.
46 R. M. MUIR AND C. HANSCH, *Plant Physiol.*, 26 (1951) 369.
47 H. VELDSTRA AND C. VAN DE WESTERINGH, *Rec. trav. chim.*, 71 (1952) 318.
48 P. W. ZIMMERMAN, A. E. HITCHCOCK AND E. A. PRILL, *Contrib. Boyce Thompson Inst.*, 16 (1952) 419.
49 H. VELDSTRA, *Rec. trav. chim.*, 71 (1952) 15.
50 C. HANSCH, R. M. MUIR AND R. L. METZENBERG, *Plant Physiol.*, 26 (1951) 812.
51 J. MAAS, G. B. R. DE GRAAFF AND H. J. DEN HERTOG, *Rec. trav. chim.*, 74 (1955) 175.
52 G. J. M. VAN DER KERK, M. H. VAN RAALTE, A. KAARS SYPESTEYN AND R. VAN DER VEEN, *Nature*, 176 (1955) 308.
53 C. W. PLUYGERS, *Thesis*, University of Utrecht, 1959.
54 C. H. FAWCETT, R. L. WAIN AND F. WIGHTMAN, *Nature*, 178 (1956) 972.
55 J. BONNER, *Harvey Lectures*, Ser. 48 (1954) 1.
56 H. VELDSTRA, W. KRUYT AND E. J. VAN DER STEEN, *Rec. trav. chim.*, 74 (1954) 23.
57 C. VAN DE WESTERINGH AND H. VELDSTRA, *Rec. trav. chim.*, 77 (1958) 1114.
58 C. VAN DE WESTERINGH AND H. VELDSTRA, *Rec. trav. chim.*, 77 (1958) 1096.
59 M. H. MAGUIRE AND G. SHAW, *J. Chem. Soc.*, (1957) 311.
60 P. CRANIADÈS AND P. RUMPF, *Bull. soc. chim. biol.*, 36 (1954) 675, 1671.
61 C. VAN DE WESTERINGH AND H. VELDSTRA, *Rec. trav. chim.*, 77 (1958) 1107.
62 C. J. SCHOOT AND K. H. KLAASSENS, *Rec. trav. chim.*, 75 (1956) 271.
63 F. KÖGL AND B. VERKAAIK, *Z. physiol. Chem.*, *Hoppe-Seyler's*, 280 (1944) 167.
64 T. MITSUI, *J. Agr. Chem. Soc. Japan*, 25 (1951) 186.
65 M. S. SMITH AND R. L. WAIN, *Proc. Roy, Soc. (London)*, B, 139 (1951) 118.
66 B. ÅBERG, *Kgl. Lantbruks-Högskol. Ann.*, 20 (1953) 241.
67 I. KATO, *Physiol. Plantarum*, 11 (1958) 200.
68 M. MATELL, *Arkiv Kemi*, 9 (1955) 157.
69 M. MATELL, *Thesis*, University of Uppsala, 1953.
70 M. MATELL, *Kgl. Lantbruks-Högskol. Ann.*, 20 (1953) 205.
71 A. FREDGA, *Festschr. Arthur Stoll*, Basel, (1957) 795.
72 H. BURSTRÖM, *Physiol. Plantarum*, 3 (1950) 277; 4 (1951) 199, 470, 641.
73 J. BONNER AND R. S. BANDURSKI, *Ann. Rev. Plant Physiol.*, 3 (1952) 59.
74 R. L. WAIN AND F. WIGHTMAN, *Ann. Appl. Biol.*, 45 (1957) 140.
75 H. VELDSTRA AND H. L. BOOIJ, *Biochim. Biophys. Acta*, 3 (1949) 278.
76 K. V. THIMAN, *Plant Physiol.*, 27 (1952) 392.
77 H. VELDSTRA, *Pharmacol. Revs.*, 8 (1956) 339.
78 A. W. GALSTON AND W. K. PURVES, *Ann. Rev. Plant Physiol.*, 11 (1960) 239.

REFERENCES ADDED IN PROOF

Section
2 C. H. FAWCETT, *Ann. Rev. Plant Physiol.*, 12 (1961) 345.
   W. L. PORTER AND K. V. THIMANN, *Plant Physiol.*, 36 (1961) XXXIX.
4 B. ÅBERG, *4th Conf. on Plant Growth Regulation*, Iowa State University Press, Ames (Iowa) 1961, p. 219.
5 B. ÅBERG, *Kgl. Lantbruks-Högskol. Ann.*, 27 (1961) 99.
6 T. FUJITA, S. IMAI, K. KOSHIMIZU, T. MITSUI AND J. KATO, *Nature*, 184 (1959) 1415.
   K. KAWAZU, T. FUJITA AND T. MITSUI, *J. Am. Chem. Soc.*, 81 (1959) 932.
   K. KOSHIMIZU, T. FUJITA AND T. MITSUI, *J. Am. Chem. Soc.*, 82 (1960) 4041.
   K. KAWAZU, T. FUJITA, T. MITSUI, J. KATO AND M. KATSUMI, *Nature*, 187 (1960) 694.
   K. KOSHIMIZU, T. FUJITA, T. MITSUI AND J. KATO, *Bull. Agr. Chem. Soc. Japan*, 24 (1960) 221.
   T. FUJITA, K. KOSHIMIZU, K. KAWAZU, S. IMAI AND T. MITSUI, *Bull. Inst. Chem. Research, Kyoto Univ.*, 38 (1960) 76.
8 B. ÅBERG, *Kgl. Lantbruks-Högskol. Ann.*, 26 (1960) 229.
9 B. ÅBERG, *Kgl. Lantbruks-Högskol. Ann.*, 26 (1960) 239.
   C. W. PLUYGERS AND G. J. M. VAN DEN KERK, *Rec. trav. chim.*, 80 (1961) 1089.
   R. M. MUIR, C. HANSCH AND J. GALLY, *Plant Physiol.*, 36 (1961) 222.
   J. L. GARRAWAY AND R. L. WAIN, *Ann. Appl. Biol.* 50 (1962) 11.
10 R. H. HAMILTON, A. KIVILAAN AND J. M. MCMANUS, *Plant Physiol.*, 35 (1960) 136.

Chapter IX

Plant Hormones

Section c

Gibberellins

CHARLES A. WEST

*Department of Chemistry, University of California,
Los Angeles, Calif. (U.S.A.)*

1. Introduction

The gibberellins are currently classed as plant growth regulating substances or plant hormones, but investigations of this class of materials really stem from attempts to identify a phytotoxic principle. Kurosawa, a Japanese plant pathologist working in Formosa in the early 1920's, undertook an investigation of the fungus *Fusarium moniliforme* Sheld. (designated *Gibberella fujikuroi* (Saw.) Wr. in the perfect stage) which had earlier been implicated as the causative agent of a disease of rice seedlings known to the Japanese as foolish seedling disease. A primary characteristic of an infected plant was the hyperelongation of leaf sheaths and leaves along with other secondary symptoms. Kurosawa demonstrated that sterile culture filtrates from the fungus grown on liquid media when applied to healthy rice seedlings induced an accelerated growth similar to that characteristic of the disease[1]. He also noted among other things that the active principle was heat stable and thus not proteinaceous and that it stimulated the growth of a number of other plants besides rice. Stodola's valuable reference volume[2] and several review articles[3-5] discuss these early phases of work on the gibberellins by Kurosawa and other Japanese groups.

By 1938 a group under Yabuta at the University of Tokyo had isolated two crystalline, growth promoting fractions[6] from *F. moniliforme* culture filtrates which they called gibberellins A and B. In succeeding years, this group, later under Sumiki, established some of the chemical characteristics of the gibberellins including the fact that they were acids which yielded fluorene derivatives on dehydrogenation and they also extended the information on their biological properties. In the early 1950's Stodola et al.[7] isolated a gibberellin fraction from *F. moniliforme* filtrates and showed it to be a mixture of two closely related, physiologically active substances which they named gibberellin A and gibberellin X. Shortly thereafter, Takahashi et al.[8] reexamined the homogeneity of their preparations of gibberellin A and found them to be variable mixtures of three closely related, active substances which were renamed gibberellins A_1, A_2, and A_3. Subsequently, they discovered a fourth active component, gibberellin A_4, which was sometimes present in the filtrates[9]. Also in the early 1950's, Curtis and Cross[10] independently isolated a single, active substance from a strain of *F. moniliforme* and named it gibberellic acid since its properties differed from those reported for gibberellin A. An exchange of samples and a comparison of properties soon showed the identity of gibberellic acid, gibberellin A_3 and gibberellin X. Gibberellin A_1 and Stodola's gibberellin A also proved to be identical.

The scope of investigations of the effects of these gibberellins on the growth and development of flowering plants broadened as these substances became more available and information about them more widely disseminated. A wide variety of flowering plants respond to treatment with small amounts of gibberellins with increased rates of stem or internode growth and often increased leaf growth. In particular some plants which show a dwarfed or stunted habit of growth because of either genetic or environmental factors assume a tall growth habit as a result of treatment with microgram quantities of gibberellins. Plants which normally require "long day" photoperiods or cold treatments in order to bolt and flower can be induced to flower under non-flowering environmental conditions by treatment with gibberellins. Seed germination, particularly in certain dormant seed, can be hastened by gibberellin treatment. In these and numerous other examples of biological effects, it seems that treatment of flowering plants with exogenous gibberellins leads to an acceleration of some phases of normal growth and development. These growth phenomena are ones which involve both cell division and cell elongation. A number of reviews summarize these observations on biological effects[2-5,11].

The effectiveness of gibberellins in small quantities in stimulating what appear to be normal growth processes in a wide variety of flowering plants naturally lead to the speculation that endogenous gibberellins serve flowering plants as normal growth regulating agents or hormones. This hypothesis has been greatly strengthened by finding gibberellins as natural constituents of flowering plants in low concentrations. Extracts of seed and seed parts, inflorescences, vegetative tissues and even tissue cultures from a wide variety of flowering plants show the presence of "gibberellin-like" substances in bioassays designed to detect gibberellins[5,11]. Gibberellin A_1 and a new gibberellin, A_5, have been isolated and identified as constituents of flowering plants and chromatographic evidence suggests that still different "gibberellin-like" substances are also present.

Some characteristics of the naturally occurring gibberellins* are summarized in the following paragraphs.

2. Physical and chemical properties

(a) Gibberellic acid

Other names include gibberellin A_3 and gibberellin X, $C_{19}H_{22}O_6$; m.p. 232–235°; $[\alpha]_D^{20} = +86°$ ($c = 0.51$ in methanol). Derivatives include methyl gibberellate, m.p. 207–209°, $[\alpha]_D^{17} = +75°$ ($c = 0.5$ in ethanol) and gibberellyl monoacetate, m.p. 233–234°, $[\alpha]_D^{17} = +152°$ ($c = 0.5$ in ethanol).

Gibberellic acid has been isolated from culture filtrates of *F. moniliforme*, frequently as the most abundant gibberellin present. Although isotope dilution studies have suggested the presence of gibberellic acid in sprouting

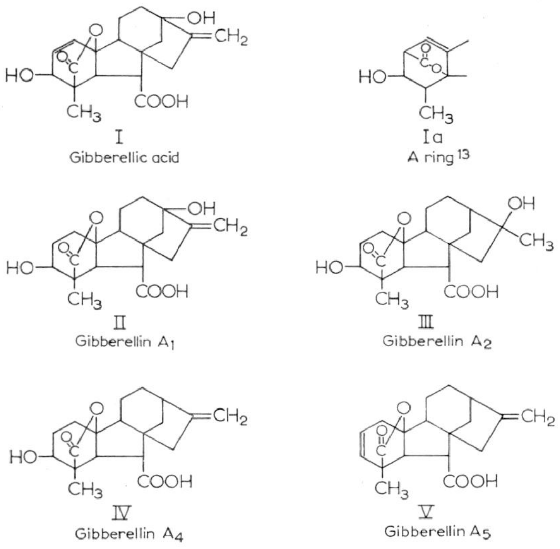

Fig. 1. Structures of the naturally occurring gibberellins.

* No convention regarding nomenclature of the gibberellins has been generally adopted. It has been suggested[11] that substances which show activity in suitable growth tests and possess the same carbon skeleton as gibberellin A_1 (see II in Fig. 1) be designated as gibberellin A series with a subscript number to denote a particular arrangement of functional groups on this carbon skeleton. Substances which have biological activities similar to the gibberellins, but of unknown structure have been referred to as "gibberellin-like" substances.

References p. 158

barley, no reports of its isolation from flowering plants in the absence of added carrier have appeared.

Numerous qualitative and quantitative bioassays for gibberellins have been described[11]. Most of these rely on the determination of net increase in the length of stem or leaves of treated, intact plants or portions of these grown in culture as compared with untreated controls. In some assays activity is also measured in terms of flowering response. In most of these assay systems, gibberellic acid is the most active of the fungal gibberellins on a weight basis.

The structural assignment for gibberellic acid (I) in Fig. I is that of Cross et al.[12], based on extensive investigations of the acid and a number of its degradation products. Sumiki and his collaborators[13] agree with all aspects of this formulation from their own studies except for the positioning of the lactone in ring A. They propose instead the arrangement shown in Ia. The Japanese argument is based in large part on the reported isolation of 1,3-dimethylfluorene (VI) as a product of dehydrogenation of a gibberellin A_1 degradation product. Since the 1-methyl is known to come from a preformed methyl in the A ring, it is assumed that the 3-methyl must be derived from the lactone carbonyl originally present in the ring. The arguments of Cross et al. for I are based in part on the demonstration of a hydroxyl with the reactivity of an allylic alcohol and on infrared and nuclear magnetic resonance spectral data, all of which are inconsistent with structure Ia. Furthermore, a scheme for the biogenesis of I related to that for diterpenes can readily be formulated. This scheme has received experimental support from studies[14] on the formation of labelled gibberellic acid from [14C]-acetate and [14C]-mevalonate. Thus, most of the evidence would seem to indicate structure I over Ia, but there are some points in the Japanese data which need to be explained.

An assignment[15] of stereochemical configuration for gibberellic acid has been made as shown in Fig. 2.

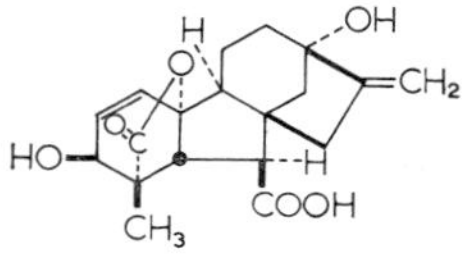

Fig. 2. Stereochemistry of gibberellic acid.

Gibberellic acid is easily decomposed in acid solution. Gibberellenic acid (VII) is formed on standing in acid at room temperature. More vigorous acid treatment (1 N hydrochloric acid at 60° for 2 h) results in aromatization of the A ring yielding allogibberic acid (gibberellin B) (VIII). Still more vigorous acid hydrolysis (refluxing with 2 N hydrochloric acid for 1 h) results in a Wagner–Meerwein type rearrangement involving the C–D rings to give gibberic acid (IX). Studies on these products were instrumental in the structure assignment for gibberellic acid. None of these degradation products has biological activity.

Treatment of gibberellic acid with dilute alkali yields an inactive isomer (X) resulting from an allylic rearrangement.

Gibberellic acid shows a characteristic fluorescence when dissolved in concentrated solutions of sulfuric acid which is unique among the reported gibberellins. This property has been used as a basis for a quantitative assay. Other assays based on isotope dilution procedures, infra-red spectroscopy and reactions with chromogenic agents have been described[11].

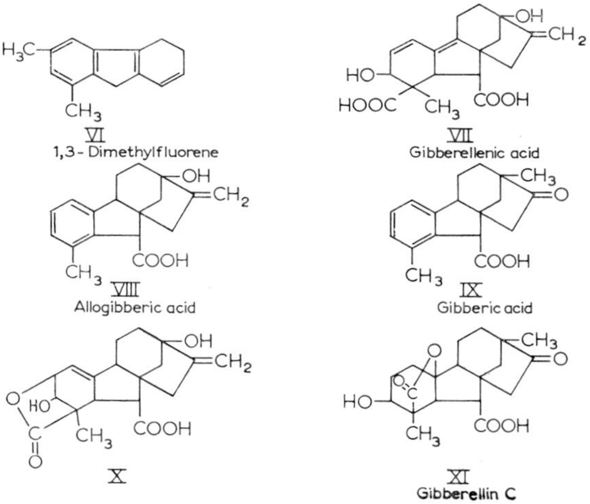

Fig. 3. Degradation products of the gibberellins.

(b) Gibberellin A₁

Other names include gibberellin A and α-dihydrogibberellic acid, $C_{19}H_{24}O_6$; m.p. 255–258° (dec.); $[\alpha]_D^{25} = +36°$ ($c = 1.74$ in 95% ethanol). Derivatives include the methyl ester of gibberellin A₁, m.p. 226–228°, $[\alpha]_D^{20} = +46°$ ($c = 0.41$ in ethanol).

Gibberellin A₁ has been obtained not only as a metabolite of *F. moniliforme*, but also has been isolated from the immature seed of two species of beans (*Phaseolus multiflorus* and *P. vulgaris*)[16] and rapidly growings shoots of the mandarin orange tree (*Citrus unshuii*)[17].

In most biological assay systems gibberellin A₁ is less active on a weight basis than gibberellic acid, but more active than either A₂ or A₄.

Partial hydrogenation of the methyl ester of gibberellic acid (I) under controlled conditions[18] gave a dihydro derivative identical with the methyl ester of gibberellin A_1. Since A_1 was known to have an exocyclic methylene group, structure II in which the A ring is saturated was assigned to it[12]. It presumably has the same steric configuration as gibberellic acid.

Gibberellin A_1 is more stable to acid catalyzed degradation than gibberellic acid, presumably since the unsaturated A ring of the latter which becomes aromatized is not present. Under the more vigorous conditions of acid hydrolysis (reflux) the C–D ring system of A_1 does undergo rearrangement to gibberellin C (XI) which retains some biological activity. Treatment of A_1 in alkaline solution gives the isomeric *pseudo*-gibberellin A_1 in which the secondary hydroxyl has been epimerized. This change is accompanied by a complete loss of biological activity.

(c) Gibberellin A_2

$C_{19}H_{22}O_6$. This compound has been obtained from *F. moniliforme* only by Takahashi *et al.*[8]. It was shown to have a carbon skeleton and A and B rings identical to those in gibberellin A_1, but the tertiary hydroxyl group of A_1 is missing and the exocyclic ethylenic double bond is hydrated[19]. For consistency, gibberellin A_2 (III) is pictured in Fig. 1 with an A ring related to II even though the Japanese formulated the A ring as in Ia. This compound appears to be the least active biologically of the fungal gibberellins.

(d) Gibberellin A_4

$C_{19}H_{24}O_5$; m.p. 222° (dec.); $[\alpha]_D = 26.8°$. This compound has been reported from filtrates of *F. moniliforme* only by Takahashi *et al.*[9], and structure IV has been assigned to it[19]. Again for consistency the A ring of IV is pictured as in II even though Kitamura *et al.* formulated it as in Ia. Thus, it may be considered a relative of A_1 in which the bridgehead tertiary hydroxyl is missing.

Gibberellin A_4 in most bioassays shows activity intermediate between that of gibberellins A_1 and A_2. However, it has been noted that many species of *Cucurbitaceae* show distinct growth responses to gibberellin A_4 at levels where none of the other gibberellins induce any response. The basis for this differential response is not understood.

(e) Gibberellin A_5

$C_{19}H_{22}O_5$; m.p. 260–261°; $[\alpha]_D^{22} = -77°$. Derivatives include gibberellin A_5 methyl ester, m.p. 190–191°, $[\alpha]_D^{25} = -75°$.

Gibberellin A_5 has been isolated only from the immature seed of two species of beans (*P. multiflorus* and *P. vulgaris*[20,21]). To date there has been no report of the presence of this component in filtrates of *F. moniliforme*.

Structure V has been assigned[20] to gibberellin A_5. It may be considered, therefore, a dehydro derivative of A_1. The dehydration of the methyl ester of A_1 (via the p-toluenesulfonyl derivative) to the methyl ester of A_5 proved an important reaction in this structural assignment.

An interesting property of A_5 is its ability to stimulate the growth of dwarf mutants of maize in a manner quantitatively unlike the other gibberellins. It is at least as active as gibberellic acid in stimulating the growth of four different dwarf mutants, but shows less than 10% the activity of gibberellic acid on a fifth mutant (dwarf-1). Since these are single-gene dwarf mutants, the possibility has been suggested that gibberellin A_5 may be an intermediate in the biosynthesis of gibberellic acid and gibberellin A_1.

(f) Other natural gibberellins

It would appear from both published and unpublished observations including chromatographic data that there are still different gibberellins from those described above produced both by *F. moniliforme* and by flowering plants. As yet, however, these substances have not been completely characterized.

(g) Other derivatives of gibberellins

A number of derivatives and degradation products of the gibberellins have been prepared and tested for biological activity in addition to those mentioned above. Although the number of examples is still relatively small, the following generalizations can be tentatively advanced. (*1*) Almost any alteration of the A or B ring results in complete loss of activity. Examples of such chemical changes include the epimerization or oxidation of the secondary alcohol, the allylic shift of the lactone ring, esterification of the carboxyl group with a number of alkyl substituents and partial or complete aromatization of the A ring. Biologically active esters of the secondary alcohol have been prepared and thus stand as exceptions to this generalization. (*2*) On the other hand, considerable alteration of the bridged C–D rings is possible without complete loss of activity. For example, gibberellin C (XI), which has undergone a Wagner-Meerwein rearrangement in its preparation, retains some activity. This is all the more striking in view of the fact that the configuration of the two carbon bridge in gibberellin C and its parent substance, gibberellin A_1 is undoubtedly opposed. Other examples of active substances prepared from natural gibberellins by alteration of the C–D rings include dihydrogibberellin A_1, dihydrogibberellin A_4 and the compound derived from gibberellin A_4 by replacement of the exocyclic methylene group with a ketone oxygen.

References p. 158

The evidence currently available clearly points to a role for at least some members of this closely related family of gibberellins along with the auxins and probably other substances as endogenously produced regulators of the growth and development of flowering plants. It is interesting to note that these gibberellins appear to be isoprenoid compounds related to the diterpenes while the steroid hormones which regulate many aspects of the growth and development of animals are isoprenoid compounds related to the triterpenes.

REFERENCES

1 E. KUROSAWA, *Trans. Nat. Hist. Soc. Formosa*, 16 (1926) 213.
2 F. H. STODOLA, *Source Book on Gibberellin, 1828–1957*, Agricultural Research Service, United States Department of Agriculture, Peoria, Illinois, 1958.
3 B. B. STOWE AND T. YAMAKI, *Ann. Rev. Plant Physiol.*, 8 (1957) 181.
4 B. B. STOWE AND T. YAMAKI, *Science*, 129 (1959) 807.
5 P. W. BRIAN, *Biol. Rev. Cambridge Phil. Soc.*, 34 (1959) 37.
6 T. YABUTA AND Y. SUMIKI, *J. Agr. Chem. Soc. Japan*, 14 (1938) 1526.
7 F. H. STODOLA, K. B. RAPER, D. I. FENNELL, H. F. CONWAY, V. E. SOHNS, C. T. LANGFORD AND R. W. JACKSON, *Arch. Biochem. Biophys.*, 54 (1955) 240.
8 N. TAKAHASHI, H. KITAMURA, A. KAWARADA, Y. SETA, M. TAKEI, S. TAMURA AND Y. SUMIKI, *Bull. Agr. Chem. Soc. Japan*, 19 (1955) 267.
9 N. TAKAHASHI, Y. SETA, H. KITAMURA AND Y. SUMIKI, *Bull. Agr. Chem. Soc. Japan*, 23 (1959) 405.
10 P. J. CURTIS AND B. E. CROSS, *Chem. & Ind. (London)*, (1954) 1066.
11 B. O. PHINNEY AND C. A. WEST, *Ann. Rev. Plant Physiol.*, 11 (1960) 411.
12 B. E. CROSS, J. F. GROVE, J. MACMILLAN, J. MOFFATT, T. P. C. MULHOLLAND AND J. C. SEATON, *Proc. Chem. Soc.*, (1959) 1302.
13 N. TAKAHASHI, Y. SETA, H. KITAMURA AND Y. SUMIKI, *Bull. Agr. Chem. Soc. Japan*, 22 (1958) 432.
14 A. J. BIRCH, R. W. RICHARDS AND H. SMITH, *Proc. Chem. Soc.*, (1958) 192.
15 B. E. CROSS, J. F. GROVE, P. MCCLOSKEY AND T. P. C. MULHOLLAND, *Chem. & Ind. (London)*, (1959) 1345; G. STORK AND H. NEWMAN, *J. Am. Chem. Soc.*, 81 (1959) 5518.
16 J. MACMILLAN AND P. J. SUTER, *Naturwissenschaften*, 45 (1958) 46.
17 A. KAWARADA AND Y. SUMIKI, *Bull. Agr. Chem. Soc. Japan*, 23 (1959) 343.
18 J. F. GROVE, P. W. JEFFS AND T. P. C. MULHOLLAND, *J. Chem. Soc.*, (1958) 2520.
19 H. KITAMURA, N. TAKAHASHI, Y. SETA, A. KAWARADA AND Y. SUMIKI, *Bull. Agr. Chem. Soc. Japan*, 23 (1959) 344.
20 J. MACMILLAN, J. C. SEATON AND P. J. SUTTER, *Proc. Chem. Soc.*, (1959) 325.
21 C. A. WEST AND B. O. PHINNEY, *J. Am. Chem. Soc.*, 81 (1959) 2424.

Chapter IX

Plant Hormones

Section d

Purines and Other Compounds

K. MOTHES

Department of Plant Biochemistry, German Academy of Sciences at Berlin, Halle/Saale (Germany)

1. Introduction

The word "hormone" was first used in animal physiology, originally meaning substances which are formed in an inner secretory gland and carried with blood or lymph to their site of action. Later on the meaning of this word was extended and became less distinct. Hormones may also be produced by tissues that are not remarkably specialized and they may act in the same tissues or in the immediate neighbourhood.

Today we may even speak of cell hormones. This widening of meaning of the word "hormone" is of the highest significance from the plant physiological point of view. In the plant we do not know at this time whether definite inner secretory glands exist. Certainly some organs and tissues produce most of the auxin, but there are several sites of formation. The higher plant as a whole is typically autotrophic; its organs, however, are mostly heterotrophic. A given essential substance can be totally or partially heterotrophic, *i.e.* a particular organ may be able to synthesize it, although insufficiently for intensive growth.

The transport of this substance from one organ to another can increase growth or other simple processes. The substance behaves like a hormone, although, in fact, it may only be a building-stone for other important substances and not really a special hormone. As long as we do not know the mode of primary chemical attack of a hormone, it is not readily possible to demarcate the borderline between hormone and primary building stones needed only in traces, and of coenzymes etc., of the cell. Therefore the word "hormone" is frequently used in an indefinite manner and assumes a deeper knowledge than is actually possessed.

At first it will be useful to restrict the word "hormone" to those cases in which an organic substance is effective in a very low concentration and well-defined for its site of formation and action. This might be demonstrated by separation and reunion of organs by graftings or by the effect of organ extracts on the growth of isolated organs or tissues.

There are many indications for the existence of such hormone-like substances. They can dominate the phenomenon of correlation of various parts and of regulations, which are so evident in the course of life of the higher plant. The investigations in this field are most difficult, since the formation of these substances is not well-localised and channels like those of blood and lymph are lacking in plants.

Only a few phenomena will be mentioned where hormones in the restricted meaning are probably involved and where these might be in the nature of purines or related substances.

2. Purines

Purines are found in all living cells, but they are mostly not free but bound as ribosides and nucleotides. Free purines are primarily found where an extensive degradation of nucleic acids takes place, as for example, in seedlings. Probably purines never arise directly from smaller building stones but rather from their nucleotides. The path of synthesis of nucleotides is very complicated, arising from 5-phosphoribosyl 1-pyrophosphate, glutamate, glycine, glutamine, CO_2, aspartate and formate (or an active 1-C-fragment) and leading to inosinic acid (IX) with ATP repeatedly participating in the process. From these nucleotides adenine (I) and guanine (II) arise after several reaction steps. The accumulation of various intermediate reaction products can induce feedback mechanisms. Doubtlessly, free purines can also react with 5-phosphoribosyl 1-pyrophosphate or with ribose 1-phosphate, giving rise to nucleotides and nucleosides in this way. These reactions, however, presumably play a role only in their reverse direction since free purines cannot be directly synthesized.

The fact that free purines exist only in very small quantities in tissues with high synthetic qualities, and bound purines in much greater amounts, may explain why free purines applied from outside occasionally develop a marked effect. Are such effects specific?

In seedlings the cotyledons are remarkable for the extent and speed of the growth of roots and leaves in the dark[1]. Therefore Went assumed that the hormone-like substances (rhizocaline, phyllocaline) other than auxin

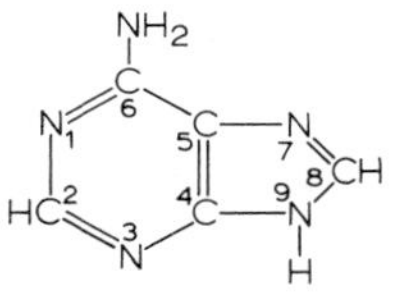

I Adenine

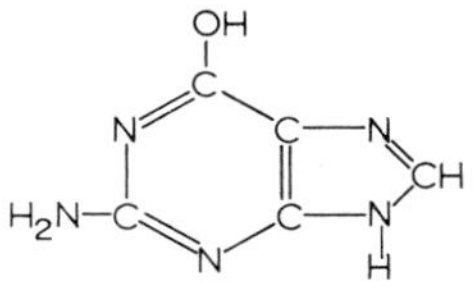

II Guanine

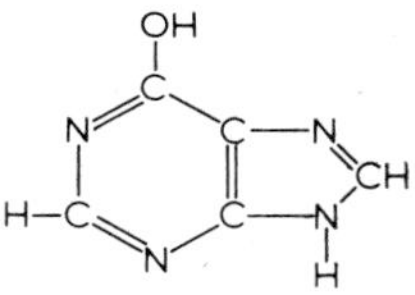

III Hypoxanthine

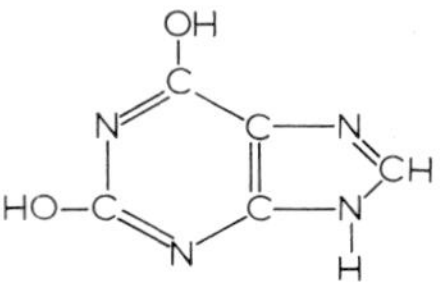

IV Xanthine

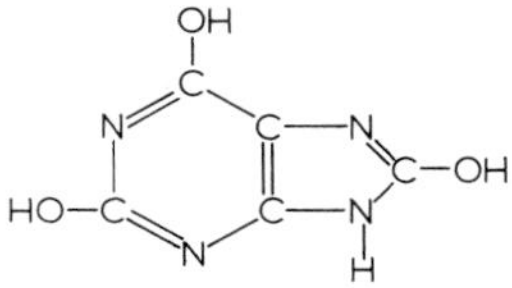

V Uric acid

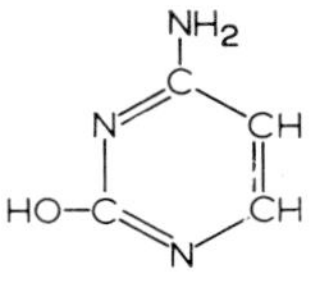

VI Cytosine

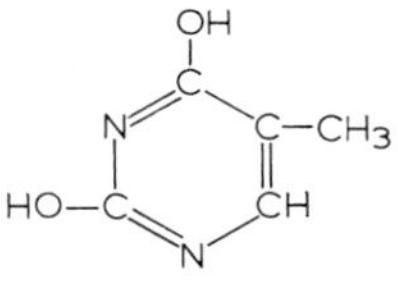

VII Thymine

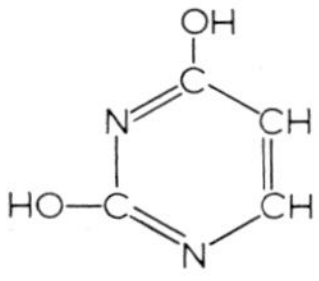

VIII Uracil

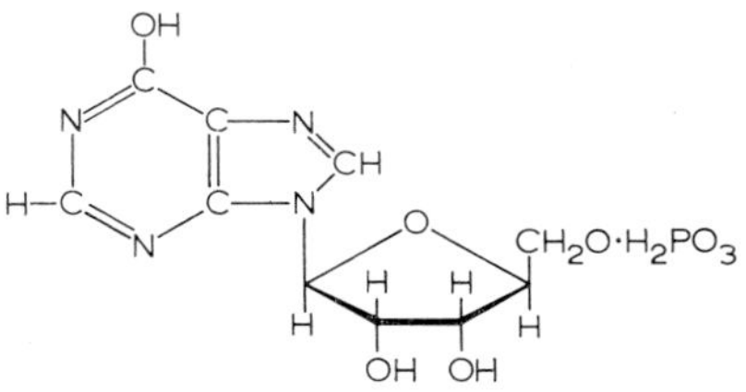

IX Inosinic acid

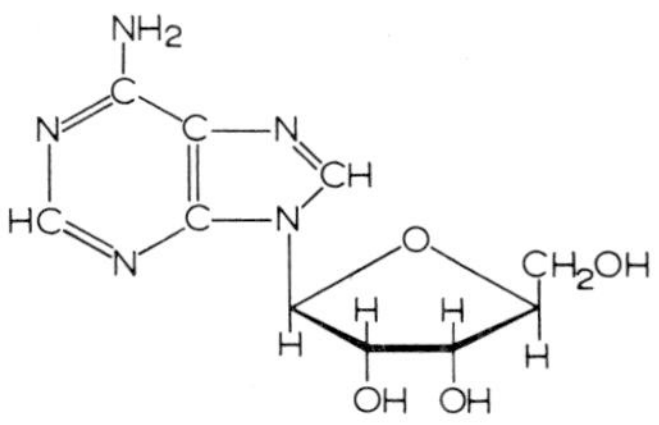

X Adenosine

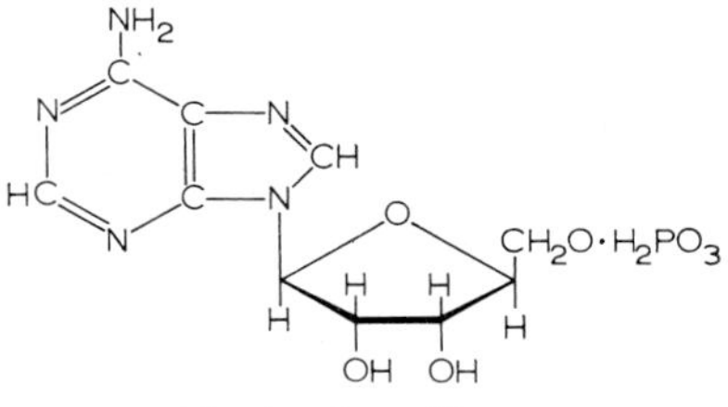

XI Adenylic acid
(Adenosine 5'– phosphate)

must be synthesized in the cotyledons and transported to the roots and shoots. Bonner, Haagen-Smit and Went[2,3], for instance, investigated cotyledon diffusates of peas for a specific growth factor for leaf growth, and found

References p. 166

among other substances adenine (I) and hypoxanthine (III) to be active (in the concentration 10 p.p.m.). These results have been confirmed by others[4,5]. Especially the regeneration of tobacco stem segments was investigated by Skoog *et al.*[6,7]. They found that adenine, adenosine (X) and guanine (II) can markedly promote shoot regeneration, whereas xanthine (IV) does not. Auxin, on the other hand, promotes root regeneration. Similar results were found by several other authors[8-10]. There are, however, certain differences among the different materials, since, for instance, oxidized purines (IV, V), pyrimidines (VI, VII) or purine ribosides (X) were sometimes effective, sometimes not.

Also the results found with the regeneration of leaves of Begonia[11] and Cardamine[12] or with the development of ovules are interesting. They show that besides adenine and guanine, occasionally also uric acid (V), adenosine (X), adenylic acid (XI), uracil (VIII), cytosine (VI) and thymine (VII) are effective[14]. However, there are also some contradictory results[15-17].

3. Kinetin and analogues

Later on Kuraishi and Okumura[18], Miller[19], Scott and Liverman[20] and others showed that the artificial purine derivative kinetin (6-aminofurfurylpurine) (XII) promotes the growth of isolated leaves and leaf discs. It is effective in the concentrations from 10^{-3} to 1.0 p.p.m. Leaves and leaf discs grow not by cell division but by cell enlargement.

Kinetin had been discovered when searching for a stimulator of cell division which was presumed to exist in aged or autoclaved DNA. It was found while working with various materials, especially with shoots and buds, that wherever adenine promoted growth, kinetin did so and generally in much lower concentrations. However, there seemed to exist an antagonism between indoleacetic acid and kinetin. Thus roots were promoted by auxin, but inhibited by kinetin. In excised roots these effects may be a matter of concentration, whereas in attached roots, living in union with leaves or shoots, they may result from the polar migration of auxin to the roots and the fixation of kinetin in the shoot. Thus kinetin by its promoting effect makes the shoot a competitor of the root[22]. Also in excised leaves or sections of shoots the regeneration of roots is accelerated by indoleacetic acid and inhibited by kinetin. The reverse is true when shoot buds are formed and developed.

Growth is a most complicated phenomenon. Much work has been done to determine a primary effect of kinetin. In these investigations some ideas of Chibnall played a role. This author assumed already in 1939 that a hormone arising from the roots stimulates protein synthesis. Later on he showed[27] that excised leaves yellowed more slowly when they were rooted. The important role of rooting the leaves for continued protein synthesis, for a positive protein balance, and for prolongating the life of the leaves was investigated by various authors. On the other hand Michael[28] found that the yellowing of leaves can be slowed down if their petioles are excised. The latter act as sinks of the amino acids arising from protein degradation. These amino acids can hardly return to the leaf blade, a fact which induces a deficiency of protein building materials.

It has been known for a long time that excised leaves and leaf parts can achieve a positive protein balance even without rooting, if there is no competition and they are well supplied with carbohydrates and nitrogen compounds. This positive protein balance, however, does not persist for a long time. Richmond and Lang[29] found that kinetin inhibited protein degradation and therefore yellowing of excised leaves, and Mothes, Engelbrecht and Kulajeva[30,31] showed that this kinetin effect depended upon an increased capacity of the cells to retain various soluble substances. Since kinetin is highly localized in those parts of a leaf to which it was applied, it could induce the capacity of an increased accumulation of soluble substances and an increased active transport to these leaf areas. Such areas therefore remain green, the rate of synthesis is increased, and they grow[30,30a]. Kinetin appeared to be a model of a root hormone affecting protein synthesis in young and growing tissues[31,32].

It has been indicated by various authors that the kinetin effect depends upon a promotion of DNA and RNA synthesis[33-35]. However, there is considerable question as to which is the primary and which is the secondary process. Since so little is known about active transport and retention of substances[36], it does not seem impossible that active transport as well as protein synthesis might depend in different ways upon nucleotide structures, the integrity of which may rest on kinetin and free adenine.

This capacity to promote growth and to inhibit the yellowing of excised leaves is characteristic of various substances. A considerable number of kinetin analogues have been synthesized[17,37]. Many of them proved to be highly active. The purine ring seems to be quite essential. The side ring, however, could be modified; thus the furan ring of kinetin (XII) might be replaced by a cyclohexyl or benzene ring.

A completely clear picture of the conditions for a kinetin-like activity has not yet been obtained. An increase in hydrophilic character of the secondary ring markedly inhibits the effectiveness. Differences in results reported in the literature may be due to the diversity of the substances used (see next page).

It is significant that yellowing in some plant species could also be inhibited by benzimidazole[31,38], indoleacetic acid, triiodobenzoic acid[31,39] or 2,4-dichlorophenoxyacetic acid[40]. It is not sufficiently known whether kinetin and substances with a similar effect correspond only in their inhibition of

KINETIN ANALOGUES

With high activity

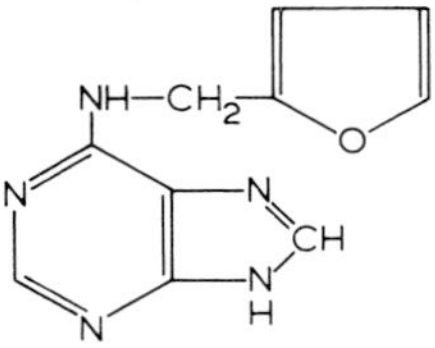

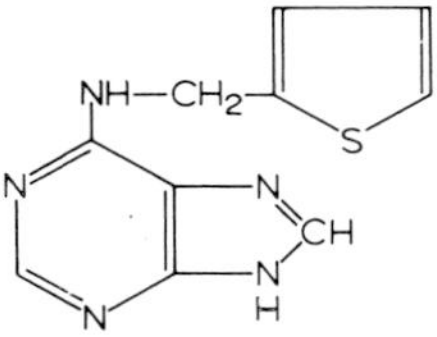

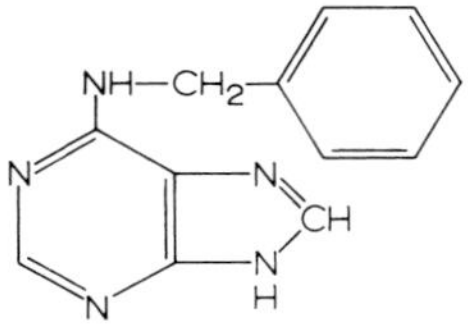

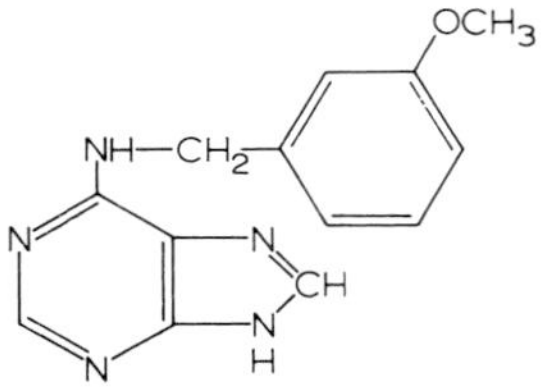

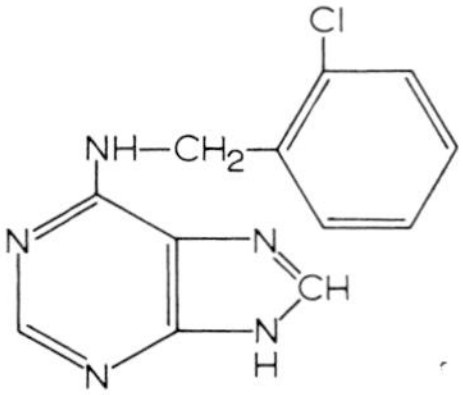

With low activity

XII Kinetin

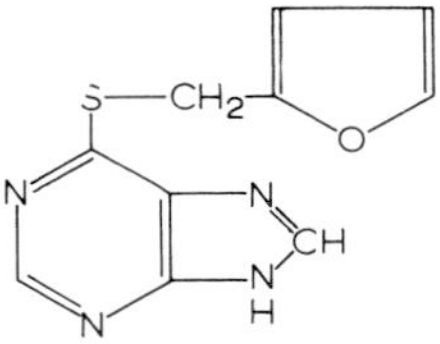

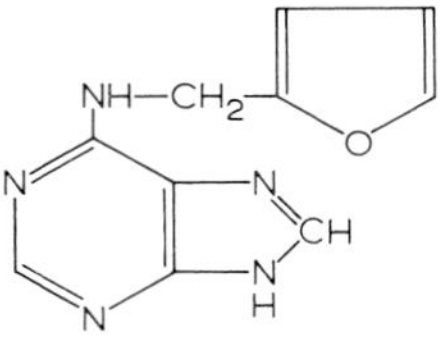

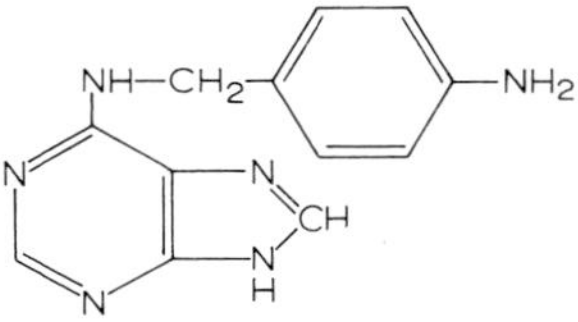

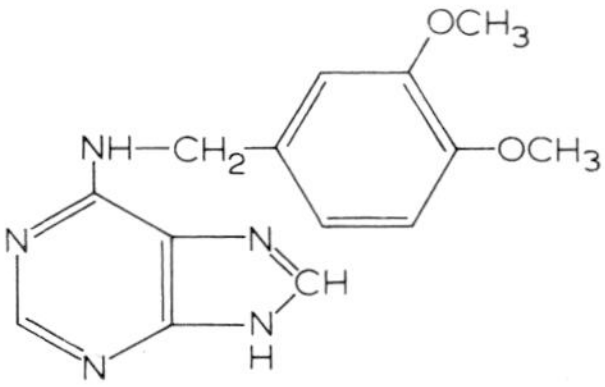

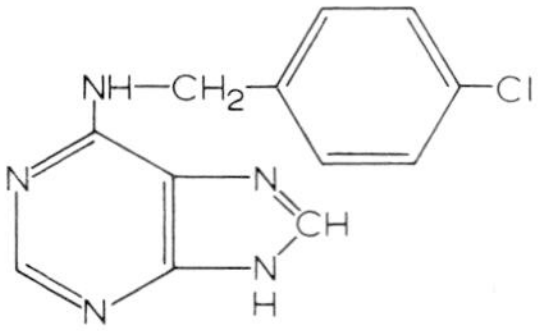

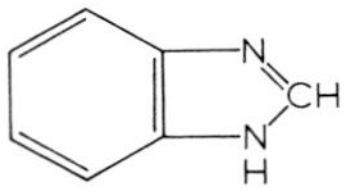

XIII Benzimidazole

yellowing or whether they also affect in a similar way the nucleic acid, protein synthesis, and active transport. Perhaps the investigation of quite different phenomena will open new possibilities for methods to be used. For instance the resistance of excised leaves to a short heating can be notably increased by (a) preheating at a somewhat lower temperature[41], (b) purines, pyrimidines, riboflavin[42-44], (c) kinetin[45] and (d) rooting (unpublished).

Such sublethal heat effects are manifested in a faster yellowing, a lower ability to accumulate and retain substances, and by the lack of competitive capacity, in contrast to non-heated leaves. This complex of manifestations is characteristic for aging leaves and apparently is implicated in a deeper sense, perhaps in the nucleic acid system.

Finally it must be mentioned that kinetin is able to overcome most of the toxic effect of chloramphenicol[32], 8-azaguanine[46] and thiouracil (unpublished). These inhibitors affect the nucleic acid metabolism. Thus kinetin seems to stabilize the metabolism of nucleic substances and consequently to promote protein synthesis. It remains, however, to be clarified by further experiments, whether active transport and nucleic acid synthesis are two completely independent fields of action of kinetin or whether they are interdependent. It is quite possible that a general principle of macromolecular and cell structure is valid in such cases. Doubtlessly, plants contain substances acting like kinetin[47-50].

The abundant literature on this subject contains a great number of observations indicating that kinetin and analogous substances influence the breaking of dormancy, the phenomenon of apical dominance[26], nucleus and cell division, branching of roots, seed germination, formation of flower buds[51] and permeability, and that they enhance or inhibit certain radiation effects. Also the synergism and antagonism of various growth substances of the purine group on the one hand and of the auxins and gibberellins on the other hand are described. These problems have also been discussed in review articles[52-56].

4. Conclusion

In summary, purines, kinetin and its artificial analogues, benzimidazole, indoleacetic acid, triiodobenzoic acid, 2,4-dichlorophenoxyacetic acid and a hypothetical root substance show certain common effects. However, they do not manifest themselves in all the investigated materials in the same way, possibly because some are quickly decomposed or translocated. One of the most general effects is the retardation of yellowing of excised leaves or leaf parts. For some of these substances, especially kinetin, other effects have been observed, but it is not known whether they are characteristic for the other substances. Among these effects are: active transport, accumulation and retention of various soluble, mostly ionized, substances, especially amino acids; promotion of the synthesis of nucleic acids, proteins, chlorophyll, lipoids, starch, etc., possibly as a consequence of accumulation; increased resistance to high temperature and dryness; increased resistance to specific inhibitors of nucleic acid and protein metabolism (chloramphenicol, thiouracil, methyltryptophan); and promotion of the growth of shoot and leaf and the suppression of bud dormancy, partial promotion of germination and of nucleus and cell division.

The total complex of these effects makes old leaves or dormant buds "young" and active. Therefore organs which possess such substances are superior in their correlative character to those which are deprived of these substances and at whose cost the former grow and accumulate metabolites for synthetic processes[32].

REFERENCES

1 F. W. Went, *Plant Physiol.*, 13 (1938) 53.
2 D. M. Bonner, A. J. Haagen-Smit and F. W. Went, *Botan. Gaz.*, 101 (1939) 128.
3 D. M. Bonner and J. Bonner, *Am. J. Botany*, 27 (1940) 38.
4 N. Fries, *Symbolae Botan. Upsalienses*, 13 (1954) 1.
5 N. Fries, *Physiol. Plantarum*, 13 (1960) 468.
6 F. Skoog and C. O. Miller, *Symposia Soc. Exptl. Biol.*, 11 (1957) 118.
7 F. Skoog and C. Tsui, *Plant Growth Subst. (Madison)*, (1951) 263.
8 L. Mayer, *Planta*, 47 (1956) 401.
9 E. Stichel, *Planta*, 53 (1959) 293.
10 K. V. Thimann and E. F. Poutasse, *Plant Physiol.*, 16 (1941) 585.
11 K. Wirth, *Planta*, 54 (1960) 265.
12 P. Paulet and J. P. Nitsch, *Bull. soc. botan. France*, 106 (1959) 425.
13 W. E. Pontovich, *Fiziol. Rastenii, Akad. Nauk, SSSR*, 6 (1959) 303.
14 Ei. Libbert, T. Kentzer and B. Steyer, *Flora (Jena)*, 151 (1961) 663.
15 R. S. de Ropp, *Plant Physiol.*, 31 (1956) 253.
16 W. Kruyt and H. Veldstra, *Koninkl. Ned. Akad. Wetenschap. Proc.*, 50 (1947) 2.
17 S. Kuraishi, *Sci. Papers Coll. Gen. Educ. Univ. Tokyo*, 9 (1959) 67.
18 S. Kuraishi and F. S. Okumura, *Botan. Mag. (Tokyo)*, 69 (1956) 300.
19 C. O. Miller, *Plant Physiol.*, 31 (1956) 318.
20 R. A. Scott and J. L. Liverman, *Plant Physiol.*, 31 (1956) 321.
21 C. O. Miller, F. Skoog, F. S. Okumura, M. H. von Saltza and F. M. Strong, *J. Am. Chem. Soc.*, 77 (1955) 2662.
22 L. Engelbrecht and K. Mothes, *Plant and Cellular Physiol.*, 2 (1961) 271.
23 C. Danckwardt-Lilieström, *Physiol. Plantarum*, 10 (1957) 794.
24 L. Chwoika, K. Weresch and J. Kosel, *Biol. Plant (Praha)*, 3 (1961) 140.
25 L. Engelbrecht and K. Mothes, *Naturwiss.*, 49 (1962) 427.
26 M. Wickson and K. V. Thimann, *Physiol. Plantarum*, 11 (1958) 62.
27 A. C. Chibnall, *New Phytologist*, 53 (1954) 31.
28 G. Michael, *Z. Botan.*, 29 (1935) 385.
29 A. Richmond and A. Lang, *Science*, 125 (1957) 650.
30 K. Mothes, L. Engelbrecht and O. Kulajeva, *Flora (Jena)*, 147 (1959) 445.
30a. B. Parthier, *Flora (Jena)*, 151 (1961) 518.
31 K. Mothes, *Naturwiss.*, 47 (1960) 337.
32 K. Mothes, *Ber. deut. botan. Ges.*, 74 (1961) 24.
33 M. J. Olszewska, *Exptl. Cell Research*, 16 (1959) 193.
34 K. V. Thimann and M. M. Laloraya, *Physiol. Plantarum*, 13 (1960) 165.

[35] R. Wollgiehn, *Flora (Jena)*, 151 (1961) 411.
[36] K. Mothes, *12. Coll. Deut. Ges. physiol. Chem. Mosbach*, (1961) 189.
[37] Ch. G. Skinner and W. Shive, *J. Am. Chem. Soc.*, 77 (1955) 6692.
[38] D. J. Samborsky, F. R. Forsyth and C. Person, *Can. J. Botany*, 36 (1958) 591.
[39] D. J. Osborne, *Trop. Agr. (Trinidad)*, 35 (1958) 145.
[40] D. J. Osborne, *Nature*, 183 (1959) 1459.
[41] C. E. Yarwood, *Science*, 134 (1961) 941.
[42] H. K. Mitchell and M. B. Houlahan, *Am. J. Bot.*, 33 (1946) 31.
[43] E. B. Kurtz, *Science*, 128 (1958) 1115.
[44] A. W. Galston and M. E. Hand, *Arch. Biochem.*, 24 (1949) 434.
[45] L. Engelbrecht and K. Mothes, *Ber. deutsch. botan. Ges.*, 73 (1960) 246.
[46] F. Moewus, *Science*, 130 (1959) 921.
[47] P. L. Goldacre and W. Bottomley, *Nature*, 184 (1959) 555.
[48] O. N. Kulajeva, *Fiziol. Rasteniĭ, Akad. Nauk, SSSR*, 9 (1962) 229.
[49] C. O. Miller, *Proc. Natl. Acad. Sci. N.Y.*, 47 (1961) 170.
[50] J. P. Nitsch, *Bull. soc. botan. France*, 107 (1960) 263.
[51] M. Kh. Chailakhian and R. G. Butenko, *Doklady Akad. Nauk SSSR*, 129 (1959) 224.
[52] G. Beauchesne, *Bull. soc. franç. physiol. végét.*, 6 (1960) 146.
[53] G. Deysson, *Bull. soc. botan. France*, 106 (1959) 369.
[54] C. O. Miller, *Ann. Rev. Plant Physiol.*, 12 (1961) 395.
[55] B. Parthier, *Pharmazie*, 15 (1960) 696.
[56] A. S. R. Pereira, *Vakblad Biologen*, 40 (1960) 105.

Chapter X

Insect Hormones

P. KARLSON

Physiological-Chemical Institute, University of Munich (Germany)

1. Survey of insect endocrinology

Our knowledge of the endocrinology of insects first arose from studies on the metamorphosis of insects, and among the insect hormones the metamorphosis hormones have been the most thoroughly studied[1-4a]. Considerably less is known about the myotropic and neurosecretory substances; it is often not chear what physiological process is actually controlled. For further information about these substances other reviews must be consulted[5,6]. On the other hand, another group of active substances will be mentioned here, namely, the pheromones. They were defined[7] as "substances which are excreted to the outside by an individual of the same species, in which they release a specific reaction, for example, a definite behaviour or a developmental process." The principle holds that minute amounts are effective. The term "pheromone" should be substituted for the somewhat ill-defined term "ectohormones".

Hormonal control of insect development

The development of insects is accomplished, as is known, through several larval stages, which are separated from one another by ecdyses. In holometabolic insects a special pupa stage is introduced between the larva and the imago. Three different hormones take part in the control of the ecdyses: (*1*) The *brain hormone*, produced by the neurosecretory cells of the pars intercerebralis, which acts on the prothoracic glands; (*2*) The *hormone of the prothoracic glands, ecdysone*, which starts the ecdysis (and also all the processes which are connected with the ecdysis); (*3*) The *juvenile hormone* of the corpora allata. According to present day knowledge the normal *larval ecdysis* is started by the brain hormone, which stimulates the prothoracic glands. These produce the molting hormone, ecdysone; simultaneously the juvenile hormone is secreted by the corpora allata and this determines the

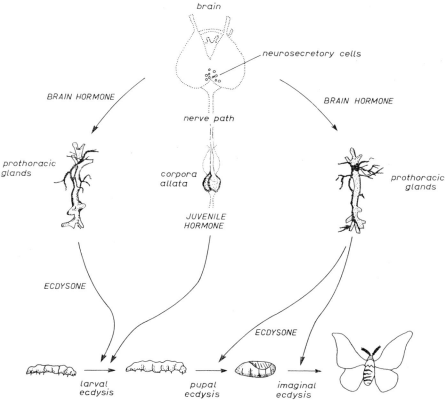

Fig. 1. Hormonal control of insect development. Three hormones are involved: the brain hormone, acting on the prothoracic glands, the juvenile hormone, secreted by the corpora allata and ecdysone, secreted by the prothoracic glands. The bottom row shows the development from the caterpillar through the pupa to the moth. The larval ecdyses are controlled by ecdysone and juvenile hormone, but the pupal and imaginal ecdyses are induced only by ecdysone. (from P. Karlson, Lehrbuch der Biochemie, with kind permission of G. Thieme Verlag, Stuttgart.)

larval character of the ecdysis. The *pupal ecdysis* of holometabolic insects comes about by a cessation, or at least, a marked reduction of the activity of the corpora allata, so that the juvenile hormone is not secreted and only the ecdysone operates. The *pupal ecdysis* can be altered so that it becomes a supernumerary larval ecdysis by implantation of active corpora allata. Finally the *imaginal ecdysis*, like the pupal ecdysis, occurs only by the co-operation of the brain and the prothoracic glands, *i.e.* peripherally through the action of the ecdysone. Fig. 1 gives a scheme of the hormonal control of insect development.

References p. 177

A further hormonal factor, the *diapause hormone*[8,9] is only indirectly related to the development. This substance is produced in the sub-esophageal ganglion and has been extracted therefrom[10]. In the silk moth it determines the diapause in the development of the eggs. Similar arrests of development have been observed in the caterpillar and pupal stages; their occurrence is often related to environmental conditions. How far the diapause factor of the sub-esophageal ganglion plays a part has not yet been determined.

2. The brain hormone

The biological evidence for a hormonal factor produced by the brain was furnished by Kopeč[11]. It was the first publication on hormonal action in the insect kingdom. Further observations followed, but nearly all investigations failed to prove the activity of extracts. Kobayashi and Kirimura[12] were the first to succeed. Starting with 8,400 brains, they obtained 4 mg of an extract which had the activity of the brain hormone. The active substance is soluble in ether and petroleum-ether. Recently, Kobayashi[12a] has claimed that the active principle is identical with cholesterol. It is more likely that the activity is due to some contaminant of the cholesterol isolated.

The implantation of a small quantity of this extract into pupae causes the development of the pupa into an imago. We know from numerous biological investigations, however, that the action must proceed through the prothoracic glands; these are stimulated to produce the ecdysis hormone, ecdysone.

A substance with similar action is present in extracts which Gilbert and Schneiderman[13] obtained during investigation of the juvenile hormone. There is much in favor of the view that the action is not to be ascribed to the juvenile hormone itself, but to the brain hormone or to a substance closely related to this.

3. Ecdysone, the hormone of the prothoracic gland

Ecdysone was the first insect hormone to be obtained in pure crystalline form. It has the action of the molting and metamorphosis hormone and has also been called, by Scharrer[14], the "growth and differentiation hormone".

(i) Bioassay

The best assay for ecdysone is still the *Calliphora test*, which goes back to the work of Fraenkel[15] and Becker and Plagge[16] and was further elaborated by Karlson[3]. The test object is the isolated abdomen of fully grown maggots. The *Calliphora unit* is defined as that amount of substance which after injection evokes the formation of a puparium in 50–70% of animals. The test is reliable and very sensitive — about 0.01 μg of the crystalline hormone, ecdysone, equals one *Calliphora* unit. So far no substance is known which can imitate the action of ecdysone. Williams[17] and Wigglesworth[18] have described other tests.

(ii) Isolation and chemical characteristics

Guided by this test procedure, Butenandt and Karlson[19] have concentrated the hormone. At first they used as their initial material the pupae of *Calliphora* and later those of *Bombyx mori* obtained from commercial silk breeders. It is clear that the content of the pure hormone in the extract is small and it is necessary to work through 500 kg of pupae to obtain 25 mg of a crystalline product which has the hormonal activity. The empirical formula appears to be $C_{27}H_{44}O_6$. An unsaturated keto group as well as hydroxyl groups could be detected by spectroscopic methods. The final elucidation of the structure may be difficult. Recent experiments have shown that it may be a steroid or a related substance[19a].

Ecdysone is sensitive to acids and alkalis. On heating with acids, a new ultraviolet-absorption maximum at 295 mμ appears, and simultaneously the activity of the hormone is lost. Rapid inactivation also occurs with alkali. On the other hand, the hormone can be kept in solution for several months without change in its activity, and it is also stable to oxygen.

In addition to ecdysone a second substance with a similar action has been isolated and has been provisionally given the name β-ecdysone. Its m.p. is 177° and it has a very similar ultraviolet and infrared spectrum, but differs from α-ecdysone (m.p. 239°) in its solubility[3,20].

(iii) Biochemical actions of ecdysone

The *Calliphora* test has not only made it possible to isolate ecdysone, but it has also provided an important insight into the mechanism by which the hormone acts. Darkening and hardening of the cuticle, which are the external signs of the action of ecdysone in *Calliphora*, are also called *sclerotization*[21-23]. This depends on the incorporation of quinones into the cuticle. Precursors of these quinones are tyrosine, dopa and dopamine. After injection of radioactively labeled samples of these substances, a high concentration of the isotope is found in the cuticle[24]. Some time before the formation of the puparium, the metabolism of tyrosine in *Calliphora* is shifted to another pathway. In young larvae tyrosine is decomposed into phenylpyruvic acid and *p*-hydroxyphenylpropionic acid, a pathway which seems to be blocked in older larvae. Instead, dopa and *N*-acetyldopamine are found as metabolites, the latter appearing partly as glucoside[25]. The biogenesis of *N*-acetyldopamine has been elucidated[25a,b]; the substance appears to be one of the most important precursors of sclerotin and it is also acted upon readily by the phenol oxidase obtained from *Calliphora*.

The phenol oxidase probably plays an important part in the sclerotization. We have purified the enzyme[26] and have studied its action on various substrates. From these studies it appears that monophenols, including tyrosine, are only very slowly attacked by the enzyme. Dopa, dopamine and *N*-acetyldopamine are the best substrates of the diphenols tested. Other substances such as 3,4-dihydroxyphenylpyruvic acid, 3,4-dihydroxyphenylacetic acid and protocatechuic acid are not attacked.

Phenol oxidase occurs in the insect organism as an inactive precursor, which is changed by a special *activating enzyme* into the active phenol-oxidase[27,28]. This change is also controlled by ecdysone. In the last larval instar the amount of both the proenzyme and the activator is at first small and increases until pupation occurs. In "permanent larvae" (obtained by destruction of the hormone-producing gland), the activator concentration is very low; an increase to normal level can be brought about by injection of ecdysone[28]. This is interpreted as being a new formation of the activator enzyme.

The biosynthesis of the enzymes which operate in tyrosine metabolism and are newly formed under the influence of ecdysone, may follow the same principles as those which operate in the well-studied protein synthesis in vertebrates and bacteria. It is assumed that the synthesis of ribonucleic acid (with the cooperation of DNA) is the first step and that protein synthesis then follows through the activated amino acids. In this connection it is interesting that a direct relationship between the genetic material and ecdysone has been found. In the midge *Chironomus* a specific "puff" could be induced in the chromosomes of the salivary glands by injection of ecdysone[29]. "Puffs" are, as is known from other investigations, sites of the activity of genes and of the synthesis of ribonucleic acid[30,31]. It is natural to suppose that a similar relationship exists between the activity of the genes and the synthesis of RNA and proteins (production of the enzymes in *Calliphora*). Over and above this, a new principle of hormone action is revealed, which is probably valid also for other hormones: the control of protein biosynthesis by the activation of genetic material[32], as outlined in Fig. 2. A specially favourable feature of our object, namely, the presence of giant chromosomes in the salivary glands, has here provided insight otherwise to be arrived at only by indirect methods.

The relationships in the development of the imagines of silk moths are less clear[33]. Here the cytochrome system is, among other things, concerned, especially cytochrome *c*. The resting stage of the diapause is biochemically characterized by a low respiration and a low concentration of cytochrome *c*. At the beginning of development, which is started by ecdysone, a rapid

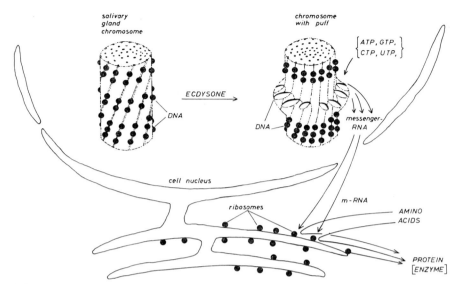

Fig. 2. Mechanism of the action of ecdysone. The hormone activates the genetic material to puff up and produce RNA. It is believed that the latter acts as messenger-RNA; it enters the cytoplasm and becomes attached to the ribosomes, where it participates in the synthesis of specific proteins.

increase of the total metabolism and of the concentration of cytochrome can be observed. These biochemical changes are, however, also caused by injury. Respiration can increase more than ten times without starting the development of the imago[34,34a]. The increased metabolism thus serves wound healing processes only. It has not yet been possible to give even a provisional interpretation of the control of these biochemical changes[35].

(iv) Further actions of ecdysone

Ecdysone has proved to be active in all the orders of insects investigated. Of major interest is the influence on symbionts in certain cockroaches. The symbionts go through a sexual cycle while the host casts its skin. The sexual cycles can be induced by means of ecdysone without the host undergoing ecdysis[36].

4. The juvenile hormone

The juvenile hormone[37] is produced in the corpora allata; nevertheless these glands seem to store up little of the hormone, because attempts to extract it have failed. This hormone was first made available for closer investigation by the work of Williams[38], who discovered that there is a relatively high content of juvenile hormone in the abdomen of the male silk moth, *Hyalo-phora cecropia*.

(i) *Bioassay*

The biological test of the action of the juvenile hormone that is most often used is inhibition of the imaginal ecdysis[39]. Williams[40] used *cecropia* pupae and an injection technique; Schneiderman *et al.*[41] described a test done on the pupal cuticle, which is very sensitive. Wigglesworth[42] has made investigations with a similar technique on various insects and found that only *Rhodnius* and *Tenebrio* were suitable. In *Tenebrio* an injection technique[43] also produced good results.

(ii) *Isolation*

A description of the method of concentration has not yet been published; it was simply stated[44] that a purification of more than 500 times had been attained. The juvenile hormone is soluble in ether and alcohol, but not in water; it thus behaves as a lipid.

It is noteworthy that extracts which have the activity of the juvenile hormone can be obtained from various starting materials. Not only insects, crabs, and other invertebrates, but also mammalian organs (adrenal glands, thymus, etc.) contain substances which act like the juvenile hormone[45]. It remains to be proved whether the activity in all these materials is due to the same factor. As has been mentioned, many of the extracts have the activity of the brain hormone.

(iii) *Inactivation and excretion*

In many insects, for example in the large silk moth *Hyalophora cecropia*, a large amount of the juvenile hormone is stored. In most species it is inactive, or is so bound that it is no longer extractable. In *Tenebrio*, excretion in the faeces has been observed[46], the substance being identified as farnesol.

5. The yolk-formation hormone (metabolic hormone) of the corpora allata

The corpora allata of most orders of insects (excepting the *Lepidoptera*) are, in addition to being the site of the production of the juvenile hormone, necessary for the development of the eggs in the ovary and primarily for the deposition of the yolk substance[47,48]. For a long time the view prevailed that it was the juvenile hormone itself which had this function in the adult animal, but more recent investigations[49,50] make it probable that a second hormone is responsible for these actions.

Various methods have been suggested for testing the effect on yolk formation, but so far no clearly positive results have been obtained with extracts; all the evidence has been obtained by transplantation experiments. We were not able to confirm the result obtained by Larsen and Bodenstein[51] on the action of extracts containing juvenile hormone in *Aedes aegypti* (see also Gillett[52]).

6. Pheromones

The name "pheromones" is given to substances which are formed in glands and effect the correlation between individuals. This field of work is well covered by some reviews[53,54]; here only those pheromones which are chemically well defined will be considered.

A typical example of a pheromone is the sex attractant substance of the silk moth, *Bombyx mori*. It is secreted by the female in special, paired glands (sacculi laterales); it is excreted to the exterior and reaches the antennae of the male through the air. There it is perceived by the chemical senses and initiates a special behavior (excitation, allurement, pairing). The biological test (bioassay) is based on this behavior[55,56].

(*i*) *Chemistry of sex attractants*

Isolation of the attractant requires a great degree of purification. To obtain the pure attractant of *Bombyx* it has been necessary to extract about 500,000 glands from the silk moth[57,58]. Although only a few milligrams of the pure substance have been obtained, Butenandt's group of workers succeeded in determining its structure and in proving it by synthesis[59-61]; it is 10-*trans*-12-*cis*-hexadecadienol-1, which has been given the name *bombykol*[58]:

$$H_3C - (CH_2)_2 CH = CH - CH = CH - (CH_2)_8 - CH_2OH$$

Bombykol is the first insect sex attractant to be obtained pure and to have its structure determined and to be synthesized[60]. It is noteworthy that its action is abolished by small changes in its structure. The synthesized isomers 10-*cis*,12-*trans*-, 10-*cis*,12-*cis*-, and 10-*trans*,12-*trans*-hexadecadienole are very many times less active[60,61]. Apparently they even inhibit the action of the natural bombykol[62].

Another attractant was isolated only a short time later[63,64], namely, that of the Gipsy moth, *Lymantria dispar*. Its structure shows similarities to the structure of bombykol. It also has a chain of 16 C-atoms and a primary alcohol group, but only one double bond and an additional acetylated hydroxyl group. The attractant of the Gipsy moth is structurally not as specific as bombykol; for example, its homologue with 18 C-atoms works well.

Yet another substance which should be mentioned in this connection was isolated from the glands of the aquatic bug *Belostoma indica*[65]. Its biological function is still not known. There is much in favor of the view that it is to be classed among the sex attractants. Its chemical structure, proved by synthesis, is the following:

$$H_3C-CH_2-CH_2-CH=CH-CHOH-CO-CH_3$$

(ii) Pheromones of bees

The pheromones of bees have important functions in the organization of the colony. The queen constantly gives off a substance which informs the members of the colony about her presence. This "Queen-substance" was isolated by Butler, Callow and Johnston[66]. It is a relatively simple substance of the following constitution:

$$H_3C-\underset{\underset{O}{\|}}{C}-(CH_2)_5-CH=CH-COOH$$

Barbier *et al.*[67], who studied the same problem independently, confirmed the findings of Butler, Callow and Johnston.

A closely related substance is decenolic acid, which has been isolated from Royal Jelly[68]. Biopterin has also been found[69] in Royal Jelly, but its biological function for the bee has not yet been determined.

NOTE ADDED IN PROOF

Additional information on Insect Hormones may be found in Proceedings of the 3rd Intern. Symp. on Comp. Endocrinol., published in *General and Comparative Endocrinology*, Suppl. 1, 1962, and in P. KARLSON, Chemie und Biochemie der Insektenhormone, *Angew. Chem.*, 75 (1963) (to appear in March 1963).

REFERENCES

[1] V. B. WIGGLESWORTH, The Physiology of Insect Metamorphosis, *Cambridge Monographs in Exptl. Biol.*, 1, University Press, London, 1954.

[2] O. PFLUGFELDER, *Entwicklungsphysiologie der Insekten*, 2nd ed., Geest u. Portig, Leipzig, 1958.

[3] P. KARLSON, *Vitamins and Hormones*, 14 (1956) 227.

[4a] P. KARLSON AND C. E. SEKERIS, *Biochemistry of Insect Metamorphosis*, in M. FLORKIN AND H. MASON, *Comparative Biochemistry*, Vol. V, Academic Press, New York, in the press.

[4] L. I. GILBERT AND H. A. SCHNEIDERMAN, *Amer. Zool.*, 1 (1961) 11.

[5] G. KOLLER, in 5. Mosbacher Colloq. Ges. physiol. Chem., Springer, Berlin, 1955; G. KOLLER, in R. AMMON AND W. DIRSCHEL, *Fermente, Hormone, Vitamine*, Vol. II, Thieme, Stuttgart, 1960, p. 814.

[6] M. GABE, P. KARLSON AND J. ROCHE, *Hormones in Invertebrates*, in M. FLORKIN AND H. S. MASON (Eds.), *Comparative Biochemistry*, Vol. V, Academic Press, New York, in the press.

[7] P. KARLSON AND M. LÜSCHER, *Nature*, 183 (1959) 55.

[8] K. HASEGAWA, *Proc. Japan Acad.*, 27 (1951) 667.

[9] S. FUKUDA, *Proc. Japan Acad.*, 29 (1953) 381, 389.

[10] K. HASEGAWA, *Nature*, 179 (1957) 1300.

[11] S. KOPEČ, *Biol. Bull.*, 42 (1922) 322.

[12] M. KOBAYASHI AND J. KIRIMURA, *Nature*, 181 (1958) 1217.

[12a] M. KOBAYASHI, J. KIRIMURA AND M. SAITO, *Nature*, 195 (1962) 515, 729.

[13] L. I. GILBERT AND H. A. SCHNEIDERMAN, *Nature*, 184 (1959) 171.

[14] B. SCHARRER, in G. PINCUS AND K. V. THIMANN, *The Hormones*, Vol. III, Academic Press, New York, 1955, p. 57.

[15] G. FRAENKEL, *Proc. Roy. Soc. (London)*, B, 118 (1935) 1.

[16] E. BECKER AND E. PLAGGE, *Biol. Zentr.*, 59 (1939) 326.

[17] C. M. WILLIAMS, *Anat. Record*, 120 (1954) 743.

[18] V. B. WIGGLESWORTH, *J. Exptl. Biol.*, 32 (1955) 650.

[19] A. BUTENANDT AND P. KARLSON, *Z. Naturforsch.*, 9b (1954) 389.

[19a] P. KARLSON, H. HOFFMEISTER, W. HOPPE AND F. HUBER, *Ann. Chem., Liebigs*, (in the press).

[20] P. KARLSON, *Proc. 3rd Intern. Congr. Biochem.*, Bruxelles, 1955, Abstr. 12–3.

[21] A. G. RICHARDS, *The Integument of Arthropods*, Minnesota University Press, Minneapolis, 1951; *Ergeb. Biol.*, 20 (1958) 1.

[22] R. DENNELL, *Biol. Revs. Cambridge Phil. Soc.*, 33 (1958) 178.

[23] R. H. HACKMAN, *Proc. 4th Intern. Congr. Biochem.*, Vol. 12, Pergamon, London, 1959, p. 48.

[24] P. KARLSON, *Z. physiol. Chem., Hoppe-Seyler's*, 318 (1960) 194.

[25] P. KARLSON, C. E. SEKERIS AND K. E. SEKERI, *Z. physiol. Chem., Hoppe-Seyler's*, 327 (1962) 86.

[25a] P. KARLSON AND C. E. SEKERIS, *Nature*, 195 (1962) 183.

[25b] C. E. SEKERIS AND P. KARLSON, *Biochim. Biophys. Acta*, 62 (1962) 103; 63 (1962) 489.

[26] P. KARLSON AND H. LIEBAU, *Z. physiol. Chem., Hoppe-Seyler's*, 326 (1961) 135.

[27] N. H. HOROWITZ AND M. FLING, in W. McELROY AND H. B. GLASS (Eds.), *Amino Acid Metabolism*, John Hopkins Press, Baltimore, 1955, p. 207.

[28] P. KARLSON AND A. SCHWEIGER, *Z. physiol. Chem., Hoppe-Seyler's*, 323 (1961) 199.

[29] U. CLEVER AND P. KARLSON, *Exptl. Cell Research*, 20 (1960) 623.

[30] W. BEERMAN, *Zool. Anz.*, (1961).

[31] G. PELLING, *Nature*, 184 (1959) 655.

[32] P. KARLSON, *Deut. med. Wochschr.*, 86 (1961) 668.

[33] C. M. WILLIAMS, *Federation Proc.*, 10 (1951) 546.

[34] H. A. SCHNEIDERMAN AND C. M. WILLIAMS, *Biol. Bull.*, 106 (1954) 238.

[34a] C. G. KURLAND AND H. A. SCHNEIDERMAN, *Biol. Bull.*, 116 (1959) 136.

[35] G. R. WYATT, *Proc. 4th Intern. Congr. Biochem.*, Vol. 12, Pergamon, London, 1959, p. 161.

36 L. R. Cleveland, A. W. Burke and P. Karlson, *J. Protozool.*, 7 (1960) 229.
37 V. B. Wigglesworth, *Quart. J. Microscop. Sci.*, 79 (1936) 91.
38 C. M. Williams, *Nature*, 178 (1956) 212.
39 H. Piepho, *Wilhelm Roux' Arch. Entwicklungsmech. Organ.*, 141 (1941) 500.
40 C. M. Williams, *Biol. Bull.*, 116 (1959) 323.
41 H. A. Schneiderman and L. I. Gilbert, *Biol. Bull.*, 115 (1958) 530.
42 V. B. Wigglesworth, *Insect Physiol.*, 2 (1958) 73.
43 P. Karlson and M. J. Nachtigall, *Insect Physiol.*, 7 (1961) 210.
44 C. M. Williams, *Anat. Record*, 128 (1957) 640; 1st Intern. Congress of Endocrinology, Copenhagen, 1960.
45 L. I. Gilbert and H. A. Schneiderman, *Science*, 128 (1958) 844; C. M. Williams, L. V. Moorhead and J. F. Pulis, *Nature*, 183 (1959) 405.
46 P. Karlson and P. Schmialek, *Z. Naturforsch.*, 14b (1959) 821; P. Schmialek, *Z. Naturforsch.*, 16b (1961) 461.
47 B. Scharrer, *Arch. ges. Physiol.*, *Pflüger's*, 255 (1952) 154; *Endocrinology*, 38 (1946) 46.
48 M. Lüscher and F. Engelmann, *Rev. suisse Zool.*, 62 (1955) 649.
49 M. Lüscher and A. Springhetti, *Insect Physiol.*, 5 (1960) 190.
50 H. Sägesser, *Insect Physiol.*, 5 (1960) 264.
51 J. R. Larsen and D. Bodenstein, *J. Exptl. Zool.*, 140 (1959) 343.
52 J. D. Gillett, *J. Exptl. Biol.*, 35 (1958) 685.
53 P. Karlson and A. Butenandt, *Ann. Rev. Entomol.*, 4 (1959) 39.
54 P. Karlson, *Ergeb. Biol.*, 22 (1959) 212.
55 A. Butenandt, *Naturw. Rundschau*, 8 (1955) 457; *Nova Acta Leopoldina*, N.F. 17 (1955) 445.
56 E. Hecker, *Umschau Wiss. u. Tech.*, 59 (1959) 499, 565.
57 A. Butenandt, R. Beckman, D. Stamm and E. Hecker, *Z. Naturforsch.*, 14b (1959) 283.
58 A. Butenandt, R. Beckmann, D. Stamm and E. Hecker, *Z. physiol. Chem.*, *Hoppe-Seyler's*, 324 (1961) 71.
59 A. Butenandt, R. Beckmann and D. Stamm, *Z. physiol. Chem.*, *Hoppe-Seyler's*, 324 (1961) 84.
60 E. Hecker, *Proc. 11th Intern. Congr. Entomol., Vienna, 1960*, Verlag Inst. Ent. Univ. Pavia, p. 69.
61 A. Butenandt and E. Hecker, *Angew. Chem.*, 73 (1961) 349.
62 E. Hecker, unpublished.
63 M. Jacobson, M. Beroza and W. A. Jones, *Science*, 132 (1960) 1011.
64 M. Jacobson, *J. org. Chem.*, 25 (1960) 2074.
65 A. Butenandt and N. D. Tam, *Z. physiol. Chem.*, *Hoppe-Seyler's*, 308 (1957) 277.
66 C. G. Butler, R. K. Callow and N. C. Johnston, *Nature*, 184 (1959) 1871.
67 M. Barbier, E. Lederer, T. Reichstein and O. Schindler, *Helv. Chim. Acta*, 43 (1960) 1682.
68 A. Butenandt and H. Rembold, *Z. physiol. Chem.*, *Hoppe-Seyler's*, 308 (1957) 284.
69 A. Butenandt and H. Rembold, *Z. physiol. Chem.*, *Hoppe-Seyler's*, 311 (1958) 79.

Volume 11

Part C

ANTIBIOTICS

Chapter XI

The Antibiotics

E. P. ABRAHAM

Sir William Dunn School of Pathology, University of Oxford (Great Britain)

1. Introduction

An antibiotic has been defined by Waksman[1] as a substance produced by one micro-organism which is capable of interfering with the growth of others. This is a convenient, though arbitrary, definition. It excludes synthetic compounds and products of the higher plants and animals which show antimicrobial activity, but includes an important collection of substances which are active *in vivo* and have found a place in medicine.

Observations on antibiosis were made and correctly interpreted by a number of bacteriologists in the second half of the nineteenth century[2]. Thus Garré reported in 1887 that the growth of *Staph. pyogenes* on gelatine plates was inhibited in the vicinity of *B. fluorescens putidus* and concluded that the second organism secreted a product that was toxic to the first. In 1896 Gosio isolated the antibiotic mycophenolic acid, produced by *Penicillium brevicompactum*, in crystalline form. As early as 1877 Pasteur and Joubert had suggested that the antagonism of one kind of bacterium to the growth of another might have therapeutic use and in 1899 Emmerich and Löw introduced a crude antibacterial product of *Bacillus pyocyaneus*, known as pyocyanase, into medicine.

In retrospect it may seem strange that the early studies on antibiotics remained isolated and sporadic and that nearly half a century passed before the subject began to acquire its present importance. This delayed development may be attributed partly to the absence of collaboration of biologists and chemists who were interested in chemotherapy, and partly to the fact that only a very small proportion of the antibiotics that are discovered have the properties required of a chemotherapeutic agent.

In 1923 Raistrick began a series of pioneer investigations on certain metabolic products of fungi. The products studied appear to have been selected mainly because they could be readily isolated in crystalline form. A number of these products were found in 1942 to be antibiotics, but only

griseofulvin, which was discovered in 1939 and first used for the treatment
of fungal infections twenty years later, has proved clinically useful.

In 1929 Fleming observed that colonies of staphylococci were undergoing
lysis in the vicinity of a fungus, *Penicillium notatum*, which was an acci-
dental contaminant on a nutrient agar plate[3]. When grown in broth the
fungus produced a bactericidal principle which Fleming named penicillin.
He showed that broth containing penicillin was not more toxic to leuco-
cytes than ordinary broth and that it could be employed as an antiseptic,
but he did not explore the possibility that penicillin could be used for the
treatment of systemic infections. Two circumstances may have contributed
to the fact that penicillin attracted relatively little attention for the next ten
years. Firstly, many attempts to find chemotherapeutic substances that
could combat bacterial infections had been unsuccessful, despite the progress
made by Ehrlich and his school in the chemotherapy of syphilis, protozoal
diseases and malaria. The view began to be held that the search for such a
substance would be fruitless and this view was not shown to be erroneous
until the therapeutic properties of prontosil, the first sulphonamide, was
discovered in 1931. Secondly, penicillin proved to be readily inactivated and
initial attempts to purify it were unsuccessful.

A report by Dubos[4] and others on tyrothricin, an antibacterial product of
Bacillus brevis, appeared in 1939. This marked the beginning of a new
approach to the study of antibiotics in that both the chemical and biological
properties of the substances were given careful attention; but unfortunately
tyrothicin proved to be too toxic for systemic use in medicine[5]. At about
this time, however, Florey and Chain planned a systematic investigation of
antibacterial substances produced by micro-organisms and chose penicillin
as the first substance for study. Together with Heatley and others they succeeded in obtaining penicillin as a crude but relatively stable sodium salt
and showed that this crude material exerted a remarkable therapeutic effect
in mice infected with streptococci[6]. In 1941 they demonstrated that crude
penicillin was effective in man[7].

Three years later the discovery of a second chemotherapeutic antibiotic,
streptomycin, was reported by Schatz, Bugie and Waksman[8]. Streptomycin
was encountered in the course of a search for antibiotics among the actinomycetes. Members of this group of micro-organisms had been the subject
of extensive study by Waksman and his colleagues. One of them had previously yielded the antibiotic streptothricin, which was too toxic to be
clinically useful.

With the demonstration of the clinical importance of penicillin, work on
the antibiotics entered a new phase. The pharmaceutical industry used its
large resources to screen many thousands of micro-organisms for antibiotic
production. Methods were developed for producing antibiotics in deep aerated

cultures on a very large scale. Yields were increased, in some cases enormously, by the use of mutant strains, obtained by irradiation or in other ways. This extensive effort has resulted in the discovery and commercial production of chloramphenicol, the tetracyclines, erythromycin, novobiocin, vancomycin and other substances that are effective in systemic bacterial infections[9]. It has also revealed certain antifungal substances, such as nystatin and amphotericin, that have therapeutic value. Antibiotics, in addition, have found non-medical uses. They are now added to animal feeds to increase the rate of growth of animals, and employed as preservatives of perishable foods and as sprays to combat plant diseases[10].

Had it not been for the skill and initiative of many pharmaceutical firms, the antibiotics would not occupy the position that they do today. Nevertheless, a number of antibiotics, including bacitracin and neomycin, have continued to be discovered by academic workers.

2. Classification of antibiotics

In the course of screening programs many hundreds of antibiotics have been isolated. An attempt to classify these substances encounters a number of difficulties. To group them according to the type of micro-organisms by which they are formed is of limited value, for a large number of antibiotics with very different properties may be synthesised by species of a single genus, such as *Streptomyces*. To group them according to the nature of their activity is natural and convenient to those who are mainly interested in their clinical use. Antibiotics such as penicillin and erythromycin, which are most effective against Gram positive bacteria, may be placed in one group; broad spectrum antibiotics, such as chloramphenicol and the tetracyclines, may be placed in another; and antibiotics with high activity against the *Mycob. tuberculosis*, such as streptomycin and neomycin, may be placed in a third group. In this classification, however, antibiotics with entirely different chemical structures and modes of action are grouped together. A third possibility is to group the antibiotics according to their chemical structures. This procedure, which is at present the most illuminating from a biochemical point of view, is the one adopted here.

3. Biochemical aspect of the antibiotics

The elucidation of the structures of a large number of antibiotics has provided a basis from which the biochemistry of this new collection of natural products may be approached. Biochemical problems raised by the antibiotics are concerned with the way in which the substances are formed, with their function, if any, in a natural environment, and with the mechanisms by which they exert their toxic effects, often highly selective, on other cells.

When considered as a whole, the antibiotics appear to comprise an extremely heterogeneous collection of compounds. Nevertheless, many of them can be placed in one of several large groups whose members have major structural features in common. Within these groups are families of antibiotics, containing substances, such as the different penicillins, bacitracins or erythromycins, that show only minor variations on a central type of structure.

Similarities in structure commonly reflect similarities in biogenesis. Consideration of the architectural patterns and structural relationships of natural products enabled Collie, Robinson, Ruzicka and others to discern the biogenetic units from which certain phenolic compounds, alkaloids and terpenes were formed[11]. A survey of the antibiotics indicates that one large collection of these substances can be derived mainly from amino acid residues, another mainly from acetate (or, on occasion, propionate) and a third from simple sugars. Some structures can be dissected into two or more different fragments that are derived from different types of biogenetic unit.

In several instances, biogenetic hypotheses that were based on structural dissections have been confirmed by the results of experiments with isotopically labelled compounds. But little is yet known about the specific biochemical processes which lead to the synthesis of antibiotics, or about the relationship of these processes to the general biochemistry of the microbial cell. The high yields of streptomycin that are obtainable from certain strains of *Streptomyces griseus* indicate that a significant fraction of the total metabolic activity of a micro-organism may sometimes be channelled into antibiotic production[12].

It is not known whether antibiotics have exerted any influence on evolutionary processes and the distribution of micro-organisms in nature. Waksman believes that many of the most powerful antibiotics are unlikely to be formed in more than trivial amounts, or if formed, to survive in the soil, while Brian has drawn attention to certain specific cases in which antibiotics appear to affect natural flora. Well defined progress has been made, however, towards an understanding of the mode of action of some of the antibiotics that are now produced under controlled conditions by man.

4. Chemical nature and biogenesis of antibiotics

(a) The penicillins

Extensive Anglo-American work during the war of 1939–45, which culminated in a complete X-ray crystallographic analysis of penicillin G, established that the penicillin molecule[2,13] was represented by the β-lactam-thiazolidine structure I. This structure may be dissected, as shown by the broken lines through I, into units of L-cysteine, D-valine, and an acyl side-chain (R·CO).

$$R \cdot CO \vdots NH \cdot \overset{L}{CH} - \overset{S}{CH} \diagdown C(CH_3)_2$$
$$\underset{CO}{|} \diagup \underset{N}{\quad} - \underset{D}{CH} \cdot CO_2H$$

I

The side-chain was found to be variable and to be dependent on the nature of precursors in the fermentation medium. Thus R was $\varDelta^2$-pentenyl in penicillin F, benzyl in penicillin G, p-hydroxybenzyl in penicillin X and n-heptyl in penicillin K. The different penicillins were then named according to the nature of the group R, penicillin G, for example, being called benzyl-penicillin. Several hundred biosynthetic penicillins, in which R·CO was derived from a mono-substituted acetic acid, were obtained from fermentations of *Penicillium notatum* or *Penicillium chrysogenum* in the presence of appropriate precursors. However, penicillins with side-chains derived from di-substituted acetic acids, or with highly polar side-chains, did not appear to be generally accessible by this route.

When the penicillins are treated with dilute alkali, or with the enzyme penicillinase, the β-lactam ring is opened and products known as peni-cilloates are formed. Early attempts to synthesise penicillins by ring-closure of the corresponding penicilloic acids (II) were unsuccessful, mainly because the N-acylamino acid substituent on the thiazolidine ring underwent an alternative cyclisation to form an oxazolone. Sheehan and Henery-

$$R \cdot CO \cdot NH \cdot CH - \overset{S}{CH} \diagdown C(CH_3)_2$$
$$\underset{CO_2H}{|} \quad \underset{NH}{|} - CH \cdot CO_2H$$

II

Logan[14] showed in 1957 that this complication could be avoided by the use of a penicilloate in which R was the phenoxymethyl group.

$$\langle \bigcirc \rangle - O \cdot CH_2$$

Phenoxymethylpenicillin, produced in fermentations to which phenoxy-acetic acid was added, had been found by Brandl and Margreiter to be much more stable than other penicillins in dilute aqueous acid[15]. The structural features of the phenoxymethyl side-chain which are responsible for this stability also confer on the corresponding penicilloate a resistance to oxazolone formation. By the action of dicyclohexylcarbodiimide on the penicilloate in aqueous solution phenoxymethylpenicillin was formed in 15–20% yield.

Subsequently Sheehan and Henery-Logan[16] described a synthesis of the nucleus of the penicillin molecule, 6-aminopenicillanic acid (III). Circum-

$$
\begin{array}{c}
S \\
H_2N \cdot CH \text{—} CH \quad C(CH_3)_2 \\
\mid \qquad \mid \qquad \mid \\
CO \text{—} N \text{——} CH \cdot CO_2H
\end{array}
$$

III

stantial evidence for the presence of this interesting compound in fermentations of *Penicillium chrysogenum* to which no side-chain precursor was added had been obtained by Kato[17]. It had been claimed by Sakaguchi and Murao that the compound could be obtained by enzymic removal of the side-chain, with an amidase from benzylpenicillin[18] and more recent studies have shown that penicillin amidases with different specificities are produced by fungi, actinomycetes, and bacteria[19]. In 1959 Batchelor, Doyle, Nayler and Rolinson reported the isolation of crystalline 6-aminopenicillanic acid from the fermentation liquor of *Penicillium chrysogenum*, and showed that it could be acylated to yield various members of the penicillin family[19]. Their work made 6-aminopenicillanic acid readily available and opened the way to the production, in quantity, of a large number of new penicillins that could not be obtained by fermentation. One of these compounds, α-phenoxyethyl-penicillin, is relatively well absorbed from the intestinal tract. Another, 2,6-dimethoxyphenylpenicillin, is highly resistant to the penicillinase produced by many strains of pathogenic staphylococci. 5-Methyl-3-phenyl-4-isoxazolylpenicillin is both absorbed from the intestinal tract and resistant to penicillinase. The activity of α-aminobenzylpenicillin against Gram negative bacteria is considerably higher than that of benzylpenicillin.

A penicillin produced by a species of *Cephalosporium* that had been isolated by Brotzu in Sardinia was shown by Newton and Abraham[20] to have a side-chain derived from a residue of D-α-aminoadipic acid.

$$
R = \quad \overset{\overset{+}{H_3N}}{\underset{-O_2C}{\diagdown}} CH \cdot CH_2 \cdot CH_2 \cdot CH_2 -
$$

This substance (D-(4-amino-4-carboxy-*n*-butyl)penicillin, also known as cephalosporin N or synnematin B) may be closely related to one of the late intermediates in the biosynthesis of the common penicillins.

Work by Arnstein and others has shown that isotopically labelled L-cysteine and L-valine are utilised by *Penicillium chrysogenum* for the formation of benzylpenicillin[21]. However, the utilisation of L-cysteinyl-L-valine was quantitatively limited and it appeared that there was a pathway leading from L-cysteine and L-valine to penicillin which did not involve the dipeptide as an obligatory intermediate. The possibility that δ-(α-aminoadipoyl)-cysteinylvaline (IV) was an intermediate arose when this tripeptide was found to be present in the mycelium of *Penicillium chrysogenum*[22]. The peptide has a formal resemblance to glutathione and, by analogy with the

$$H_3\overset{+}{N}$$

$$\underset{^-O_2C}{\diagdown}CH \cdot CH_2 \cdot CH_2 \cdot CH_2 \cdot CO \cdot NH \cdot \underset{|}{CH} \cdot CH_2SH$$

$$CO \cdot NH \cdot CH - CH(CH_3)_2$$

$$\underset{|}{CO_2H}$$

IV

latter, may be formed by the coupling of α-aminoadipic acid with cysteine followed by the coupling of the resulting dipeptide with valine. It is conceivable that the biosynthesis of benzylpenicillin involves an enzyme-catalysed exchange of a residue of α-aminoadipic acid for one of phenylacetic acid and that one pathway to 6-aminopenicillanic acid involves the hydrolytic removal of α-aminoadipic acid. An enzyme that is present in extracts of *Penicillium notatum* catalyses an exchange of side-chains between benzylpenicillin and phenoxymethylpenicillin. It is also conceivable that the α-aminoadipic acid in the tripeptide has the L-configuration and that D-(4-amino-4-carboxy-*n*-butyl)penicillin is formed by the *Cephalosporium* sp. because a mechanism exists in this organism for converting the α-aminoadipic acid to the D-form.

The formation of the β-lactam ring in the penicillin structure may involve an oxidative condensation of the type shown by V or VI. The formation of the thiazolidine ring may then occur by αβ-dehydrogenation of the L-valine residue followed by addition of sulphur to the double bond to yield a residue with the D-configuration at the α-carbon atom.

R·CO·NH·CH—CH=S
CO—N — CH—CH(CH₃)₂
H CO₂H

V

R·CO·NH·CH—CH—SH
CO—N—CH—CH(CH₃)₂
[O⁺] H CO₂H

VI

D-Penicillamine, $(CH_3)_2$–CSH–CH·NH₂·CO₂H, which was the first degradation product to be obtained from penicillin and is one of the starting materials for total chemical synthesis, plays no part in the biosynthesis of the penicillin molecule and does not appear to be formed in nature as an independent unit.

References p. 221

(b) Cephalosporin C

Abraham and Newton found that crude preparations of cephalosporin N contained a second acidic antibiotic which they named cephalosporin C. This substance contained two more carbon and two more oxygen atoms than cephalosporin N and unlike the latter, it showed an absorption band in ultraviolet light at 260 mμ. It was much more stable than cephalosporin N to dilute acid and to penicillinase[23,24].

The results of degradative studies, together with data provided by infra-red spectra, nuclear magnetic resonance spectra, and electrometric titra-tions, led Abraham and Newton[25] to propose the structure VII for cephalo-sporin C. An X-ray crystallographic study by Hodgkin and Maslen led to the same structure and showed that the hydrogen atoms on the β-lactam ring are cis, as they are in the penicillins[26].

When cephalosporin C is kept in dilute acid at room temperature various hydrolytic changes slowly occur. One change involves the removal of the acetyl group and subsequent lactonisation to yield a compound named cephalosporin C_C (VIII). Another involves the removal of the side-chain to

form the nucleus of the cephalosporin C molecule (X) which has been named 7-aminocephalosporanic acid.

When cephalosporin C is kept in an aqueous solution of pyridine the ace-toxy group is replaced by a pyridinium ion and the product, known as cephalosporin C_A, shows no net charge at pH 7. A variety of heterocyclic tertiary bases react in a similar manner to give other members of the cepha-losporin C_A family.

Cephalosporin C contains a β-lactam-dihydrothiazine ring system in place of the β-lactam-thiazolidine ring system in the penicillins. Its structure can be dissected into residues of D-α-aminoadipic acid, L-cysteine, and an oxidation product of valine. This indicates that it is related biogenetically to the penicillins and to cephalosporin N in particular.

(c) Polypeptide antibiotics

Penicillin may be regarded as the product of oxidative intramolecular condensations in a tripeptide. A collection of antibiotics formed by members of the genus *Bacillus* and the genus *Streptomyces* contain between six and twelve amino acid residues linked through peptide bonds. The discovery of these substances has been contemporaneous with the introduction, by Martin and Synge, by Sanger and by Moore and Stein, of new and powerful chromatographic methods for the determination of amino acid sequences in polypeptides, and with the development by Craig of countercurrent distribution as a tool for the separation of peptides from each other. It was thus quickly established that a number of the polypeptide antibiotics were members of families and that they showed unusual structural features. They contained amino acids with the D-configuration and their chains contained large rings closed by peptide or ester linkages. N-terminal portions of their chains often ended in an uncommon structural unit.

(i) The tyrocidines and gramicidins S

These substances, produced by strains of *Bacillus brevis*, are examples of the simplest type of polypeptide antibiotic. They consist of 10 amino acid residues linked head-to-tail in an endless chain.

Dubos showed that tyrothricin could be separated into two components, gramicidin and tyrocidine. Craig showed that tyrocidine could be resolved into three components, tyrocidines A, B and C. Tyrocidine A has the structure XI and tyrocidine B differs from XI only in containing an L-tryptophan residue in place of an L-phenylalanine residue[27].

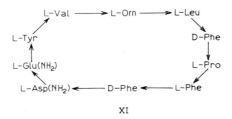

XI

Gramicidin S, first isolated by Gause and Brazhnikova in the U.S.S.R., has been resolved by counter-current distribution into at least four peptides[27]. The major component of the mixture consists of two units of the pentapeptide L-Val–L-Orn–L-Leu–D-Phe–L-Pro linked head-to-tail to give a macrocyclic structure. The pentapeptide unit contains the same sequence of amino acids as one half of the molecule of tyrocidine.

The biosynthesis of gramicidin S may occur through the doubling of the pentapeptide unit. Schwyzer and Sieber[28] attempted to cyclise an activated ester of the pentapeptide, but found that two molecules of the latter combined to give gramicidin S. They suggested that doubling occurred because the L-residues of the two molecules aggregated in a manner corresponding to the antiparallel pleated sheet of Pauling and Corey. This would lead to the structure XII for gramicidin S, a structure which is also favoured by the results of X-ray crystallographic investigations.

XII

(ii) *The bacitracins and related substances*

An antibiotic produced by a strain of *Bacillus licheniformis* that had been isolated in the U.S.A. from debrided tissue of a patient named Tracey was called bacitracin. The same antibiotic was found to be formed by a strain of *Bacillus licheniformis* that had been brought to England from Chile[24,29,30].

Crude bacitracin was resolved by counter-current distribution into a number of similar peptides. Work in two laboratories showed that the major component of the mixture, bacitracin A, had the structure XIII. The dotted line symbolises the fact that a small amount of a peptide containing the sequence Phe–Ileu was found among the products of partial hydrolysis, possibly in consequence of a rearrangement. Bacitracin B appears to consist of a mixture of peptides in which isoleucine residues are replaced by valine at various positions in the chain of XIII.

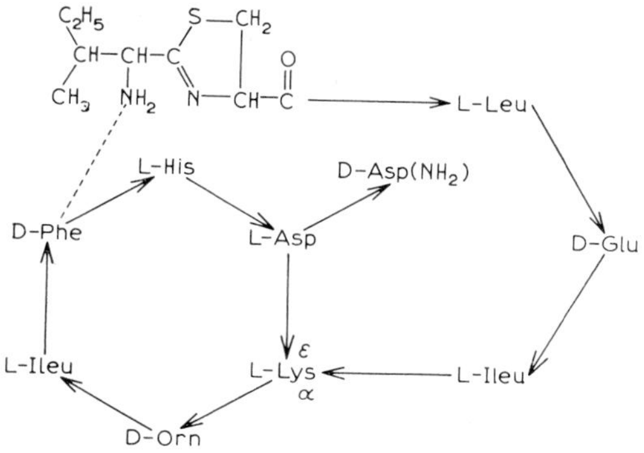

XIII

The structure XIII might be formed by two condensations in a dodeca-peptide containing only α-peptide bonds. Condensation in an N-terminal isoleucylcysteinyl sequence (XIV) would yield the thiazoline containing fragment (XV) of the molecule:

XIV → XV

Condensation of a carboxyl group of the L-aspartic acid with the ε-amino group of the lysine would yield the ring of six residues.

Oxidation of thiazoline rings that have been formed by condensations in N-acylcysteinyl peptides may represent the biosynthetic pathway to thia-zole rings that are present in a number of antibiotics. Bacitracin A under-goes oxidation, in a neutral solution exposed to air, to form bacitracin F, which contains the N-terminal fragment XVI. Micrococcin, an antibiotic

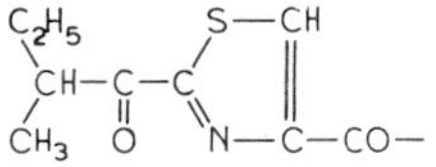

XVI 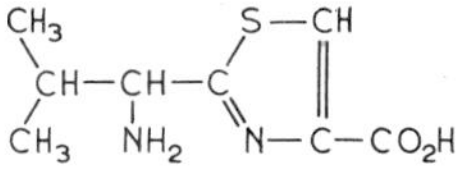　　　　　　　　XVII 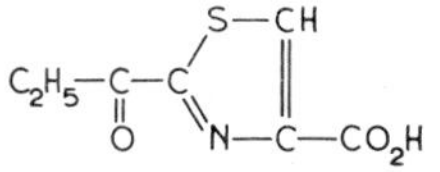　　　　　　　　XVIII

produced by a micrococcus and *Bacillus pumilus*, yields the thiazoles XVII and XVIII on hydrolysis[31]. Bottromycin, a peptide antibiotic formed by a *Streptomyces* sp., gives the dipeptide XIX on treatment with acetic anhydride[32]. Part of this fragment could be synthesised by the *Streptomyces* from α-aspartylcysteine, the steps involving decarboxylation, ring closure and

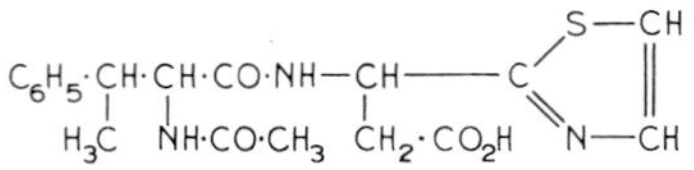

$$C_6H_5 \cdot \underset{\underset{H_3C}{|}}{CH} \cdot \underset{\underset{NH \cdot CO \cdot CH_3}{|}}{CH} \cdot CO \cdot NH - \underset{\underset{CH_2 \cdot CO_2H}{|}}{CH} - C \begin{array}{c} S - CH \\ \| \\ N - CH \end{array}$$

XIX

oxidation. Thiostrepton yields on hydrolysis a racemate of XVII and two other thiazoles derivable from glycylcysteine and α-aminobutyrylcysteine respectively[33].

(iii) *The polymyxins and related substances*

A family of basic polypeptide antibiotics is produced by *Bacillus polymyxa*. Different strains of this organism[34] form polymyxins A, B, C, D and E. Circulin A produced by *Bacillus circulans*[35], and colimycine, produced by *Bacillus colistinus*[36], are related substances. All these antibiotics are cyclic polypeptides containing α,γ-diaminobutyric acid (DAB) and a fatty acid linked to the amino group of an amino acid residue.

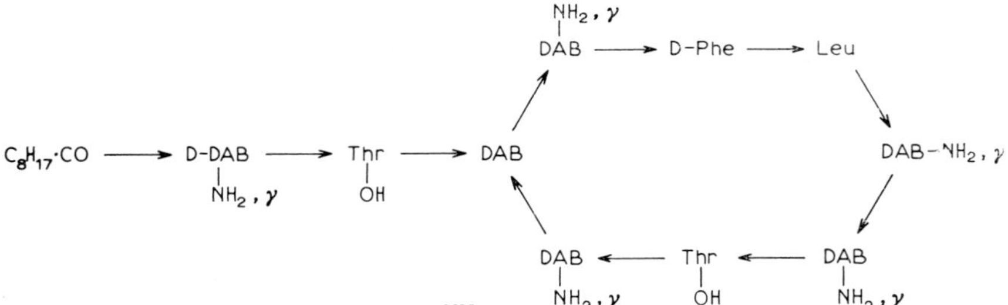

XX

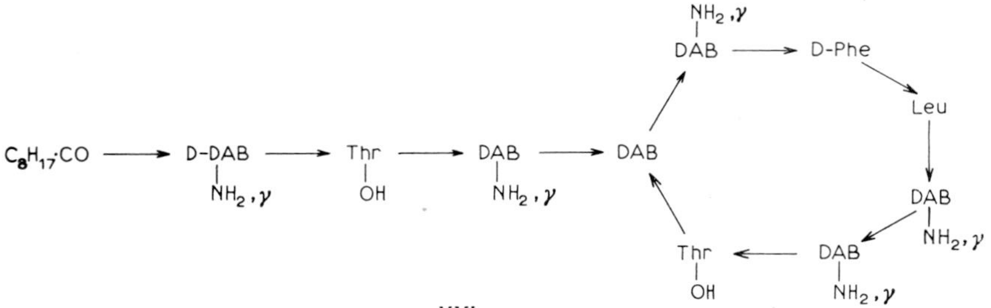

XXI

Polymyxin B has been resolved by countercurrent distribution into two components, B_1 and B_2. Polymyxin B_1, which has been studied by Hausmann[37] and by Biserte and Dautrevaux[38], appears to be represented by XX or XXI, the latter being more likely. An N-terminal residue of α,γ-diaminobutyric acid is acylated by 6-methyloctanoic acid. Isooctanoic acid occurs in this position in polymyxin B_2. In polymyxin B_1 a residue of α,γ-diaminobutyric acid (like lysine in bacitracin A) is used to link a macrocyclic portion of the peptide to a side-chain. If there were an α-linkage between the ring and the side-chain, the ring could be formed from a single chain containing only α-peptide bonds. Two forms of XXI have now been synthesized in which there is an α- and γ-linkage, respectively, between ring and side-chain. Both forms showed high antibacterial activity and an unequivocal decision between them was not made[39].

(iv) The actinomycins

Waksman and Tishler found that a bright red antibiotic, which they named actinomycin, was produced by *Streptomyces antibioticus*. Subsequent work showed that a considerable number of different actinomycins are produced by *S. antibioticus* and *S. chrysomallus*. Different systems of nomenclature have been used with reference to these compounds. In one employed by Brockmann the actinomycins are described by capital letters and subscripts (*e.g.* C_3). The one used here is that suggested by Waksman, Katz and Vining[40] in which each actinomycin is assigned a roman numeral. Actinomycins I to V are produced by *S. antibioticus* and actinomycins IV, VI and VII by *S. chrysomallus*.

The work of Brockmann[41] and of Johnson[42] and their colleagues has indicated that the actinomycins have the general structure XXII, although

XXII

it has been suggested that lactone formation might also occur between the C-terminal residue of one chain and the threonine residue of the other. Structure XXII represents the same phenoxazone chromophore linked to different, though similar, peptides containing lactone rings. In actinomycins I to V sites B and B^1 are occupied by D-valine. In actinomycin VI one of these valine residues is replaced by D-*allo*isoleucine and in actinomycin VII (C_3) both are replaced by D-*allo*isoleucine. Actinomycins I to V differ in the residues occupying sites A and A^1. These are hydroxyproline and proline (I), sarcosine and sarcosine (II), sarcosine and proline (III), proline and proline (IV), or 4-ketoproline and proline (V). In actinomycins VI and VII as in actinomycin IV, both of these sites are occupied by proline. Actinomycin VII (C_3) has been obtained by total synthesis[41].

The phenoxazone fragment of XXII may be dissected, as shown by the broken line, into two residues of 3-hydroxy-4-methylanthranilic acid. Phenoxazones are found in the ommochrome pigments of the eyes of insects. Butenandt has shown that the biosynthesis of one of these pigments involves the oxidative condensation of two molecules of 3-hydroxykynurenine, a derivative of 3-hydroxyanthranilic acid that is formed from tryptophan[43]. Katz and Weissbach have shown that 4-methyl-3-hydroxyanthranilic acid, which is presumably formed from tryptophan via 3-hydroxyanthranilic acid, is converted to the chromophore of the actinomycins by a cell-free extract of *S. antibioticus*[44]. The fact that some of the actinomycins contain two peptide fragments that are not identical could be accounted for by the random coupling of two 3-hydroxy-4-methylanthraniloylpeptides.

Certain changes in the proportion of different actinomycins synthesized by a given *Streptomyces* sp. may result from changes in the amino acid composition of the culture medium. Studies by Katz and Goss have indicated that addition to the medium of proline, hydroxyproline, or sarcosine respectively may result in an increased synthesis of actinomycins with these particular residues at sites A and A^1, and that the addition of pipecolic acid or azetidine-2-carboxylic acid results in the production of new actinomycins in which residues of the added compounds occupy these sites[44]. It seems that the peptide synthesizing mechanism does not distinguish perfectly, at sites A and A^1, between amino acids of similar structure.

Katz[45] has reported that D-valine inhibits actinomycin synthesis and suggested that L-valine is the precursor of the D-valine which may occur in the molecule at sites B and B^1.

(v) Etamycin (viridogrisein) and echinomycin

These antibiotics, produced by *Streptomyces* spp., resemble the actinomycins in that they contain an unusual N-terminal unit linked to the amino group of threonine and that the hydroxyl group of threonine is involved in the formation of a large lactone ring. They also contain N-methylamino acids, etamycin containing the previously unknown α-phenylsarcosine and β-N-dimethylleucine. In etamycin (XXIII) the N-terminal structure is 3-hydroxypicolinic acid[46] and in echinomycin (XXIV) it is quinoxaline-2-carboxylic acid[47].

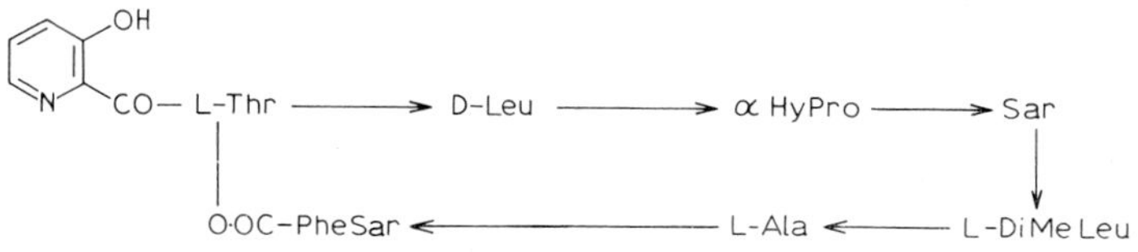

XXIII

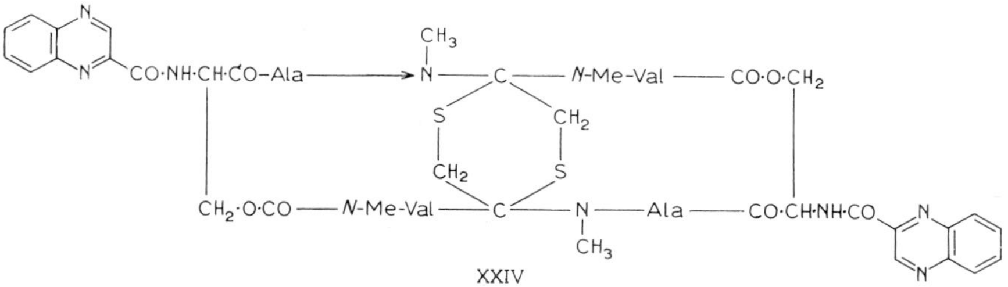

XXIV

(vi) The enniatins, valinomycin and amidomycin

Three antibiotics that were isolated from the mycelium of a species of *Fusarium* were named enniatin A, B and C respectively. The related antibiotics valinomycin and amidomycin were obtained from the mycelia of *Streptomyces* spp. These antibiotics contain a new type of ring in which alternate residues of certain α-hydroxy and α-amino acids are linked by peptide and ester bonds. The enniatins[48] have the general structure XXV. In enniatin A the amino acid is N-methyl-L-isoleucine, in enniatin B it is N-methyl-L-valine and in enniatin C it is probably N-methyl-L-leucine.

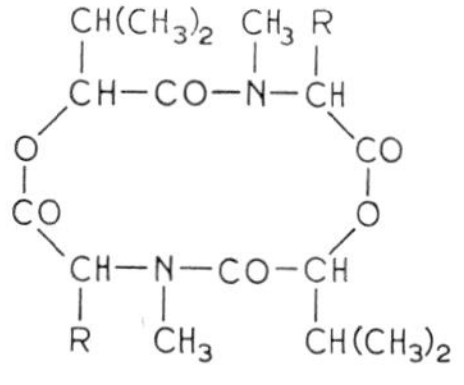

XXV

Amidomycin contains 4 residues of D-α-hydroxyisovaleric acid[49] and 4 of D-valine while valinomycin contains 2 units of D-α-hydroxyisovaleryl-D-valine and 2 of L-lactyl-L-valine[50].

(vii) *The nisins, subtilin and cinnamycin*

Nisin, produced by *Streptococcus lactis*, has been resolved into several components by countercurrent distribution. Subtilin consists of a family of peptides produced by *Bacillus subtilis*. Cinnamycin is formed by *Streptomyces cinnamoneus*. All these peptide antibiotics[51,52] contain the unusual amino acids, lanthionine and β-methyllanthionine (XXVI). Subtilin A appears to contain 5 ring structures. None of its sulphur-containing amino acid residues has free NH_2 groups, and lanthionine may form a bridge between a side-chain [Sar–(Glu–Leu–Sar–Asp)–Lan] and a cyclic structure[53].

$$\begin{array}{l} CH_3 \\ \quad \diagdown \\ \quad\quad CH \cdot CH(NH_2) \cdot CO_2H \\ \quad \diagup \\ S \\ \quad \diagdown \\ \quad\quad CH_2 \cdot CH(NH_2) \cdot CO_2H \end{array}$$

XXVI

(d) Chloramphenicol

Chloramphenicol, which is produced by *Streptomyces venezuelae*, was the first antibiotic with a broad antibacterial spectrum to be introduced into medicine. It was isolated in the Parke Davis Research Laboratories and characterized as D(–)threo-2-dichloracetamido-1-*p*-nitrophenyl-1,3-propanediol (XXVII). It was synthesized by several routes[54–56].

$$O_2N-\!\!\!\!\bigcirc\!\!\!\!-\overset{\overset{\displaystyle H}{|}}{\underset{\underset{\displaystyle OH}{|}}{C}}-\overset{\overset{\displaystyle NH \cdot CO \cdot CHCl_2}{|}}{\underset{\underset{\displaystyle H}{|}}{C}}-CH_2OH$$

XXVII

Chloramphenicol has the common C_6–C_3 skeleton which appears in amino acids such as phenylalanine and its C_3 fragment is also structurally related to serine, but it contains a nitro group and dichloroacetyl group which are unusual in natural products. The condensation of *p*-nitrophenylserinol and dichloroacetic acid appears to have been excluded as a step in the biosynthesis of this antibiotic[57]. However, dechloro analogues of chloramphenicol are produced by a *Streptomyces* sp. in a culture medium to which no chloride ion has been added. These analogues include compounds in which the dichloroacetyl group of XXVII is replaced by acetyl, propionyl, butyryl, and pentanoyl or hexanoyl[58].

Chloramphenicol is degraded in a number of different ways by bacterial enzymes[59].

(e) *Miscellaneous antibiotics derivable from amino acids*

A few antibiotics that are produced by *Streptomyces* spp. have structural affinities to single amino acids. Thus D-cycloserine[60] (oxamycin), which has the structure XXVIII, could formally be obtained from D-serine amide by removal of the elements of water, or from D-alanine by an oxidative process.

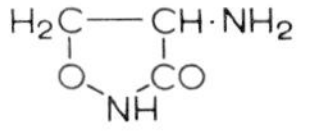

XXVIII

$N_2CH \cdot CO \cdot O \cdot CH_2 \cdot CH \cdot NH_2 \cdot CO_2H$

XXIX

$N_2CH \cdot CO \cdot CH_2 \cdot CH_2 \cdot CH \cdot NH_2CO_2H$

XXX

L-Azaserine (XXIX) and 6-diazo-5-oxo-L-norleucine (DON) (XXX), which contain a reactive aliphatic diazo group[61], could be regarded as oxidation products of ornithine and lysine respectively. Thiolutin (XXXI, R = CH_3CO) and aureothricin (XXXI, R = CH_3CH_2CO)[62] have structural affinities to cystine.

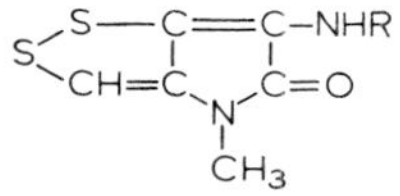

XXXI

In addition to the penicillins, a number of antibiotics produced by fungi have structures that could arise from the condensation of two or three amino acids. For example, gliotoxin, which is formed by *Trichoderma viride* and *Aspergillus fumigatus*, may be regarded as an anhydrodipeptide containing the skeletons[63] of phenylalanine and serine, as shown by the broken line in XXXII.

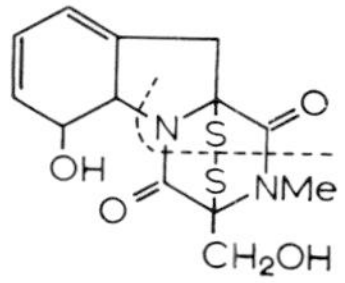

XXXII

Phenylalanine labelled with ^{14}C has been shown to be a direct precursor of the indole fragment of the molecule[64]. The positions of the sulphur atoms are such that they form part of α-thio-α-amino acid residues, and they might be introduced, together with nitrogen, via the corresponding keto acids. Sulphur occurs in this or a related structural situation in echinomycin and actithiazic acid.

Several antibiotics from *Streptomyces* spp. contain structures that may be

References p. 221

dissected into amino acids and other types of unit. The dilactone structure
XXXIII has been proposed for a family of antibiotics known as antimycin
A, with R and R′ representing different hydrocarbon chains[65,66]. This

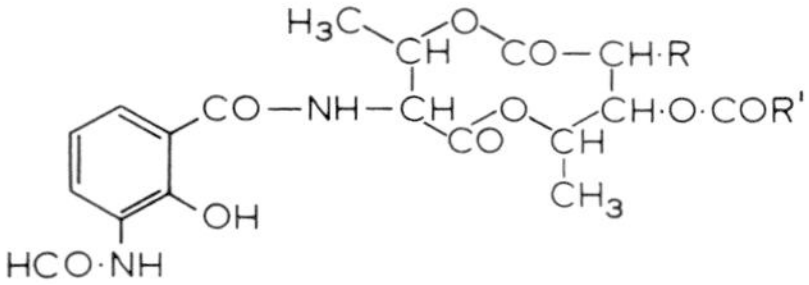

XXXIII

structure, which contains a residue of *N*-(3-aminosalicyloyl)-L-threonine,
shows a general resemblance to the N-terminal portion of etamycin and
similar polypeptide antibiotics. The antibiotics puromycin, cordicepin,
nebularine, nucleocidin and amicetin have nucleoside structures[67]. Thus, puromycin (XXXIV) may be dissected into 6-dimethylaminopurine, D-3-ami-
noribose, and *p*-methoxyphenylalanine.

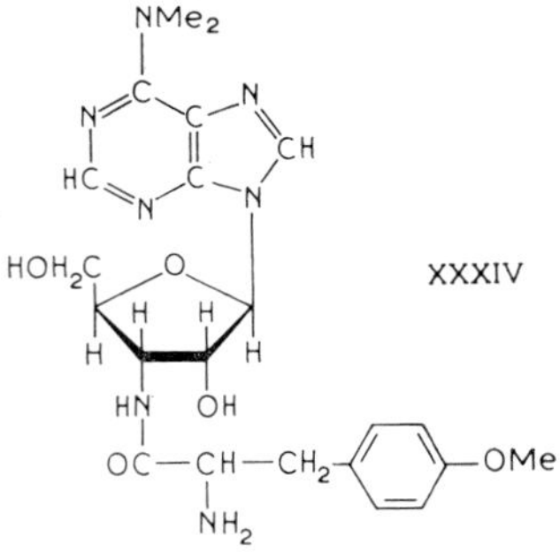

XXXIV

(f) Griseofulvin

Griseofulvin was first isolated by Oxford, Raistrick and Simonart from the
mycelium of *Penicillium griseofulvum*. "Curling-factor", an antibiotic
discovered by Brian, Curtis and Hemming which caused characteristic
changes in the germ tubes of certain fungi, was later shown to be identical
with griseofulvin. Grove[68] and others established the structure of griseofulvin as XXXV.

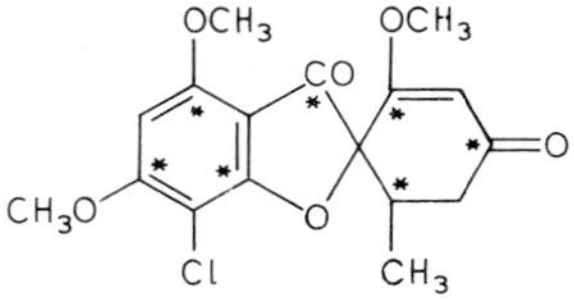

XXXV

The oxygen atoms in XXXV appear on alternate carbon atoms of the carbon skeleton. Collie, Robinson, Birch and others have pointed out that this distribution of oxygen in a natural product may indicate that the latter is derived from a poly β-keto acid which is itself formed from acetate. Birch[69] and his colleagues found that the distribution of ^{14}C in griseofulvin formed by *P. griseofulvum* in the presence of [I-^{14}C]acetate (shown by * in XXXV) was precisely that to be expected if the skeleton of the molecule had been produced by intramolecular condensation in the poly β-keto acid,

XXXVI

XXXVI. The latter could be synthesized from 7 molecules of acetate, with malonyl coenzyme A as an intermediate as it is in the synthesis of fatty acids. O-Methylation and the introduction of a chlorine atom into the carbon skeleton would be required to yield XXXV. But the biosynthesis of the skeleton itself appears to be independent of the process of chlorination, for dechlorogriseofulvin has been isolated from culture fluids of *Penicillium griseofulvum* and *Penicillium janczewskii*, and the bromo analogue of griseofulvin may be formed when chloride in the culture medium is replaced by bromide[70].

(g) The tetracyclines

Soon after the introduction of chloramphenicol into medicine a second antibiotic with a broad antibacterial spectrum was discovered in the Lederle Laboratories[71]. This substance was produced by *Streptomyces aureofaciens* and was named aureomycin. Later, a similar substance, terramycin, was isolated at Chas. Pfizer Inc. from the culture fluid of *Streptomyces rimosus*[72]. The complete structure of terramycin[73] was elucidated in 1953 and that of aureomycin[74] a year later.

TABLE I

RELATIONSHIP OF SOME TETRACYCLINES PRODUCED BY *Streptomyces* spp.

Compound (see structure XXXVII)	R_1	R_2	R_3
Tetracycline	H	CH$_3$	H
7-Chlorotetracycline (aureomycin)	Cl	CH$_3$	H
5-Oxytetracycline (terramycin)	H	CH$_3$	OH
6-Demethyltetracycline	H	H	H

Aureomycin contained a chlorine atom which was removed by catalytic hydrogenation with the formation of a substance that was given the generic name tetracycline. Subsequently, this and other substances of the same family were also found to be produced by *Streptomyces* spp. These antibiotics have the general structure XXXVII and the relationship between them is shown in Table I. In addition, 6-deoxytetracyclines can be obtained from tetracyclines by hydrogenolysis[75], and an aminomethyl group can be introduced onto the amide nitrogen by treatment of tetracyclines with formaldehyde and an amine[76].

In the tetracyclines, oxygen appears on a series of alternate carbon atoms. Robinson pointed out that the naphthalene ring system could be derived from octaketostearic acid and that the latter could be formed from 9 moles of acetate[11]. The addition of single carbon atoms and an amino

XXXVII   XXXVIII

group, together with other plausible changes, might then lead to tetracycline. Degradation of tetracycline produced in the presence of isotopically labelled precursors has indicated that a major part of the molecule, but probably not all of it, is derived from acetate units linked head-to-tail.

[1-14C] Acetate and [2-14C] acetate were found to be good precursors of labelled tetracyclines and the results of partial degradations of the labelled compounds were consistent with the assumption that the skeletons of rings D and C and part, at least, of ring B were formed from a polyketomethylene. A polymerisation involving malonyl coenzyme A, itself formed from acetyl coenzyme A, may thus play an important role in the biosynthesis of the molecule. However, glutamic acid, rather than acetate, may be a precursor of part, at least, of ring A.

The introduction of a methyl group at C-6, a halogen atom at C-7, or an oxygen at C-5 is independent of the synthesis of the main skeleton, for 6-demethyl analogues of tetracycline, 7-bromotetracycline, and 5-oxytetracycline are formed by *Streptomyces* spp. The methyl carbon of methionine acts as a source of the methyl group at C-6 and the N-methyl groups. The nature and relative amounts of the halogen substituted tetracyclines that are synthesised depend on the halide content of the culture medium. The relationship of these facts to the biogenesis of the tetracyclines is summarised in XXXVIII, in which carbons b and a are derived from C-1 and C-2 of acetate respectively[77].

Microbiological hydroxylation of 12α-deoxytetracycline to tetracycline has been shown to occur[78] and also the reduction of 5α(11α)-dehydrotetracycline[79]. It may be that these processes occur at late stages in the biosynthesis of the tetracycline molecule.

(h) Polyacetylene antibiotics

In 1952 Anchel reported that a number of antibiotics produced by *Basidiomycetes* were polyacetylenes[80]. Compounds of this class had been known since 1935 to be produced by plants and those of the *Compositae* had been investigated systematically by Sörensen. The general chemistry of polyacetylenes was studied by Jones and his colleagues and by Bohlmann[81,82]. Many of these energy-rich compounds are extremely unstable and polymerise rapidly in the solid state. However, they show characteristic ultraviolet absorption spectra which are useful in structural determinations.

Some of the polyacetylene antibiotics are highly toxic and none has found clinical use.

Agrocybin, produced by *Agrocybe dura*, has the structure XXXIX and diatretynes I and II, produced by *Clytocybe diatreta*, have the structures XL and XLI respectively.

Mycomycin, which was isolated by Celmer and Solomons[83] from the culture fluid of the actinomycete, *Nocardia acidophilus*, was shown to contain a polyacetylenic structure and also an optically active allene unit (XLII). Van 't Hoff had predicted that the allene unit should show optical activity, but mycomycin provided the first example of its existence in nature. Nemotin (XLIII) and nemotinic acid (XLIV), which are formed by *Poria corticola* and *Poria tenuis*, are also allenes. A related compound, odyssic acid (XLV), is produced by the same fungi.

Biformin, obtained from the culture fluid of *Polyporus biformis*, may have

$$HOCH_2.C \equiv C.C \equiv C.C \equiv C.CONH_2 \qquad XXXIX$$

$$HO_2C.CH = CH.C \equiv C.C \equiv C.CONH_2 \qquad XL$$

$$HO_2C.CH = CH.C \equiv C.C \equiv C.CN \qquad XLI$$

$$HC \equiv C.C \equiv C.CH = C = CH.CH = CH.CH = CH.CH_2CO_2H \qquad XLII$$
$$\qquad cis \qquad trans$$

$$HC \equiv C.C \equiv C.CH = C = CH.CH.CH_2.CH_2.CO \qquad XLIII$$
$$\qquad\qquad | \qquad\qquad\qquad\qquad |$$
$$\qquad\qquad O$$

$$H\overset{*}{C} \equiv C.\overset{*}{C} \equiv C.\overset{*}{C}H = C = \overset{*}{C}H.CHOH.\overset{*}{C}H_2.CH_2.CO_2H \qquad XLIV$$

$$CH_3.C \equiv C.C \equiv C.CH = C = CH.CHOH.CH_2.CH_2.CO_2H \qquad XLV$$

$$HC \equiv C.C \equiv C.C \equiv C.CHOH.CHOH.CH_2OH \qquad XLVI$$

a triynediol structure. The main quadrifidin produced by *Coprinus quadri-fidus* is the triacetylenic triol[82], XLVI.

The natural polyacetylenes were shown to have unbranched chains of carbon atoms and a group of polyacetylenes from seed oils contained the C_{18} chain of stearic acid. It thus seemed possible that these substances were produced by modifications of the process of fatty acid synthesis. In conformity with this hypothesis, Bu'Lock and Gregory[84] found that nemotinic acid produced by a *Basidiomycete* in the presence of [1-14C] acetate contained 14C equally distributed in its odd numbered carbon atoms (denoted by * in XLIV).

Several possible mechanisms for the formation of triple bonds have been considered. One involves the dehydration of enols corresponding to polyketo acids. Examples of the reverse of this reaction are known. The conversion of acetylene dicarboxylic acid to oxaloacetic acid has been shown to be brought about by extracts of *Enterobacteriaceae*, and the conversion of acetylene monocarboxylic acid to malonic semialdehyde is catalysed by an enzyme from a strain of *Pseudomonas fluorescens*[85].

A number of the polyacetylenic antibiotics contain carboxyl groups, or groups easily derived from carboxyl, at both ends of their carbon chains. Diatretyne II (XLI) can be placed in this group, for its unusual nitrile may be formed by dehydration of the amide in diatretyne I. These antibiotics contain an even number of carbon atoms. If they are synthesised entirely from acetate (via malonyl coenzyme A) one of their terminal groups may thus arise from the oxidation of a methyl group. In contrast, the polyacetylene antibiotics which contain a terminal HC≡C group have an odd number of carbon atoms. This would be accounted for if the oxidation of a terminal methyl group to a carboxyl were followed by decarboxylation. The production of the C_{11} nemotinic acid (XLIV) and the C_{12} odyssic acid (XLV) by the same fungus would also be consistent with such a biosynthetic pathway. Other possibilities, such as the generation of a terminal ethynyl (HC≡C) group by the dehydration of a malonic semialdehyde fragment, are less easily reconciled with the distribution of labelled carbon in nemotinic acid.

(j) The macrolide (erythromycin) group of antibiotics

In 1956 structures began to be reported for a new class of antibiotics produced by *Streptomyces* spp. The term macrolide has been applied to these substances because they all contain a large lactone ring. The ring is joined glycosidically to one or more amino sugars and also, in some cases, to a non-nitrogenous sugar. Several macrolide antibiotics have proved clinically useful. Erythromycin, which is probably the best known, was developed in the Lilly Research Laboratories.

Properties of some of the macrolide antibiotics are given in Table II. The same sugars are found in a number of different substances. Most of these sugars had not previously been encountered but oleandrose, obtained from oleandomycin, had been found in the cardiac glycoside oleandrin.

TABLE II

PROPERTIES OF SOME MACROLIDE ANTIBIOTICS

Substance	Molecular formula	Number of atoms in macrolide ring	Sugars obtained on hydrolysis	
			Dimethylamino sugar	Non-nitrog-enous sugar
Methymycin[87]	$C_{25}H_{43}O_7N$	12	Desosamine	None
Neomethymycin	$C_{25}H_{43}O_7N$	12	Desosamine	None
Pikromycin[88]	$C_{25}H_{43}O_7N$	12	Desosamine	None
Oleandomycin[89]	$C_{35}H_{61}O_{12}N$		Desosamine	Oleandrose
Erythromycin[90]	$C_{37}H_{67}O_{13}N$	14	Desosamine	Cladinose
Erythromycin B	$C_{37}H_{67}O_{12}N$	14	Desosamine	Cladinose
Erythromycin C	$C_{36}H_{65}O_{13}N$	14	Desosamine	Unnamed
Magnamycin[86]	$C_{42}H_{67}O_{16}N$	17	Mycaminose	Mycarose
Magnamycin B	$C_{42}H_{67}O_{15}N$	17	Mycaminose	Mycarose
Spiramycin A[91]	$C_{45}H_{78}O_{15}N_2$		Mycaminose	Mycarose
Spiramycin B	$C_{47}H_{80}O_{16}N_2$		and another	Mycarose
Spiramycin C	$C_{48}H_{82}O_{16}N_2$			Mycarose

Methymycin (XLVII) and pikromycin (XLVIII) appear to differ only in the position at which the dimethylamino sugar, desosamine, is attached to the lactone ring. Neomethymycin has a hydroxyl group at C-12 in place of that at C-10 in methymycin.

Erythromycin has the structure XLIX. Erythromycin B differs from erythromycin only in containing no hydroxyl substituent at C-12.

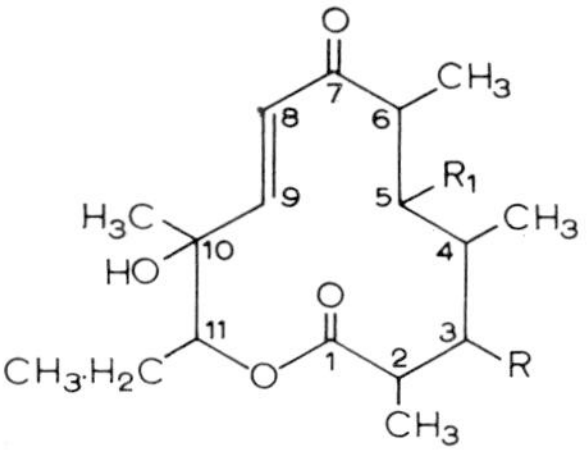

XLVII and XLVIII

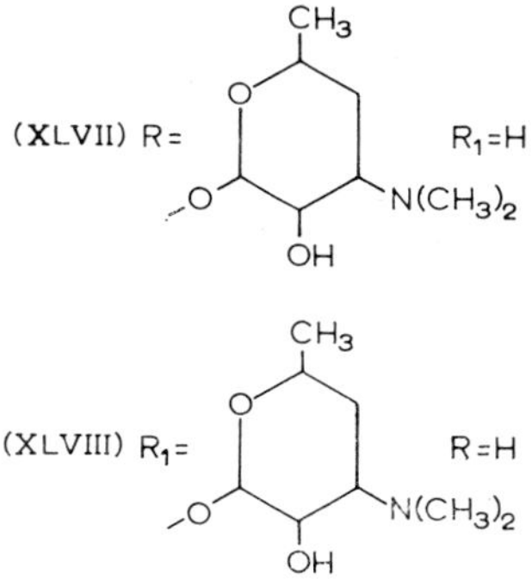

Erythromycin C contains a sugar with the composition $C_7H_{14}O_4$ in place of cladinose.

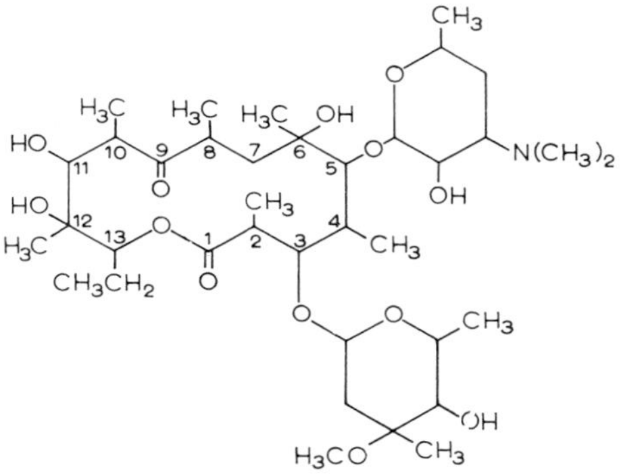

XLIX

Magnamycin (L) contains a dimethylamino sugar to which the isovaleryl derivative of non-nitrogenous sugar (mycarose) is linked glycosidically. In magnamycin B there is a double bond in place of the epoxide group in the macrocyclic lactone.

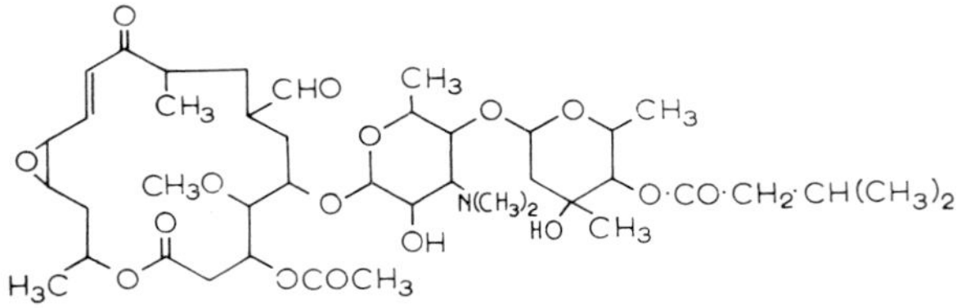

L

The general structural patterns of the large lactone rings of the macrolide antibiotics suggest that these rings may be formed from poly β-keto acids. Thus, in the lactone of methymycin (named methynolide) oxygen is found on each odd numbered carbon atom except C-5, and in the lactone of erythromycin (erythronolide) it is found on each odd numbered carbon except C-7. Certain features of the individual ring structures, however, raise specific biogenetic problems.

If a lactone were formed from a poly β-keto acid derived from acetate (with malonyl coenzyme A as an intermediate) the ring should contain an even number of atoms. To account for the presence of an odd number of atoms in the lactone of magnamycin Woodward suggested that the aldehyde group at C-7 in this ring is extruded from the chain of a hypothetical precursor, protomagnamycin, by a pinacol–pinacolone rearrangement[86].

Protomagnamycin would have a C_{18} carbon skeleton very similar to that of tuberculostearic acid.

In the lactone rings of methymycin and pikromycin, methyl groups occur on most of the even numbered carbon atoms, and in erythronolide they occur on all the even numbered carbon atoms. Methyl groups can sometimes be added separately to a carbon skeleton, but those in the macrolides may originate in a different way. The fact that erythronolide can be dissected into 7 three-carbon units has led to the hypothesis that this lactone is formed from propionate rather than from acetate and one-carbon fragments. The suggestion has been made that it may be possible to apply to some compounds a "propionate rule", analogous to the "isoprene rules" which have facilitated the prediction of structures among the terpenes[90]. Propionyl coenzyme A is known to undergo carboxylation to methylmalonyl coenzyme A (LI). Polymerisation of the latter could yield a poly β-keto acid of the type required for the biosynthesis of erythronolide[92].

$$2x\ CH_3 \cdot CH_2 \cdot COCoA \xrightarrow{CO_2} 2x\ \underset{\underset{CO_2H}{|}}{\overset{\overset{CH_3}{|}}{CH}} \cdot COCoA \longrightarrow x\ (-\overset{\overset{CH_3}{|}}{CH} \cdot CO \cdot \overset{\overset{CH_3}{|}}{CH} \cdot CO-) + CO_2$$

LI

When erythromycin is formed in the presence of [1-^{14}C]acetate or [1-^{14}C]propionate the labelled carbon is incorporated into the erythronolide portion of the molecule but not into either of the sugars, cladinose and desosamine, to which this portion is linked[93]. Different types of biosynthetic pathway are thus involved in the formation of the sugars and of the lactone ring. [^{14}C]Propionate is incorporated into the lactone ring as an intact unit[93].

(k) Polyene antibiotics

A group of antibiotics that are produced by *Streptomyces* spp. contain polyene groupings. These antibiotics inhibit the growth of certain fungi and some of them have proved effective against fungal infections in man.

(i) Nystatin and amphotericin B

Nystatin, obtained from *Streptomyces noursei*, has the molecular formula $C_{46}H_{77}O_{19}N$. Its ultraviolet absorption spectrum indicates that it contains a tetraene grouping. Amphotericin B, obtained from another species of *Streptomyces*, has the formula $C_{46}H_{73}O_{20}N$ and contains a heptaene grouping[94,95]. Both antibiotics are amphoteric and both consist of C_{40} structures linked to an amino sugar named mycosamine.

(ii) Pimaricin

This antifungal polyene, with the molecular formula $C_{34}H_{49}O_{14}N$, has been shown to consist of mycosamine linked to a large lactone ring containing a tetraene grouping[96]. Its structure (LII) thus has an architectural pattern similar to that of the erythromycin group of macrolides. Nystatin and amphotericin B may be compounds of a similar type.

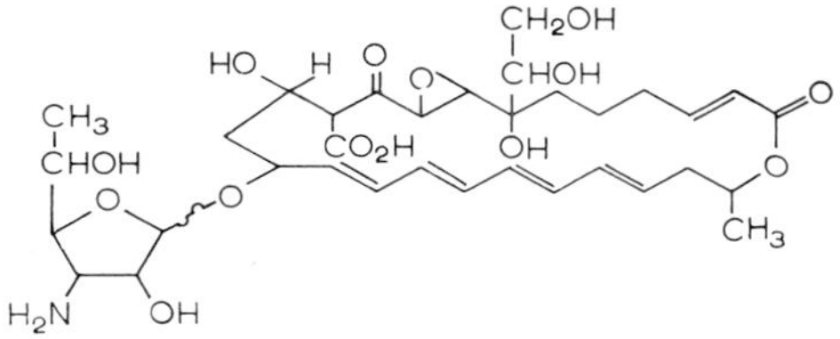

LII

(l) Terpenoid antibiotics

Several antibiotics have terpenoid structures or contain terpenoid fragments.

Mycophenolic acid ($C_{17}H_{20}O_6$), which is produced by several species of *Penicillium*, consists of a terpenoid chain attached to an aromatic nucleus. When the antibiotic is produced in culture fluid containing labelled acetate the latter is incorporated into both side-chain and nucleus. Labelled mevalonic acid, on the other hand, is incorporated only into the side-chain[97]. Helvolic acid ($C_{32}H_{42}O_8$), cephalosporin P ($C_{32}H_{48}O_8$) and fucidin ($C_{31}H_{48}O_6$), which are acidic antibiotics produced by *Aspergillus fumigatus*, a *Cephalosporium* sp., and *Fusidium coccineum*, respectively, appear to belong to the triterpene group[98]. The terpenoid hydrocarbon, squalene, formed from mevalonic acid, is thus probably involved in their biosynthesis[24].

(m) The streptomycins

Streptomycin, produced by *Streptomyces griseus*, is a strongly basic antibiotic which has the structure LIII. It consists of three fragments linked

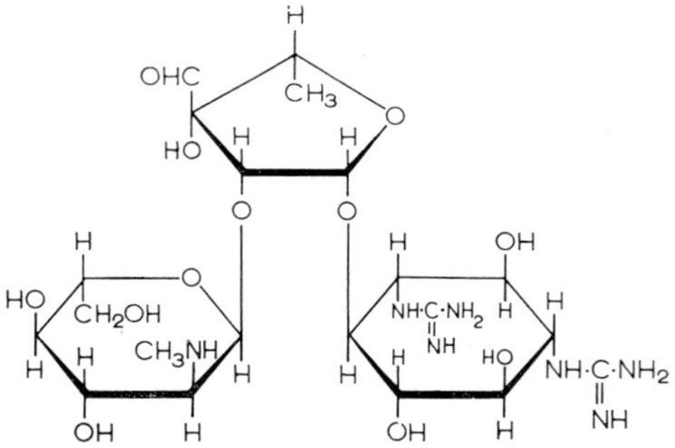

LIII

glycosidically: streptidine, streptose, and N-methyl-L-glucosamine[99]. Streptidine is a *meso* diguanidocyclohexitol and streptose is a sugar with a branched aldehyde group.

Two substances that are closely related to streptomycin are also produced by *Streptomyces* spp. In one, mannosidostreptomycin, a residue of D-mannose is attached by a glycosidic linkage to C-4 of the N-methyl-L-glucosamine fragment of LIII. In the other, hydroxystreptomycin, the methyl group of the streptose fragment of LIII is replaced by a hydroxymethyl group. Catalytic reduction of the aldehyde group in streptomycin leads to the biologically active dihydrostreptomycin.

The whole carbon skeleton of streptomycin is synthesised by *Streptomyces griseus* from D-glucose. On the other hand, the label of [14C] acetate or glycine is only incorporated into the guanidine side-chains. The carbon of the guanidine groups can be derived from carbon dioxide and it may be these groups are transferred to a streptomycin precursor from arginine.

Streptidine does not appear to be an intermediate in the biosynthesis of streptomycin, but N-methyl-[14C]-L-glucosamine is incorporated into both the streptidine and the N-methyl-L-glucosamine fragment of the molecule. There are apparently enzyme systems in *Streptomyces griseus* which link D-glucose with L-glucose and N-methyl-L-glucosamine[100]. Multiple epimerisations and multiple oxidation and reduction have been considered as possible mechanisms for the inversion of all the asymmetric centres of D-glucose[100].

(n) Kanamycin, the neomycins and paromomycin

(i) Kanamycin

Kanamycin, produced by *Streptomyces kanamyceticus*, has been shown by

LIV

workers in Japan and in the U.S.A. to have the structure LIV. Like streptomycin, it consists of three C_6 units joined by glycosidic linkages. These
units are 6-amino-6-deoxy-D-glucose, 3-amino-3-deoxy-D-glucose and 2-
deoxystreptamine respectively[101,102]. The 2-deoxystreptamine is related to
the streptidine of streptomycin, but differs from it in containing amino
groups in place of guanidyl groups and in containing hydrogen in place of a
hydroxyl group at C-2.

(ii) Neomycin

Neomycin was first obtained by Waksman and Lechevalier from the
culture fluid of *Streptomyces fradiae*[103]. Later, it was shown to consist of
closely related antibiotics, neomycins B and C. Both substances consist of
three C_6 units and one C_5 unit linked glycosidically and neomycin B can be
assigned the tentative structure LV. A fragment composed of a diaminohexose and 2-deoxystreptamine, known as neamine, is common to neomycins B and C. The difference between the two substances resides in a second
fragment, known as neobiosamine B or C, which consists of D-ribose linked
to a diaminohexose. The latter[104], which is different in the two neomycins,
is known as neosamine B or C.

LV

(iii) Paromomycin

Paromomycin (LVI), produced by a *Streptomyces* sp., resembles neomycin
in its structural pattern. It contains D-glucosamine, 2-deoxystreptamine,
D-ribose, and a new diaminohexose, named paromose, linked glycosidically[105].

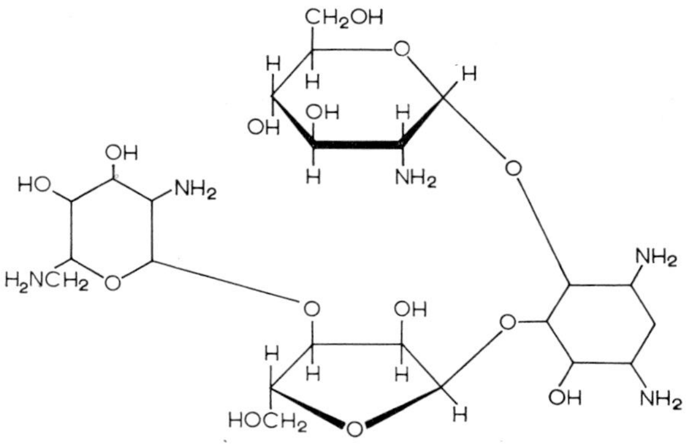

LVI

(o) Novobiocin

An antibiotic which was isolated from culture fluids of *Streptomyces niveus* and *Streptomyces spheroides* by members of the Upjohn Co. and of Merck, Sharp and Dohme respectively has been named novobiocin.

The structure of novobiocin (LVII) may be dissected into three fragments: a substituted benzoic acid, a substituted coumarin, and a new sugar, noviose. Optical rotational data suggest that it is an α-glycoside[106]. The enolic group of the coumarin imparts acidic properties to the molecule.

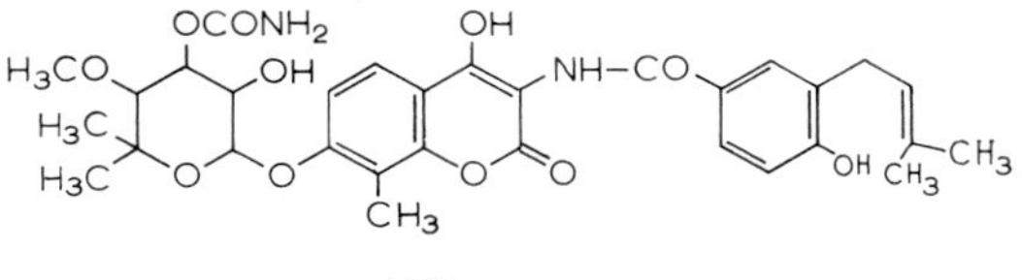

LVII

(p) Vancomycin and ristocetins A and B

Vancomycin, which is produced by *Streptomyces orientalis*, is an amphoteric substance with a molecular weight of 3,200 to 3,500. It appears to contain amino and phenolic groups and yields aspartic acid and D-glucose, among other products, on hydrolysis[107].

Ristocetins A and B are produced by *Nocardia lurida*. They are amphoteric substances which contain amino and phenolic groups and carbohydrate. They appear to be related chemically to vancomycin[108].

5. Structure and activity

Antibiotics with widely different structures may have a similar range of activity. For example, the common penicillins, erythromycin, novobiocin, bacitracin and vancomycin are effective mainly against Gram positive bacteria and *Neisseria*. Chloramphenicol and the tetracyclines have broad spectra. On the other hand, antibiotics that are related chemically may have very different antibacterial activities. Cephalosporin N is much less active than benzylpenicillin against Gram positive bacteria, but more active against certain Gram negative bacteria, in particular the *salmonellae*. Nevertheless, antibiotics in the same or related chemical families often resemble each other, as might be expected, in their biological properties. The various polymyxins are more active against Gram negative than against Gram positive organisms. Streptomycin, kanamycin and neomycin all show high activity against *Mycob. tuberculosis*. Among members of a single group or family this resemblance may extend to different strains of single bacterial species. Staphylococci that have acquired resistance to one of the macrolide (erythromycin) antibiotics are normally resistant to others, though they may be sensitive to antibiotics of a different type, such as penicillin.

The antimicrobial properties of different members of a single antibiotic family show that variations can often be made in certain portions of a structure without the loss of the specific characteristics which endow the molecule with activity. For example, the substituents R_1, R_2 and R_3 on the upper periphery of the tetracycline structure (XXXVII) can all be varied without great effect on the activity of the molecule against *Staph. aureus*. 6-Deoxytetracyclines also show a high activity. Similarly, many changes involving non-polar groups can be made in the penicillin side-chain which have relatively little influence on the antibacterial properties of the molecule. About two thirds of the original activity of novobiocin is retained when the carbamyl group migrates from C-3 to C-2.

However, certain variations in structure which appear to fall into this category nevertheless result in quantitative changes in activity, possibly because they affect the ability of the antibiotic to reach its point of action in the cell. Cephalosporin N, a penicillin in which the side-chain carries a negatively charged carboxyl group and positively charged amino group, provides one example. A similar example is provided by the *N*-phenylacetyl derivative of 7-aminocephalosporanic acid, an analogue of cephalosporin C (VII) which is very much more active against *Staph. aureus* than cephalosporin C itself[109]. Dechlorogriseofulvin and the dechloro analogue of chloramphenicol are less active than the normal antibiotics. Changes in pharmacological or other biological properties may also occur. Phenoxymethylpenicillin is relatively stable in dilute acid and is useful, partly for this reason, for oral administration. 2,6-Dimethoxyphenylpenicillin is hydrolysed much less rapidly than benzylpenicillin by staphylococcal penicillinase under conditions such that the enzyme is saturated with substrate and it appears, in addition, to have a much lower affinity for the enzyme. In consequence, 2,6-dimethoxyphenylpenicillin is much more active than benzylpenicillin against penicillinase producing strains of *Staph. aureus* though it is much less active against other strains.

Changes in other portions of an antibiotic molecule, and particularly changes in configuration at asymmetric centres, may result in a virtually complete loss of activity. For example, conversion of the amide group in tetracycline to the nitrile yields an inactive product. Hydrogen bonding of the phenolic hydroxyl at C-10, which can be brought about by the introduction of a nitro group at C-9 in the 6-deoxytetracyclines, results in a great reduction in activity[110]. 4-*Epi*tetracycline and 5-*epi*tetracycline, which differ only in their configuration at C-4 and C-5 respectively from the natural products (XXXVII), have less than 5% of the activity of the latter against *Staph. aureus*. The (+) L-*erythro* isomer of chloramphenicol (XXVII) has only about 1% of the activity of the natural D-*threo* product and the L-*threo* and D-*erythro* forms are inactive[111]. D-Azaserine, in contrast to the natural L compound, is inactive. Both the integrity of the thiazoline ring in bacitracin (XIII) and the correct configuration at the N-terminal asymmetric centre appear to be essential for the full activity of the peptide. In the penicillin series it seems that the thiazolidine-β-lactam ring system of the 6-aminopenicillanic acid nucleus must be intact and all the asymmetric centres in this nucleus must have the natural configuration for the corresponding penicillin to show high activity. Thus, a penicillin with the L-configuration at C-3 appears to be inactive.

Cephalosporin C, which contains a dihydrothiazine-β-lactam ring system, shows at least 10% of the activity of cephalosporin N against *Staph. aureus* and induces the formation of the enzyme penicillinase by *Staph. aureus* and *Bacillus cereus*[112]. This may be attributed to the fact that the stereochemistry of a major part of the cephalosporin C nucleus is similar to that of 6-aminopenicillanic acid. The precise factors which determine the ability of a substance to act as an inducer of penicillinase are clearly different from those which make the substance a good substrate of the enzyme. The β-lactam ring in cephalosporin C is insensitive to penicillinase. However, the affinity of a substance for a penicillinase varies with the source of the enzyme. Cephalosporin C acts as a competitive inhibitor of the action of penicillinase from *Bacillus cereus*, but not from *Staph. aureus*, on benzylpenicillin. In contrast, the N-phenylacetyl derivative of 7-aminocephalosporanic acid is a powerful inhibitor of the staphylococcal enzyme[24,112].

6. Biochemical effects of antibiotics on micro-organisms

The stereospecificity of many of the antibiotics indicates that they interact at several points, like the substrates of enzymes, with structures that themselves contain asymmetric centres. Antibiotics which are highly selective in their action presumably react with structural entities in sensitive cells which do not exist, or are inaccessible, in cells that are resistant.

A number of antibiotics damage the structure, or inhibit the synthesis, of the cell membranes or walls of micro-organisms. Others interfere with reactions, such as those involved in the production of energy of formation of protein, which are essential for the general growth of the cell.

(a) Antibiotics which cause defects in the cell membrane

(i) Tyrocidine and polymyxin

Both these antibiotics damage the cytoplasmic membrane of sensitive bacteria. Newton has shown that a fluorescent 1-dimethylaminonaphthalene-5-sulphonyl derivative of polymyxin (DANSP) combines with the cytoplasmic membrane[113].

The fragile cytoplasmic membrane controls the osmotic equilibrium of the cell. When it is damaged, amino acids, nucleotides and other essential cellular constituents escape into the external medium. The membrane is surrounded by, or interwoven with, a more rigid cell wall structure. The walls of a number of polymyxin sensitive bacteria, including *Pseudomonas aeruginosa*, absorb DANSP much more readily than those of polymyxin-resistant bacteria. It has been suggested that the resistance of many Gram positive bacteria to polymyxin may be due to an inability of the antibiotic to penetrate the wall and reach the underlying membrane.

(ii) Streptomycin and novobiocin

Anand and Davis found that streptomycin was rapidly lethal to a culture of *E. coli* which was growing exponentially in a medium of glucose and mineral salts[114]. The bactericidal action was accompanied by the excretion of 5'-ribonucleotides and amino acids into the medium. Streptomycin thus appears to cause damage to a permeability barrier, presumably the cytoplasmic membrane, of the bacterial cell. But its action on the membrane, unlike that of polymyxin, is an indirect one. Both the lethal and excreting action of streptomycin were found to be blocked when protein synthesis was inhibited by chloramphenicol. It was thus suggested that streptomycin affects the process of membrane synthesis, so that new membrane formed in the presence of the antibiotic is defective. However, it does not follow that breakdown of the permeability barrier is alone responsible for the lethal effect of the drug. Umbreit believed that streptomycin was a powerful inhibitor of an enzyme system involved in the oxidation of pyruvate and oxaloacetate. Hancock has reported that inhibition of growth by streptomycin is accompanied by a reduction in the oxidative activities of the cells, but that the latter are still able to yield stable protoplasts when growth inhibition is complete. Other work indicates that streptomycin rapidly inhibits the synthesis of protein in *E. coli*, possibly because it is bound to the ribosomes.

Experiments with radioactive streptomycin showed that there was an immediate uptake of the antibiotic by the cells and that this was followed, after a short interval, by a secondary uptake. The secondary uptake may be due to the entry of streptomycin into the cell through the defective growing membrane, and may thus enable the drug to damage intracellular enzymes. Hurwitz and Rosano have concluded that streptomycin exerts its effect in two phases and that the secondary phase, in which the antibiotic is directly lethal, is insensitive to chloramphenicol. However, an attempt to confirm the existence of a chloramphenicol insensitive phase has been unsuccessful.

Brock and Brock have shown that the addition of novobiocin to a growing culture of *E. coli* results in a leakage of RNA from the cells to the surrounding medium[115]. This phenomenon was accompanied by an increased permeability of the cells to *o*-nitrophenyl-β-D-galactoside, as shown by a great increase in the rate of hydrolysis of this compound by a normally inaccessible β-galactosidase. Novobiocin does not show these effects on non-growing cells and it appears, like streptomycin, to interfere with the synthesis of membrane material.

(b) Antibiotics which interfere with cell wall synthesis

(i) Penicillin, cephalosporin C and bacitracin

Small amounts of ^{35}S-labelled penicillin are bound irreversibly by sensitive bacteria and the penicillin binding component (PBC) appears to be present in a lipoprotein fraction of the cells that is derived from the cytoplasmic membrane.

Park and Johnson found that three uridine nucleotides accumulated in *Staph. aureus* treated with penicillin[116]. The major nucleotide (LVIII) was later shown to consist of uridine 5′-pyrophosphate (UDP) linked to a new *N*-acetylamino sugar that is linked in turn to a peptide. The new amino sugar occurs in the cell walls of a number of bacteria and has been named muramic acid. It is an ether of D-glucosamine and lactic acid (GNAc-lactic) and is structurally related to the neuraminic acid that occurs in mucins synthesised by mammalian cells. Muramic acid, L- and D-alanine, D-glutamic acid, and L-lysine are present in the same proportions in the nucleotide and in the cell wall. It has thus been suggested that the nucleotide (UDP–GNAc-lactyl–L-Ala–D-Glu–L-Lys–D-Ala–D-Ala) is an intermediate in cell wall synthesis and that its muramic acid peptide fragment is incorporated into new cell wall material[117].

A specific inhibition of cell wall synthesis would account for the fact that resting staphylococci are insensitive to penicillin, but that growing organisms undergo lysis in the presence of the drug in normal media. When

LVIII

synthesis of the rigid cell wall is inadequate, the fragile cytoplasmic membrane is unprotected from rupture by the high internal osmotic pressure of the cell.

Independent evidence for this sequence of events was obtained by Lederberg and by Hahn, who showed that the rod shaped *Salm. typhi* and *E. coli* formed large spherical organisms known as spheroplasts when grown in the presence of penicillin in a medium containing a high concentration of sucrose, and that these spheroplasts underwent lysis when the osmotic concentration of the medium was reduced by dilution with water[118,119].

Cephalosporin C resembles penicillin in its ability to cause the accumulation of the uridine nucleotide (LVIII) in *Staph. aureus* and to bring about the lysis of growing organisms. Bacitracin behaves similarly, but it does not follow that this substance interferes with cell wall synthesis at the same point as the penicillins[120].

(ii) Cycloserine

The nucleotide UDP–GNAc-lactyl–L-Ala–D-Glu–L-Lys accumulates in *Staph. aureus* treated with D-cycloserine. This accumulation is inhibited competitively by D-alanine, but not by its L-isomer. It has thus been suggested that the antibacterial activity of D-cycloserine (XXVIII) depends on its structural similarity to D-alanine, which enables it to inhibit the incorporation of the latter into the muramic acid-peptide of the cell wall.

Strominger, Ito and Threnn[121] have reported that D-alanine is incorporated into the nucleotide, under normal conditions, by the following series of reactions

$$\text{L-Ala} \underset{\longleftarrow}{\overset{\text{pyridoxal}}{\rightleftharpoons}} \text{D-Ala} \qquad (1)$$

$$\text{D-Ala} \longrightarrow \text{D-Ala–D-Ala} \qquad (2)$$

$$\text{UDP–GNAc-lactyl-L–Ala–D-Glu–L-Lys} + \text{D-Ala–D-Ala} \rightarrow$$
$$\text{UDP–GNAc-lactyl–L-Ala–D-Glu–L-Lys–D-Ala–D-Ala} \qquad (3)$$

D-Cycloserine is a powerful inhibitor of reactions (1) and (2), but not of (3).

L-Cycloserine is active against *E. coli* but its mode of action is different from that of the natural D-isomer.

(iii) Griseofulvin

This antibiotic induces swelling of the hyphae of a sensitive fungus in the region, just behind the growing tip, where new hyphal wall is being formed. Mature cells are unaffected. It thus appears that griseofulvin interferes with wall synthesis[122].

The dermatophytes, which are highly sensitive to griseofulvin, have chitinous cell walls, whereas the oomycetes, which are resistant, have cellulosic walls. The presence of chitin in the wall, however, is not in itself sufficient to endow the cell with sensitivity, for some fungi with chitinous walls are resistant.

(c) *Antibiotics with inhibit protein synthesis*

(i) Chloramphenicol and the tetracyclines

Gale and Folkes reported in 1953 that chloramphenicol, aureomycin and terramycin inhibited protein synthesis in *Staph. aureus* at antibacterial concentrations, but that they did not inhibit the synthesis of nucleic acid[123,124]. Later, chloramphenicol was shown to inhibit the formation of inducible enzymes by *E. coli*[119] and to inhibit the incorporation of labelled amino acids into cytoplasmic protein in *Staph. aureus*, but to have no effect on the synthesis of the muramic acid peptide structure of the cell wall.

Chloramphenicol also inhibits protein synthesis in animal cells, but much higher concentrations of the drug are required than is the case with bacteria. It may be that the sites of protein synthesis are more accessible to chloramphenicol in bacteria than in animal cells.

At least three stages are now believed to be involved in protein synthesis in animal cells. In stage (1), amino acids (AA) are activated by the formation of amino acyl adenylates in the presence of appropriate activating enzymes (E). In stage (2), the activated amino acid reacts with ribonucleic acids of relatively low molecular weight, known as soluble (or transfer) ribonucleic acids (sRNA). In stage (3), the amino acid is transferred to the RNA of the microsomes (Ms) where it is incorporated into new protein:

$$AA + ATP + E \rightleftharpoons E\text{-}AMP\text{-}AA + PP \qquad (1)$$

$$E\text{-}AMP\text{-}AA + sRNA \rightleftharpoons sRNA\text{-}AA + AMP + E \qquad (2)$$

$$sRNA\text{-}AA + Ms \xrightarrow[ATP]{GTP} Ms \cdot protein + sRNA \qquad (3)$$

Chloramphenicol has been reported to have no effect on amino acid activation or incorporation of amino acids into sRNA. In high concentration, however, it inhibits nearly completely the incorporation of labelled amino acid into the protein of calf thymus nuclei[125]. The antibiotic thus appears to interfere at a late stage in the process of protein synthesis. It is of interest that its L-*erythro* isomer has little effect on protein synthesis but inhibits the synthesis of a D-glutamyl polypeptide by *Bacillus subtilis*[119].

The tetracyclines inhibit the synthesis of bacterial protein in low concentrations, but their action is less specific than that of chloramphenicol. In higher concentrations they also inhibit oxidative processes and the synthesis of nucleic acids and cell walls. Some of these secondary effects may be attributed to the fact that the tetracyclines are chelating agents for metal ions.

(ii) Puromycin

This antibiotic, which is toxic to a wide variety of different cells, inhibits the incorporation of [^{14}C] leucine into protein in a rat liver extract containing microsomes[126]. As with chloramphenicol, the inhibition of protein synthesis does not occur at the stage of amino acid activation or of amino acid linkage to sRNA. It apparently involves the stage between sRNA and microsomal protein. Puromycin (XXXIV) consists of an amino-nucleoside linked to an amino acid (*p*-methoxyphenylalanine) and its activity may be associated with the fact that it shows a general structural resemblance to the amino acid-bearing end of the sRNA-AA complex[127].

(d) Inhibition of purine or nucleic acid synthesis

(i) Azaserine and 6-diazo-5-oxonorleucine (DON)

These antibiotics, which show antitumour activity, strongly inhibit the synthesis of purines in liver extracts and cause the accumulation of the formyl derivative of N-glycylribosylamine 5-phosphate (LIX). Under normal conditions the latter reacts with glutamine and ATP, in the presence of a liver enzyme, to form the amidine LX. Buchanan has shown that azaserine (XXIX) and DON (XXX) inhibit this reaction specifically, by competing with glutamine for the enzyme site[128]. After combining with the enzyme the

LIX   LX

antibiotics inactivate the latter irreversibly, possibly by acting as alkylating agents.

(ii) Actinomycin

Low concentrations of actinomycin D have been reported to inhibit the synthesis of RNA by a system from HeLa cells whose functioning is dependent on the presence of DNA and all four ribonucleotides. The anti-tumour activity of the actinomycins might be the consequence of an interference with such RNA synthesis. It has been suggested that this interference depends on the ability of the actinomycins to form complexes with DNA.

(e) Inhibition of oxidative processes

Antimycin A

Low concentrations of antimycin A were found in 1949 to inhibit almost completely the oxygen uptake of respiring yeast[129]. Later it was shown that the antibiotic is a powerful inhibitor of succinoxidase. Chance and Williams[130] have established that antimycin A inactivates a specific component of the electron transport system in mitochondria, with the result that reduced cytochrome b is not oxidised by cytochrome c. The antibiotic thus causes a block at point X in the terminal stages of respiration.

DPNH $\longrightarrow$ Flavoprotein $\longrightarrow$ Cytochrome b $\xrightarrow[X]{\quad}$ Cytochrome c $\longrightarrow$ Cytochrome a $\longrightarrow$

Antimycin A is highly active against yeasts and a number of fungi, but it shows little activity against many aerobic bacteria. This may be because the antibiotic fails to penetrate to the electron transport system of the bacterial cell. The accessibility of the electron transport system may also determine the relative activities of different members of the antimycin A complex. Antimycin A_3 is 13 times as active as antimycin A_1 against *Torula utilis*, although the two compounds are equally effective as inhibitors of the terminal oxidation system of rat kidney mitochondria[131].

7. Conclusion

The study of antibiotics has revealed a series of natural products with a wide variety of new structures. These products have been discovered, in most cases, because they have antimicrobial properties, and their place within the wider range of the synthetic activities of micro-organisms remains unknown. It may be that large numbers of chemically analogous but non-antibiotic substances would be revealed by other methods of selection. Nevertheless, certain biochemical patterns have begun to emerge among the antibiotics whose structures have now been established.

The members of a single antibiotic family commonly differ in their content of simple groups, such as alkyl, halogen or hydroxyl, attached to a main skeleton, or in containing different but related units, such as valine or iso-leucine, at specific points in their structures. Some of these differences are associated with biochemical processes of a type that is widely distributed. Thus, the transfer of methyl groups and the addition of hydroxyl groups are well known enzymic reactions and the replacement of isoleucine by valine is encountered in polypeptide hormones from the higher animals. Similarly, the main skeletons of antibiotics of different families are commonly formed from types of unit, such as amino acids, acetate, and sugars, which have an essential function in all living cells. It thus seems that the novelty of many of the antibiotic structures is a consequence of the ability of micro-organisms to effect hitherto unrecognized modifications in such basic processes as peptide and fatty acid synthesis.

A number of antibiotics contain amino acid residues that differ structurally from those found in proteins. Examples are α,γ-diaminobutyric acid in the polymyxins, D-α-aminoadipic acid in cephalosporin N and C, β-methyl-lanthionine in subtilin, nisin and cinnamycin, α-phenylsarcosine and L-α,N-dimethylleucine in etamycin, $(+)$-β,ε-diamino-n-caproic acid (β-lysine) in streptothricin[132], and L-β-methylaspartic acid (which can be formed from glutamic acid), α,β-diaminobutyric acid and D-α-pipecolic acid in asparto-cin[133]. A more general peculiarity of these antibiotics, however, is that some of their amino acid residues have the D-configuration. With few exceptions D-amino acids have only been encountered in microbial products and they appear to occur as components of cellular structures only in the cell walls of bacteria and actinomycetes.

Certain D-amino acids can be formed in bacteria by processes involving a racemase and D-amino acid transaminases. Amino acid activating systems have been found for D-alanine in *Staph. aureus* and a number of other bacteria[134]. It is thus possible that free D-amino acids are sometimes incorporated as such into peptide antibiotics. On the other hand, the D-valine fragment of the penicillins arises from changes in an intermediate peptide that contains an L-valine residue. L-Valine in the culture fluid appears to be the precursor of the D-valine residue found in some of the actinomycins, but this relationship does not reveal the stage at which the inversion of configuration occurs. Differences in the permeability of cells or intracellular structures to L- and D-amino acids are liable to complicate the interpretation of experiments in this field.

A striking feature of many different families of antibiotics is their macrocyclic nature. The structure of the polypeptide substances gives the impression that peptide synthesis has been brought to an end by the formation of large rings and the addition, in some cases, of abnormal terminal residues. The lactone rings of some of the macrolide (erythromycin) group of antibiotics are derived from hydroxy acids that are comparable in chain length to the common fatty acids and it has been suggested that the nature of cellular matrices on which such substances are formed sets an upper limit to their size.

Some of the structural fragments of antibiotics are evidently synthesised by the aid of enzymic systems that occur much more widely in microorganisms than the antibiotics themselves. The thiazoline ring in bacitracin appears to be biogenetically related to the thiazole rings in micrococcin and thiostrepton; the unusual ε-aspartyllysine sequence in bacitracin occurs in the cell walls of certain lactobacilli and strains of *Actinomyces bovis*[24]. The same amino sugar occurs in a number of different macrolides, and structures closely related to that of streptamine are found in streptomycin, neomycin, kanamycin and paromomycin. Antibiotic production often occurs in cells or mycelia that have passed the stage of rapid growth. It may thus be associated with a reorganisation of synthetic activities that are used for more vital purposes in vigorously growing organisms[135].

A variety of antibiotics, including some of those used in medicine, appear to exert their antimicrobial activity by inhibiting biochemical processes that are of general occurrence in living organisms. With D-azaserine and antimycin A the precise reactions that are involved have been established. With chloramphenicol and puromycin the inhibited reactions are concerned with late stages in the process of protein synthesis. Antibiotics which interfere with these widespread biochemical processes may nevertheless differ greatly in their relative toxicity to different kinds of cells. This fact is most simply accounted for by the assumption that there are differences in the accessibility of a sensitive cellular structure, in different cells, to a given antibiotic. For example, the inability of streptomycin to enter animal cells may be one of the reasons for its relatively low toxicity to man.

A number of other antibiotics appear to damage enzymic systems or cellular structures that are restricted to micro-organisms. Studies of the mode of action of these substances can throw new light on the biochemical differences between microbial and animal cells and on those features of the former which should be open to selective attack by chemotherapeutic agents. Thus, changes which result from the action of penicillin and certain other antibiotics on staphylococci can now be interpreted in terms of a derangement of the synthesis of the highly specific structure of the bacterial cell wall. The finding that D-cycloserine interferes with cell wall synthesis by competing with D-alanine raises the question whether it may not be possible, eventually, to design new analogues of essential microbial structures that are sufficiently specific in their action to find clinical use, and thus bring success to the rational approach to chemotherapy that was envisaged by Woods and Fildes during their work on the competitive inhibition of p-aminobenzoic acid by the sulphonamides.

REFERENCES

[1] S. A. WAKSMAN, *Microbial Antagonisms and Antibiotic Substances*, Commonwealth Fund, New York, 1945.

[2] H. W. FLOREY, E. CHAIN, N. G. HEATLEY, M. A. JENNINGS, A. G. SANDERS, E. P. ABRAHAM AND M. E. FLOREY, *Antibiotics*, Oxford University Press, 1949.

[3] A. FLEMING, *Brit. J. Exptl. Pathol.*, 10 (1929) 226.

[4] R. J. DUBOS AND C. CATTANEO, *J. Exptl. Med.*, 70 (1939) 249.

[5] R. D. HOTCHKISS, *Advances in Enzymol.*, 4 (1944) 153.

[6] E. CHAIN, H. W. FLOREY, A. D. GARDNER, N. G. HEATLEY, M. A. JENNINGS, J. ORR-EWING AND A. G. SANDERS, *Lancet*, ii (1940) 226.

[7] E. P. ABRAHAM, E. CHAIN, C. M. FLETCHER, H. W. FLOREY, A. D. GARDNER, N. G. HEATLEY AND M. A. JENNINGS, *Lancet*, ii (1941) 177.

[8] A. SCHATZ, E. BUGIE AND S. A. WAKSMAN, *Proc. Soc. Exptl. Biol. Med.*, 55 (1944) 66.

[9] L. P. GARROD AND E. F. SCOWEN, *Brit. Med. Bull.*, 16 (1960) 23.

[10] H. S. GOLDBERG (Ed.), *Antibiotics, Their Chemistry and Non-Medical Uses*, Van Nostrand, New Jersey, 1959.

[11] R. ROBINSON, *The Structural Relations of Natural Products*, Clarendon Press, Oxford, 1955.

[12] S. A. WAKSMAN, *Antibiotics Ann.*, (1958–1959) 22.

[13] H. T. CLARKE, J. R. JOHNSON AND R. ROBINSON (Eds.), *The Chemistry of Penicillin*, Princeton University Press, 1949.

[14] J. C. SHEEHAN AND K. R. HENERY-LOGAN, *J. Am. Chem. Soc.*, 79 (1957) 1262.

[15] E. BRANDL AND H. MARGREITER, *Österr. Chemiker-Ztg.*, 55 (1954) 11.

[16] J. C. SHEEHAN AND K. R. HENERY-LOGAN, *J. Am. Chem. Soc.*, 81 (1959) 5838.

[17] K. KATO, *J. Antibiotics (Japan), Ser. A*, 6 (1953) 130.

[18] K. SAKAGUCHI AND S. MURAO, *J. Agr. Chem. Soc. Japan*, 23 (1950) 411.

[19] F. R. BATCHELOR, F. P. DOYLE, J. H. C. NAYLER AND G. N. ROLINSON, *Nature*, 183 (1959) 257; G. N. ROLINSON, F. R. BATCHELOR, D. BUTTERWORTH, J. CAMERON-WOOD, M. COLE, G. C. EUSTACE, M. V. HART, M. RICHARDS AND E. B. CHAIN, *Nature*, 187 (1960) 236; C. A. CLARIDGE, A. GOUREWITCH AND J. LEIN, *Nature*, 187 (1960) 237.

[20] G. G. F. NEWTON AND E. P. ABRAHAM, *Biochem. J.*, 58 (1954) 103.

[21] H. R. V. ARNSTEIN, *Ann. Repts. on Progr. Chem.*, 54 (1957) 339.

[22] H. R. V. ARNSTEIN AND D. MORRIS, *Biochem. J.*, 76 (1960) 357.

[23] E. P. ABRAHAM AND G. G. F. NEWTON, *Biochem. J.*, 62 (1956) 658.

[24] E. P. ABRAHAM, *Biochemistry of Some Peptide and Steroid Antibiotics*, John Wiley, New York, 1957.

[25] E. P. ABRAHAM AND G. G. F. NEWTON, *Biochem. J.*, 79 (1961) 377.

[26] D. HODGKIN AND E. N. MASLEN, *Biochem. J.*, 79 (1961) 393.

[27] L. C. CRAIG, *Proc. 3rd Intern. Congr. Biochemistry, Brussels.*, Academic Press, New York, 1956, p. 417.

[28] R. SCHWYZER in *Amino Acids and Peptides with Antimetabolic Activity* (Ciba Foundation Symposium), Churchill, London, 1958, p. 171.

[29] E. P. ABRAHAM AND G. G. F. NEWTON in *Amino Acids and Peptides with Antimetabolic Activity* (Ciba Foundation Symposium), Churchill, London, 1958, p. 205.

[30] L. C. CRAIG, W. KONIGSBERG AND R. J. HILL in *Amino Acids and Peptides with Antimetabolic Activity* (Ciba Foundation Symposium), Churchill, London, 1958, p. 226.

[31] P. BROOKES, R. J. CLARK, A. T. FULLER, M. P. V. MIJOVIĆ AND JAMES WALKER, *J. Chem. Soc.*, (1960) 916.

[32] J. M. WAISVISZ, M. G. VAN DE HOEVEN AND B. TE NIJENHUIS, *J. Am. Chem. Soc.*, 79 (1957) 4524.

[33] G. W. KENNER, R. C. SHEPPARD AND C. E. STEHR, *Tetrahedron Letters*, 1 (1960) 23.

[34] G. BROWNLEE, *Ann. N.Y. Acad. Sci.*, 51 (1949) 875.

[35] H. KOFFLER AND T. KOBAYASHI, *4th Intern. Congr. Biochem., Vienna, 1958*, Abstracts of Communications, 1958, p. 1

[36] M. DAUTREVAUX AND G. BISERTE, *Compt. rend. soc. biol.*, 153 (1959) 1346.

[37] W. Hausmann, *J. Am. Chem. Soc.*, 78 (1956) 3663.
[38] G. Biserte and M. Dautrevaux, *Bull. soc. chim. biol.*, 39 (1957) 795.
[39] K. Vogler, R. O. Studer, P. Lanz, W. Lergier and E. Böhni, *Experientia*, 17 (1961) 223.
[40] S. A. Waksman, E. Katz and L. C. Vining, *Proc. Natl. Acad. Sci. U.S.*, 44 (1958) 602.
[41] H. Brockmann, G. Bohnsack, B. Franck, H. Gröne, H. Muxfeldt and C. Süling, *Angew. Chem.*, 68 (1956) 70; H. Brockmann and H. Lackner, *Naturwissenschaften*, 47 (1960) 230.
[42] A. W. Johnson in *Amino Acids and Peptides with Antimetabolic Activity* (Ciba Foundation Symposium), Churchill, London, 1958, p. 123.
[43] A. Butenandt in *Perspectives in Organic Chemistry*, Interscience, New York, 1957.
[44] E. Katz and W. A. Goss, *Biochem. J.*, 73 (1959) 458; E. Katz and H. Weissbach, *J. Biol. Chem.*, 237 (1962) 882.
[45] E. Katz, *J. Biol. Chem.*, 235 (1960) 1090.
[46] J. C. Sheehan, H. G. Zachau and W. B. Lawson, *J. Am. Chem. Soc.*, 79 (1957) 3933.
[47] W. Keller-Schierlein, M. L. Mihailovic and V. Prelog, *Helv. Chim. Acta*, 42 (1959) 305.
[48] P. A. Plattner and U. Nager, *Helv. Chim. Acta*, 31 (1948) 2192.
[49] L. C. Vining and W. A. Taber, *Can. J. Chem.*, 35 (1957) 1109.
[50] H. Brockmann and H. Geeren, *Ann. Chem., Liebigs*, 603 (1957) 216.
[51] G. Alderton, *J. Am. Chem. Soc.*, 75 (1953) 2391.
[52] G. G. F. Newton, E. P. Abraham and N. J. Berridge, *Nature*, 171 (1953) 606; G. C. Cheeseman and N. J. Berridge, *Biochem. J.*, 71 (1959) 185.
[53] A. Stracher and L. C. Craig, *J. Am. Chem. Soc.*, 81 (1959) 696.
[54] M. C. Rebstock, H. M. Crooks, J. Controulis and Q. R. Bartz, *J. Am. Chem. Soc.*, 71 (1949) 2458.
[55] J. Controulis, M. C. Rebstock and H. M. Crooks, *J. Am. Chem. Soc.*, 71 (1949) 2463.
[56] L. M. Long and H. D. Troutman, *J. Am. Chem. Soc.*, 71 (1949) 2469, 2473.
[57] D. Gottlieb, P. W. Robbins and H. E. Carter, *J. Bacteriol.*, 72 (1956) 153.
[58] C. G. Smith, *J. Bacteriol.*, 75 (1958) 577.
[59] G. N. Smith and C. S. Worrel, *Arch. Biochem.*, 28 (1950) 1, 232.
[60] F. A. Kuehl, F. J. Wolf, N. R. Trenner, R. L. Peck, E. Howe, B. D. Hunnewell, G. Downing, E. Newstead, K. Folkers, R. D. Buhs, I. Putter, R. Ormond, J. E. Lyons and L. Chaiet, *J. Am. Chem. Soc.*, 77 (1955) 2344.
[61] H. C. Reilly in *Amino Acids and Peptides with Antimetabolic Activity* (Ciba Foundation Symposium), Churchill, London, 1958, p. 62.
[62] W. D. Celmer and I. A. Solomons, *J. Am. Chem. Soc.*, 77 (1955) 2861.
[63] M. R. Bell, J. R. Johnson, B. S. Wildi and R. B. Woodward, *J. Am. Chem. Soc.*, 80 (1958) 1001.
[64] R. J. Suhadolnik and R. G. Chenoweth, *J. Am. Chem. Soc.*, 80 (1958) 4391.
[65] A. J. Birch, D. W. Cameron and R. W. Rickards, *Proc. Chem. Soc.*, (1960) 22.
[66] F. M. Strong, J. P. Dickie, M. E. Loomans, E. E. van Tamelen and R. S. Dewey, *J. Am. Chem. Soc.*, 82 (1960) 1513.
[67] N. G. Brink and R. E. Harman, *Quart. Revs.(London)*, 12 (1958) 93.
[68] J. F. Grove, J. MacMillan, T. P. C. Mulholland and M. A. T. Rogers, *J. Chem. Soc.*, (1952) 3949, 3977.
[69] A. J. Birch, R. A. Massy-Westropp, R. W. Rickards and H. Smith, *J. Chem. Soc.*, (1958) 360.
[70] J. MacMillan, *J. Chem. Soc.*, (1954) 2585.
[71] B. M. Duggar, *Ann. N.Y. Acad. Sci.*, 51 (1948) 177.
[72] A. C. Finlay, G. L. Hobby, S. Y. P'an, P. P. Regna, J. B. Routien, D. B. Seeley, G. M. Shull, B. A. Sobin, I. A. Solomons, J. W. Vinson and J. H. Kane, *Science*, 111 (1950) 85.
[73] F. A. Hochstein, C. R. Stephens, L. H. Conover, P. P. Regna, R. Pasternack, P. N. Gordon, F. J. Pilgrim, K. J. Brunings and R. B. Woodward, *J. Am. Chem. Soc.*, 75 (1953) 5455.

74 C. R. Stephens, L. H. Conover, R. Pasternack, F. A. Hochstein, W. T. More-
   land, P. P. Regna, F. J. Pilgrim, K. J. Brunings and R. B. Woodward, *J. Am.
   Chem. Soc.*, 76 (1954) 3568.
75 C. R. Stephens, K. Murai, H. H. Rennhard, L. H. Conover and K. J. Brunings, *J. Am. Chem. Soc.*, 80 (1958) 5324.
76 W. J. Gottstein, W. F. Minor and L. C. Cheney, *J. Am. Chem. Soc.*, 81 (1959)
   1198.
77 J. F. Snell, A. J. Birch and P. L. Thomson, *J. Am. Chem. Soc.*, 82 (1960) 2402.
78 C. E. Holmlund, W. W. Andres and A. J. Shay, *J. Am. Chem. Soc.*, 81 (1959)
   4748.
79 J. R. D. McCormick, N. O. Sjolander, P. A. Miller, U. Hirsch, N. H. Arnold
   and A. P. Doerschuk, *J. Am. Chem. Soc.*, 80 (1958) 6460.
80 M. Anchel, *J. Am. Chem. Soc.*, 74 (1952) 1588.
81 F. Bohlmann, *Angew. Chem.*, 67 (1955) 389.
82 J. D. Bu'Lock, *Quart. Rev. Chem. Soc.*, 10 (1956) 371; E. R. H. Jones, *Proc. Chem.
   Soc.*, (1960) 199.
83 W. D. Celmer and I. A. Solomons, *J. Am. Chem. Soc.*, 75 (1953) 1372.
84 J. D. Bu'Lock and H. Gregory, *Biochem. J.*, 72 (1959) 322.
85 E. W. Yamada and W. B. Jakoby, *J. Biol. Chem.*, 234 (1959) 941.
86 R. B. Woodward, *Angew. Chem.*, 68 (1956) 13.
87 C. Djerassi and J. A. Zderic, *J. Am. Chem. Soc.*, 78 (1956) 6390.
88 H. Brockmann and R. Oster, *Ber.*, 90 (1957) 605.
89 H. Els, W. D. Celmer and K. Murai, *J. Am. Chem. Soc.*, 80 (1958) 3777.
90 K. Gerzon, E. H. Flynn, M. V. Sigal, P. F. Wiley, R. Monahan and U. C.
   Quarck, *J. Am. Chem. Soc.*, 78 (1956) 6396.
91 R. Paul and S. Tchelitcheff, *Bull. soc. chim. France*, (1957) 443, 734, 1059.
92 F. Lynen in *The Centennial Lectures, E. R. Squibb & Sons*, Putnam, New York,
   1959, p. 75.
93 Z. Vaněk, J. Majer, A. Babický, J. Liebster, K. Vereš and L. Doležilová,
   4th Intern. Congr. Biochem., Vienna, 1958, p. 135; K. Toshi et al., *J. Biol. Chem.*,
   237 (1962) 322.
94 D. R. Walters, J. D. Dutcher and O. Wintersteiner, *J. Am. Chem. Soc.*, 79
   (1957) 5076.
95 R. Donovick, B. A. Steinberg, J. D. Dutcher and J. Vandeputte, *Giorn.
   Microbiol.*, 2 (1956) 147.
96 J. B. Patrick, R. P. Williams and J. S. Webb, *J. Am. Chem. Soc.*, 80 (1958) 6689.
97 A. J. Birch, R. J. English, R. A. Massy-Westropp and H. Smith, *Proc. Chem.
   Soc.*, (1957) 233.
98 H. S. Burton, E. P. Abraham and H. M. E. Cardwell, *Biochem. J.*, 62 (1956) 171.
   W. Godtfredsen, K. Roholt and L. Tybring, *Lancet*, i (1962) 928.
99 F. A. Kuehl, R. L. Peck, C. E. Hoffhine, E. W. Peel and K. Folkers, *J. Am.
   Chem. Soc.*, 69 (1947) 1234.
100 G. D. Hunter, *Giorn. Microbiol.*, 2 (1956) 312; M. Silverman and S. V. Rieder,
   J. Biol. Chem., 235 (1960) 1251.
101 M. J. Cron, D. L. Evans, F. M. Palermiti, D. F. Whitehead, I. R. Hooper,
   P. Chu and R. U. Lemieux, *J. Am. Chem. Soc.*, 80 (1958) 4741.
102 H. Ogawa, T. Ito, S. Kondo and S. Inone, *J. Antibiotics (Japan), Ser. A*, 11 (1958)
   169.
103 S. A. Waksman (Ed.), *Neomycin*, Bailliere, Tindall & Cox, London, 1958.
104 K. L. Rinehart and P. W. K. Woo, *J. Am. Chem. Soc.*, 80 (1958) 6463; K. L.
   Rinehart et al., *J. Am. Chem. Soc.*, 82 (1960) 2970.
105 T. H. Haskell, J. C. French and Q. R. Bartz, *J. Am. Chem. Soc.*, 81 (1959) 3482.
106 E. Walton, J. O. Rodin, C. H. Stammer, F. W. Holly and K. Folkers, *J. Am.
   Chem. Soc.*, 80 (1958) 5168.
107 M. H. McCormick, W. M. Stark, G. E. Pittenger, R. C. Pittenger and J. M.
   McGuire, *Antibiotics Ann.*, (1955–56) 606.
108 J. E. Philip, J. R. Schenck and M. P. Hargie, *Antibiotics Ann.*, (1956–1957)
   699.

109 B. Loder, G. G. F. Newton and E. P. Abraham, *Biochem. J.*, 79 (1961) 408.
110 J. J. Beereboom, J. J. Ursprung, H. H. Rennhard and C. R. Stephens, *J. Am. Chem. Soc.*, 82 (1960) 1003.
111 R. E. Maxwell and V. S. Nickel, *Antibiotics & Chemotherapy*, 4 (1954) 289.
112 M. R. Pollock, *Biochem. J.*, 66 (1957) 419; M. Crompton, M. Jago, K. Crawford, G. G. F. Newton and E. P. Abraham, *Biochem. J.*, 83 (1962) 52.
113 B. A. Newton, *Bacteriol. Rev.*, 20 (1956) 14; *Giorn. Microbiol.*, 2 (1956) 388.
114 N. Anand and B. D. Davis, *Nature*, 185 (1960) 22.
115 T. D. Brock and M. L. Brock, *Arch. Biochem. Biophys.*, 85 (1959) 176.
116 J. T. Park and M. J. Johnson, *J. Biol. Chem.*, 179 (1949) 585.
117 J. T. Park and J. L. Strominger, *Science*, 125 (1957) 99.
118 J. Lederberg, *Proc. Natl. Acad. Sci. U.S.*, 42 (1956) 574; J. Lederberg and J. St. Clair, *J. Bacteriol.*, 75 (1958) 143.
119 F. E. Hahn, *4th Intern. Congr. Biochem., Vienna, 1958*, Symp. No. 5.
120 E. P. Abraham and G. G. F. Newton in *Amino Acids and Peptides with Antimetabolic Activity* (Ciba Foundation Symposium), Churchill, London, 1958, p. 205.
121 J. L. Strominger, E. Ito and R. H. Threnn, *J. Am. Chem. Soc.*, 82 (1960) 998.
122 A. H. Campbell, *Brit. Med. Bull.*, 16 (1960) 82.
123 E. F. Gale, *Brit. Med. Bull.*, 16 (1960) 11.
124 E. F. Gale, *Synthesis and Organisation in the Bacterial Cell*, John Wiley, New York, 1959.
125 J. W. Hopkins, *Proc. Natl. Acad. Sci. U.S.*, 45 (1959) 1461.
126 M. B. Yarmolinsky and G. L. de la Haba, *Proc. Natl. Acad. Sci. U.S.*, 45 (1959) 1721.
127 L. I. Hecht, M. L. Stephenson and P. C. Zamecnik, *Proc. Natl. Acad. Sci. U.S.*, 45 (1959) 505; P. C. Zamecnik, *Harvey Lectures, 1958–59*, Academic Press, New York, 1960, p. 256.
128 J. M. Buchanan in *Amino Acids and Peptides with Antimetabolic Activity* (Ciba Foundation Symposium), Churchill, London, 1958, p. 75.
129 F. M. Strong, *Topics in Microbial Biochemistry*, John Wiley, New York, 1956.
130 B. Chance and G. R. Williams, *Advances in Enzymol.*, 17 (1956) 65.
131 Wen-Chih Liu and F. M. Strong, *J. Am. Chem. Soc.*, 81 (1959) 4387.
132 S. B. Binkley, *Ann. Rev. Biochem.*, 24 (1955) 597; A. W. Johnson and J. W. Westley, *J. Chem. Soc.*, (1962) 1642.
133 J. H. Martin and W. K. Hausmann, *J. Am. Chem. Soc.*, 82 (1960) 2079.
134 J. Baddiley and F. C. Neuhaus, *Biochem. J.*, 75 (1960) 579.
135 R. W. Bernlohr and G. D. Novelli, *Arch. Biochem.*, 87 (1960) 232.

SUBJECT INDEX

COMPREHENSIVE BIOCHEMISTRY

SECTION III (VOLUMES 12–16)

Biochemical Reaction Mechanisms

PRINTED IN THE NETHERLANDS BY
NEDERLANDSE BOEKDRUK INRICHTING N.V. — 'S-HERTOGENBOSCH